Glowing Praise for
"UPSTAIRS, DOWNSTAIRS"
TV's Best Drama Series*

"Pure joy"   —*Christian Science Monitor*

" 'Upstairs, Downstairs' is too good to miss . . . great fun and marvelous television."
                    —*The New York Times*

"It holds an elegantly framed mirror up to a perennially fascinating historical moment."
                    —*Time*

"Our favorite series"   —*New York Daily News*

   * "Upstairs, Downstairs" is winner of the Emmy Award for Best Drama Series.

ROSE'S STORY
was originally published by
Sphere Books Limited of London.

Books in the Upstairs, Downstairs Series

Mr. Hudson's Diaries
Rose's Story
Sarah's Story

Published by POCKET BOOKS

ROSE'S STORY

◆

Terence Brady
and
Charlotte Bingham

PUBLISHED BY POCKET BOOKS NEW YORK

ROSE'S STORY

Sphere Books edition published 1972
POCKET BOOK edition published March, 1975

Standard Book Number: 671-78791-8.
This POCKET BOOK edition is published by arrangement with Sagitta Productions. Copyright, ©, 1972, by Terence Brady and Charlotte Bingham. All rights reserved. This book, or portions thereof, may not be reproduced by any means without permission of Sagitta Productions, c/o International Famous Agency, 1301 Avenue of the Americas, New York, N.Y. 10019.
Printed in the U.S.A.

ROSE'S STORY

Ever since she could remember Rose had always brushed her hair one hundred times, as her mother had taught her, while repeating the Lord's Prayer ten times. Tonight she did so with a little less of her usual vigour. She was tired. It had been a long day at Eaton Place, and she felt sleepy.

She opened her Bible, and started to read.

It was not long before she realised that her concentration was not as it usually was. A contributing factor might have been that she knew the piece in question off by heart, having learnt it once at school, but more than that perhaps, was the fact that tomorrow was her birthday. She was not in the habit of celebrating it, particularly since she was about to reach one of those ages that ladies like to forget, situated as they are between one thing and another, or as in her case, between twenty-nine and thirty-one.

Her Bible held the essence of most of her life between its leaves, because she had long ago developed the habit of keeping mementoes in between its pages.

In this way when she turned the pages, a picture the vicar had given her at confirmation would fall out, or a flower pressed on the occasion of a former birthday; or another picture given to her by the housekeeper at Southwold many years ago before she left to come to Eaton Place. Little things that mean nothing to anyone else, but hold the scent of the past for their owner as strongly as a perfume.

Here was poor Eddie's medal, sent to her after he'd been killed. There was a picture of her dog Tatty painted by her brother Tim, and a ribbon worn on her hat at Lady Marjorie's wedding celebrations. And then towards the back, letters sent from Southwold over the years from her friend Albert, now a school teacher there.

All those years! And yet touching each object by turn brought back each memory, as if they were merely doors that she had only to step through, or push open with her hand.

Chapter 1

Rose pushed open the kitchen door.

At least she began to push open the kitchen door, but first she wished for the thousandth time that her grandmother would go and live somewhere else, with someone else's family. Grandmother was about as gay as a funeral, but unlike a funeral, she went on and on.

It wasn't as if you could ignore her either. She was such a large woman. Tall, and big boned. Having Grandmother around on a birthday, or at Christmas, was like sitting around with a suet pudding on your head. Grandmother weighed everything down. Fun, as far as Grandmother was concerned, was something wicked people had when people like her had their backs turned, and of course they always came off worse for having had it.

Rose didn't like her grandmother, but she made a practice of not admitting it. This morning she was busy not admitting that she hoped very much that her grandmother would not already be up and standing by the stove, ready to spoil Rose's tenth birthday right from the start. And that was another thing about her, there was no getting away from her, because she was always first up and last to go to bed. Afraid to miss anything. Afraid that someone might start having a good time without her being able to be there and spoil it for them. Rose gave the kitchen door a little kick; it got rid of some of her feelings, but it was gentle enough so that Grandmother wouldn't notice.

Having kicked the door she then turned the handle and went into the kitchen. It was warm from the oven, and there were two round, freshly baked loaves on the table but no Grandmother. It was too good to be true. Just for one glorious second Rose wondered if she could possibly be dead, but that was too much to hope for, even if it was your birthday. Then she suddenly remembered that Mrs. Burrows, Grandmother's friend in the next village, was ill, and that last night Grandmother had talked of taking her over something.

Only Mrs. Burrows could drag Grandmother away from the Lodge, particularly on a birthday. Rose imagined her hurrying along the lanes to Mrs. Burrows' cottage, her head filled with the uncomfortable thought that Mother and Father and Rose and Tim might all be having a nice time without her being there to spoil it. No doubt she would hurry back as fast as she could so as not to miss having a go at someone (having a go was Grandmother's second best pastime after spoiling a good time) but hurry as much as she could Rose knew that Grandmother could not possibly get back to the Lodge until the afternoon. For one thing Mathilda Burrows had a tongue as sharp as Grandmother's and if Grandmother didn't stay at least until after dinner time Mathilda would give her what for, and for another thing Mrs. Burrows, ill or not, would fill her ear with such gossip that Grandmother wouldn't be *able* to tear herself away until after dinner time. So by and large, and the thought made Rose skip twice round the kitchen table, by and large they were all safe—Father, Mother, Tim and she, for, well, for a good long while anyway.

When Rose had stopped skipping round the table she bent over the kitchen table and smelt the loaf that Grandmother had baked prior to leaving the Lodge. It smelt so good, and it was still warm from the oven. She would have loved to have stuck her fingers in and broken off a piece, but it would show, and even Father would whip her for doing such a thing. Not that Father wasn't gentle, as gentle as Mother, but he would most certainly whip her or Tim if they touched any food.

Rose knew that they were luckier than most because they lived on an estate and folk that lived on an estate were better looked after, it seemed, than folk that didn't and had to fend for themselves. Her father was someone, and she was lucky enough to be his daughter. The daughter of the Earl of Southwold's Lodge Keeper—it was on account of this that they would never starve. Even when the harvests were as bad as they had been this year and the last year, even then they never went hungry, they always got their flour to bake their bread and they could grow as many vegetables as they wanted, "enough for four or five families" Father would say when he stood in front of the rows of cabbages in the back garden. But it was all right to grow as much as you wanted so long as they could not be viewed from the road when the gentry went by, and that went for washing, or anything else too. The only thing the gentry must see when they went by were pretty things, like flowers, and Father being the sort he was, he made sure the flowers they saw were a proper eyeful. His spring flowers were something of a feature nowadays. And on the first warm day the Countess would make a point of getting her coachman to stop by the Lodge gate so that she could look out of her carriage window and admire the display.

Of course Father loved that, and he would bow from the waist down, and then blush as red as a poppy when she told him how much she looked forward to seeing his display each year. Father would give his life for the Countess, and not just because she was the Countess of Southwold either, as he was so fond of pointing out to Rose and Tim, but because she was a great and wonderful lady. Often when he had just said that, his eyes would stray to where Mother was sitting sewing in front of the fire, or darning at the table, and his eyes would sort of run over Mother, and Rose knew that he thought that Mother was the same

—a great and wonderful lady. Someone you could really look up to and admire.

"Where's Grandmother?" Tim stood blinking in the sunlight, and doing up the bottons of his breeches.

"She's gone to see Mrs. Burrows," said Rose gleefully, and then she eyed her five year old brother warily, waiting to see if he had forgotten that it was her birthday.

Tim touched her on the arm. "Did you manage it Rose?"

Rose looked down into his large blue eyes which were unaccountably framed by black eyelashes—contrasting with his yellow hair, like the contrasting fringe on a shawl.

Rose frowned. "Did I manage what?"

"You know, Rose."

She did know, but she liked to pretend sometimes that she didn't understand Tim, that he was too young to make himself quite clear to her.

"Yes, I did manage it, if you really want to know."

Tim sighed thankfully, and Rose was glad she had lied to him. Well, not exactly lied so much as fibbed. She was glad she had fibbed to him. After all an elder sister was meant to be an elder sister, and part of being an elder sister was doing older kind of things, like staying awake until after midnight so that you can see the birthday ghost. The fact that she couldn't remember hearing the stable clock strike twelve didn't mean that she hadn't actually been awake at midnight. She probably just hadn't heard it that was all, although she had definitely seen her birthday ghost, quite definitely. It had been fairly tall, and wearing old fashioned clothes, like someone in a picture.

Tim sidled on to a chair, waiting expectantly for what was to come. He knew that Rose would not let him down, and by the time she had got to the bit about her ghost being as tall as a hayrick with boots that came over his knees, Tim's eyes were as round as round apples.

"I suppose I didn't hear anything at all?" he asked hopefully.

"You? You were snoring fit to bust, louder than Father."

"I just thought I might have heard one of his chains rattling, that's all."

"Well, you did turn over rather quickly when he came in through the window, as if you *nearly* heard him," Rose admitted graciously.

"Did I?"

"Yes, you did, but you definitely didn't *see* anything, most definitely not."

"No, well I couldn't if I were asleep. But I'm glad I *nearly* heard something," Tim looked gratefully at his sister.

"Oh, you nearly heard something all right."

Rose stood on tiptoe to reach the plates on the dresser, and then she very carefully lifted them down, and put them on the table. They were blue and white plates with a design of birds on them. Mother had bought them last year on market day, and Grandmother had grumbled that she wasted Father's money. As if Mother would waste anything of Father's, as if Father wouldn't buy Mother the whole of Southwold estate, if he had the money for it. But then that was Grandmother. Always making remarks about other people which made them seem nasty, and remarks about herself that made *her* seem nice.

It was like the way Grandmother always referred to Mother as 'poor Lucy', and 'your poor Mother,' and even Father would become 'poor John', as if Grandmother felt deeply sorry for him, although why she should was a mystery to everyone, most of all Father.

Sometimes it occurred to Rose that Grandmother was afraid of Mother. She would speak about Mother's waist length black hair as if it was unnatural, and although Rose loved to see her mother coil her hair up into the massive chignon that she always wore, Grandmother would eye it with disfavour. Rose felt that

Grandmother thought there was something improper about having such thick black hair, just like Rose knew that Grandmother thought Mother was giving herself airs and graces by wearing lace collars, and when Father was out of ear shot Grandmother would mutter 'it wouldn't surprise me if she had Romany blood'. Rose was sorely tempted to kick her on her ankles when she said that, because she knew that no-one proper had Romany blood, and that Grandmother had never forgiven Father for not marrying someone from his own village, and that was why she said such things.

"Happy birthday," her mother bent to kiss Rose, and Rose put up her cheek to be kissed, loving the smell that came from her Mother's clothes and hair, a smell so fresh and clean that it could only remind you of Father's garden on a warm day when all the flowers were out. Not like the way Grandmother smelt of carbolic soap, or cooking, and Mother's cheek was as soft as Tim's, not prickly like Father's and Grandmother's. She put her finger under Rose's chin and stared seriously into her face. "You are ten years old Rose," she looked grave, "ten years old, that is a wonderful age."

Rose caught Lucy's hand and kissed it, and rubbed her cheek against the back of it. She didn't like to ask if she was going to get a present. It didn't really matter if she was or not when Mother was around.

"Will you come with me to the end of the lane this morning since there is no school?"

"Yes Mother, please."

"Can I too?" Tim looked across at Rose imploringly.

"If Rose says yes, it's her birthday Timothy."

Mother always called Tim 'Timothy', and the way she said 'Rose' was quite different to anyone else. She rolled her 'r' sort of softly making it seem as if 'Rose' was a real rose that grew on a bush, which was rather how she always felt when she was near Mother. Mother made you feel delicate and special, and as if you were about to break, while Grandmother made you feel thin and ugly. Only last week when Rose had cut her knee Grandmother had said 'your bones are too fine wove, like your poor Mother's,' and Rose in spite of the fact that she was busy trying not to cry from Grandmother's having rubbed salt into the cut to clean it, in spite of that, she had been secretly thrilled at Grandmother's words, although she knew for certain she didn't mean them to be nice.

"Tim can come if he promises not to be noisy."

"I won't, Rose, promise I won't."

"Very well then."

Going with Mother down the back path to the end of the hedge was one of their treats, just as waiting for her at the same place at dinner time was one of the highlights of the day. Rose actually preferred to perform this ceremony of waiting for her mother on her own, as if it were a secret, but she knew that Tim was just as happy as her that Grandmother was away today, so it was difficult not to share their delight.

Half an hour later they set off, walking quietly beside their mother. Occasionally she would stop by a flower and ask them the name of it, and when they got it right she would look pleased. Mother smiled quite often, but she hardly ever laughed (not like Father who liked laughing nearly as much as a good dinner). It was as if laughing was something that other more ordinary folk did, while Mother could put as much into a smile as other folk put into their laughs.

At the end of the hedge Lucy bent and kissed each of the children in turn, and then, as she always did, she went a little way across the wide lawns that crept up to the big house and waved. The children waved back watching her intently. She made a delicate outline against the large cedar trees whose branches spread across the lawns. She was slender and grey in her simple frock and shawl, while they, like giants from a story, frowned down on her looking as if their wide arms would like to bend and scoop her up.

Rose shivered. 'Someone walking across your grave,'

Grandmother would say. Grandmother was full of phrases like that. Phrases full of death and sadness. She had once seen a hanging when she was young. She loved to tell Tim about it. Poor Tim, his eyes would start out of his head, because when you're only five you do frighten easily, not like ten. He couldn't even walk past the graveyard without breaking into a run. Father loved to tell stories about the graveyard. Particularly the one about the boy who dared to spend the night there, and was found dead in the morning. Father loved that one. It seemed that when he was a boy they'd all had a bet about who should dare to spend the night in the graveyard, and this one boy said he would. Well, it appears that Father and his friends left the boy in the graveyard, and from what they think happened, it must have been that he sat against a gravestone and his shirt got hooked on a nail, and he must have thought it was a corpse come to grab him and he died from the shock of it.

"Race you back."

Rose glanced sideways at Tim running beside her down the lane to the Lodge. She loved her brother, even though he was only five.

"For you, Rose." Tim pushed the little parcel into her hand. "I waited till Mother had gone, to surprise you."

"Not your best snail shell Tim?"

Tim looked at the contents of the parcel longingly, and then nodded. "I wanted you to have it Rose."

"I'll keep my little ring Mother gave me in it."

Tim looked a little doubtful about keeping a ring in it, but then remembering that you had to make allowances for girls, he nodded approval, and really when Rose tucked a piece of material into it, and then placed the ring carefully inside it, it didn't look quite as silly as you might have thought.

"What would you like to play, Tim?"

"It's *your* birthday Rose."

"Never mind that, what would you like to play?"

"Could we play with my horse?"

"Very well."

They took the carved wooden horse into the garden. Father's garden was as neat as anything on the South-wold estate. Now in the summer it had everything from lavender to cabbages. Tim ran the horse along the path.

"Let's pretend it's the Queen's horse, and it's winning a race."

"No, the Prince of Wales'. He's much nicer."

Tim considered this, and then was forced to agree. After all, little though he knew of this person called the Prince of Wales, there was no doubt about it that he had a singular advantage over even the Queen—he was a man.

"All right. It's the Prince of Wales' horse, and it's winning."

They played until the stable clock struck twelve. Although the Southwold stables were some distance from the Lodge they could hear the clock striking in the still air of that summer morning, and as soon as they heard it they caught up the little wooden horse, and ran back to meet their mother. Down the lane again to the end of the hedge where they could again view the lawns and the cedar trees.

Possibly it might have surprised them if a visitor had stood behind them and exclaimed at the beauty that lay before them. Even so, a child will not wholly be able to ignore beauty however accustomed they are to it, and although they were ignorant of the fact that the old house that they could just glimpse through the trees was Palladian in style, nevertheless they knew it to be beautiful, even though they couldn't say why it was. And they were proud of it, and as people living in the shadow of some natural phenomena will talk about 'our mountain' they would talk about 'our house' as if they in part owned it.

When Lucy re-appeared walking slowly back across the lawns, Tim skipped ahead leaving Rose to walk beside her mother holding back her disappointment that it now looked more than ever as if she would not be getting a present this year. She ate her bread and bacon dinner in silence, and then having duly thanked the Almighty for providing her with the same she got down from the table, unable to bring herself to go out and rejoin Tim in the garden, and at the same time at a loss as to what to do next. She had a very lively sense that something should happen on a person's birthday, but at the same time she knew that it was bad manners to expect something to happen. There was nothing for it but to go on hoping.

"Rose," Lucy wiped her hands carefully, "I want you to go and put your best dress on, and your shoes and stockings."

Rose stared at her mother. She had a very strong feeling that she was not hearing things quite well.

"Go quickly, Rose dear."

Rose went quickly, her heart not beating but hammering. She struggled into her shoes and stockings, having given her feet a good scrub, and then pulled on her best dress. She caught up its matching cotton bonnet, undecided whether 'best dress' meant just 'best dress' or whether it also meant 'bonnet to match'.

Her mother looked at her critically.

"Very nice, dear," she nodded, and taking the bonnet from her she tied its strings under Rose's chin, while smoothing her hair neatly to each side. She stepped back, and then after a little she nodded once more, and again said "Very nice, dear," which rather made Rose want to scream. But she knew that if she asked her mother why it was that she was required to put on her best dress and bonnet, as well as shoes and stockings, she knew that her mother would say something like 'you'll see', or just smile and touch her on the cheek, because Lucy loved giving surprises, and one of Lucy's surprises was always just that—surprising. She had once sewed Father a whole set of shirts without his ever finding out, and on another occasion made Grandmother a patchwork cushion for Christmas without her once suspecting.

They left Tim playing with his snails in the sunshine, and set off once again down the little lane that led back from the Lodge to the big house. Rose walked in some discomfort because her shoes were a little tight. She hoped that her mother wouldn't notice. After all if you grew out of your shoes it could be quite a long while before you ever set eyes on another pair. And these were red, a present from the shoemaker to Father because he had done him a favour last year, and by way of thanking him he had made Rose a pair of shoes, the envy of all the other children at the village school.

She would have liked to have held her mother's hand as they grew nearer and nearer to the big house, but her mother was staring thoughtfully ahead, possibly not realising that this was the first time that Rose had ever been quite so near to the great building because, as everyone on the Southwold estate knew, ten years was the age that children had to be before they were allowed up to the big house for the annual Christmas party. Rose wondered suddenly if her Mother had suddenly taken leave of her senses when she opened a side door, and beckoned for her to follow.

Rose did follow her, but climbing the broad stone staircase in her wake, she wished her shoes were made of as soft a leather as her mother's, as were everybody's who worked in the big house, so that they wouldn't make a noise going up and down stairs. The Earl hated noise, in fact it was said that the merest clatter could put him in a bad mood for days and days. Father had said that this was on account of his having always been very bookish, since he was quite young. Apparently people who were bookish were inclined to want very little noise, so that they could read their books better.

Lucy knocked very quietly on the door in front of them. When a voice said 'come in, come in' Rose suddenly had a feeling that she was going to faint, which was very silly, because that was the sort of thing that little Lottie Collins was always doing, not Rose Buck.

Rose stood in the shadow of the doorway, and then very carefully just inside the door when her mother shut it behind them. She wasn't going to risk doing anything wrong, and letting Mother down in the big house. To let Mother down in the big house would be so terrible, and what would be much worse it would please Grandmother, something to be avoided at all costs.

At first, because it was dark, Rose could not take in just how large the room she was standing in was. It seemed to stretch endlessly in front of her. She watched her mother moving quietly down the length of it until she came to the fireplace where she curtsied in front of an old lady dressed in black.

"Ah, Lucy, there you are—pour my tea."

The old lady's voice was not English, in fact it wasn't like anything Rose had ever heard before, and then she remembered that of course the Earl's mother came from a place very far away called Russia, a place even further away from England than France, it appeared. Having remembered that, Rose felt a little faint once more at the realisation that she was not only standing in the big house, but that this was more likely the person referred to by everyone on the estate as 'the old Countess'.

The old Countess' face was old, but when she looked at you her eyes were of such a brilliance that they looked as brown and polished as the furniture in the room, and you could almost imagine that you could see your image in them if you wanted to brush your hair or see if your face was clean. Her hair on the other hand was as white as a handkerchief. It was said that it had gone that colour when she was only twenty-eight and her first baby had died. Father could remember that time although he was only a boy then and not considered of any account. Apparently she had shut herself away, seeing no-one but her husband, until one day she had another baby—the present Earl, and started to go about again.

"She is only a little like you, Lucy," the Countess' hand lay on Rose's shoulder like the claw of the sick bird that they had released last winter. "Only a little like you," she said again, studying Rose's face intently, and then she looked at Lucy, "but enough to count."

Rose stepped carefully backwards to avoid making an unseemly noise, and also there were several footstools and things, so you had to watch exactly where you placed your feet.

"Sit down," the old lady indicated one of the stools. "Sit down."

Rose did as she was told, keeping her eyes fixed firmly on her red shoes.

"Give her a biscuit, Lucy. Do you like biscuits, child?"

Rose nodded.

"Your mother tells me you are ten today. Do you like being ten?"

Rose nodded again and tried to chew her biscuit in as delicate a fashion as her mother poured out the Countess' tea. The Countess had hands that were shaky, like Father's after Harvest Festival, so for a few minutes that was the only noise in the room, the rattle of her china cup on her china saucer as she drank her tea—that and the clock ticking on the mantelpiece in front of the big gold mirror that hung over the fireplace.

Eventually when she had finished her tea, the old lady beckoned Rose to stand near her chair. "Do you like telling the truth, little girl?"

"Sometimes," said Rose, and then somehow felt she had made the sort of answer that Mother might not like.

"Sometimes, yes, like most of us. Well, Mademoiselle Sometimes, tell me what you are thinking about as you stand looking at an old lady?"

Rose was silent.

"Of what do you think child?"

"I was thinking you had shaky hands, like Father after Harvest Festival."

The Countess laughed. In fact she laughed so much that Rose began to wonder if she would ever stop. And then she stopped and asked Rose what presents she had received on this, her tenth birthday?

"A snail shell only? I think that such a truthful little girl should have more than a snail shell on the day she has reached ten years. Fetch me that little box, Lucy. You may have this, ma petite, so that whenever you see it you will know there is a reward in speaking the truth."

Rose looked down at the little box. It had roses wreathed around the outside, and a knot of blue forget-me-nots in the middle.

"Roses for Rose, ca c'est bien, but don't you forget why you came by it. Now go and play somewhere while your mother reads to me."

Rose wandered down the length of the long room until she came to a window seat. How strange it was to be sitting listening to Mother reading actually inside the big house. It was like a dream, and any minute she would wake up to hear Tim's snores, and try and cover herself with whichever bit of blanket he hadn't pulled off her. Of course she knew it wasn't a dream because she could feel the cold of the little box in her hand. She put it against her cheeks which were hot and red from sitting by the old lady's fire.

The view from the window was of green hills and trees, but directly below her she could see a garden that she had never seen before. It had fountains, and pillars, and a little house at one end of it and a pool with water lilies on it. Someone was sitting reading in the entrance to the little house. It looked to Rose as if it was a lady who was quite young. Her dress was very pretty. It was the colour of cream. And she wore a straw hat with roses and ribbons to match her dress. Rose liked things to match. Last week when there had been a garden party at the big house Rose had seen lots of dresses and hats going through in the carriages for which Father held open the Lodge gates. Her favourite had been one in pale blue worn by a lady with blonde curls who looked like a princess. Now she almost preferred the outfit below—blue was very pretty, but cream was almost better. She would have liked to have called to her mother to look, as she sometimes did when she and Tim were counting the carriages that went through the Lodge gates, but Mother was still reading. Mother read wonderfully well. That was another thing that Grandmother didn't like about Mother, the fact that she could read. And speak French.

In Grandmother's often voiced opinion, anyone who could read or speak French like Mother could wasn't proper. 'Leastaways, not when they're folk like us.' Folk like them, according to Grandmother, had no business with books and talking foreign tongues.

No-one knew how Mother came to speak French, or read for that matter, not even Father, which was rather exciting. There were quite a few things that Father didn't know about Mother, because she never told him, and Father would never ask. It was enough for him, he said, that Lucy was a lady. And of course Rose could see that when he said that, in his mind he nearly always put 'great and wonderful' in front of 'lady', even if he didn't actually say it. If Father had taken the Countess of Southwold herself as a wife, he couldn't be more proud than he was of having had the privilege of marrying Mother.

The lady down below in the garden got up from her seat, and carefully shut her book. Rose noticed that she was wearing an engagement ring on her wedding finger, and that made her think that perhaps she was the Lady Marjorie, the Earl's daughter, who was getting married next year, but to someone of whom the old Countess didn't really approve, not being, Mother said, of a great and historic family like the Talbot-Careys, even though he was an honest gentleman, and had been at school with Lady Marjorie's brother.

Rose wondered if she would ever possess a parasol like the lady below. She hoped so.

It was late afternoon now. Her mother took her hand, and Rose bobbed her thanks to the old lady, and they walked back to the Lodge, neither saying anything. Not that Lucy talked very often, but Rose normally did. It was just that this afternoon there was so much to think about. First of all going inside the big house, and then meeting the old Countess, and her giving Rose the box, and then seeing the lady in the cream dress. Gracious heavens! There was enough in just this one afternoon to keep her and Tim going in games forever and ever. Already she could see herself making Tim pretend to be the old Countess, all doubled up, with a leaf on his head for her cap. And then walking to school next week she could pretend to be young Lady Marjorie walking graciously in the garden with her parasol.

She let go of her mother's hand, and ran into the kitchen to find Tim. He wasn't there—only Grandmother, back from seeing Mrs. Burrows.

Rose automatically hid the little box behind her back. She had no intention of showing it to Grandmother. She would only make some remarks about it being too good, or think of some way that really she, Grandmother, should have it, because she always did. Even if Father bought a tiny piece of lace for Rose from a gypsy, or some sweets off a stall in the market, she would always find some reason why he should be giving whatever it was to her. It was as if Grandmother was determined to make Father be grateful to her all the time, although grateful for what Rose had never yet discovered.

"What will you be doing in your best dress and bonnet, Miss?"

"Mother took me to the big house," Rose could hardly keep herself from sounding boastful, although the Bible was always telling you not to be.

"And why should she be going up to the big

house?" Grandmother looked at Lucy. "They're so short they be needing her for dusting, no doubt."

Grandmother always said 'no doubt' when she was saying something she meant to be nasty, but she'd said as if she'd meant it to be nice.

Not very many minutes later she was saying 'no doubt' again, because if it wasn't enough that Rose had been given a box, and a snail shell to put her ring in, and a visit to the big house, and that she'd met the old Countess, if all this wasn't enough on her tenth birthday, then Father had to walk in the door carrying a puppy.

A puppy!

Just for a minute neither Rose, nor her mother, nor Grandmother, nor Tim who'd just wandered in from the garden, none of them could speak, they all just stared.

And then Father said very sheepishly, looking at no-one but Mother, "well but Lucy, I'd ha' loved one when I was a boy," and waited for her to smile, which she did, thank heavens, before he put the puppy into Rose's arms.

"Can I share him, Rose?" Tim looked at her so anxiously, it made her love him a little bit more even than she did already. She nodded, and they ran together into the garden and let it go on the grass. "What shall we call him, Rose?" Rose looked at the puppy. "We'll have to see what he's like," she said carefully. "You have to call animals a name that suits them."

"Yes, you're right, Rose," Tim agreed hastily, "you mean as if it's like my snails. One being slimy I call him 'Slimy', and that kind of a thing?"

Rose nodded, but she didn't take her eyes off the puppy. At the back of them in the kitchen she could hear Grandmother arguing with Father and telling him he didn't ought to have brought home a fool thing like a puppy, and Father saying why not, and Grandmother carrying on about mouths to feed, and he had no more sense than a hen.

Rose sighed happily. Not even Grandmother mattered now she had a puppy.

"Come on," said Tim, "let's see if he'll fetch a stick."

Chapter 2

Rose grew to know the Countess' rooms almost as well as the Lodge. Once or twice a week after her tenth birthday she would go across the lawns to the big house, and sit playing while her mother read to the Countess, or poured her endless cups of tea from something they called a 'samovar.' The old lady appeared to like Rose. Rose knew this because she would often make Rose sit near her, and then she would pinch her cheek and talk to her in a language that wasn't either English or French.

Sometimes the old lady would show Rose big books of drawings, and talk to her about what the drawings were about in her funny accent. Rose knew she was very fortunate to be allowed to sit in such a beautiful room, and look at books. She knew this, but sometimes she couldn't help wishing she was back in the garden of the Lodge playing with her dog Tatty. Of course she never said this to anyone because it would be very ungrateful, and she knew that she was more privileged than any other child on the estate. Not only that but the old lady often gave her sweeties, which she called 'bon-bons', and that was extraordinary because she gave them to her on days that weren't Sundays, and she and Tim would take them to the bottom of the garden and eat them, on a day that wasn't Sunday, and not even Grandmother could say anything because it was the old Countess who had given them to her.

The rooms that Rose sat in with the old Countess would have been magnificent to even the most sophisticated observer, but to Rose, who only dared to examine her surroundings little by little as her visits progressed, they were almost unbelievable. Naturally enough she knew that they must have cost a lot of money because there was so much gold paint, but it wasn't just the gold paint that she marvelled at, it was the details of each room, which she—sitting quietly by a window, or playing with the pieces of an old chess set—had time to take in. And it was this very detail, rather than any one magnificent painting or piece of furniture, which imbued in her an even more fervent awe of the people she and her family were wont to call 'gentry'. She often wondered what it felt like to be the old Countess and go to sleep in a room with a ceiling with cherubs and angels all over it and to sit in a drawing room that had so many paintings in it that you could hardly tell what the wallpaper underneath was made of.

It was one of these paintings in the old Countess' drawing room that caught her imagination. An oval painting, not very big, of a young man with brown eyes and a large lace collar that sat crisply on his brown velvet suit. Rose thought him beautiful, and sometimes when she was closing her eyes to go to sleep she would imagine him stepping out of the picture and coming down to the Lodge to play with her and Tim and Tatty. The visits to the old Countess were less of an ordeal once she had the young man to think about. In fact, however much her shoes pinched, or however long her mother sat reading out aloud to the old lady, Rose didn't mind because she had her young Lord to think about. She knew he was a young Lord from the way he was looking down at everyone with an expression that only Lords and gentry were entitled to wear, and besides that—his features were that of a Lord. Only a Lord could possess such a fine straight nose, and such a proud curving mouth, and the feathers on his hat were so magnificent—only a Lord could afford them.

In her mind she and Tatty and Tim followed the young man all over the world, doing whatever he required of them. They were his faithful servants, and it was enough that he allowed them to serve him.

There were other pictures of course. But they weren't very interesting, nothing to compare with her young Lord. In fact some of them she found quite ordinary, and wondered how people who were so rich and could afford to buy anything they wanted, could keep such dull paintings. One was of an old lady— very like the old Countess—stitching a piece of material. She looked just like real life which was more than some of the other pictures did but there didn't seem much sense to that. Why, Rose wondered quite frequently, why have a painting of something that you can see every day? There were lots of old ladies in the village that the Earl and Countess could come and look at. It was so strange that they should choose to hang pictures on their walls of such things. Just as it was very strange how many people in the paintings at Southwold had no clothes on at all. Not even a single stitch. Obviously there were reasons for this, but although Rose couldn't think what they could be, she knew that the ways of the gentry, like the ways of the Lord, were not to be questioned.

"Lucy, bring your daughter to sit beside me," the old lady said and shifted her feet on her embroidered footstool. Rose sat on the chair her mother pushed forward for her and then waited to see what this afternoon's lecture would be about. The old lady appeared to like to talk about all sorts of different things, and Rose appreciated that she was very lucky to be allowed to listen to her, but her mind would sometimes turn to other things, like the big emerald and diamond ring that the old Countess wore.

"Why are you staring at my ring, child?"

"Because it is so big."

"Do you think it is vulgar, Miss Truthfulness?"

"No, but it must have cost a lot of money."

"There is no value to be put on a piece like this, did you know that? Did you know that there are some things to which we cannot put a price?"

Because the old lady was a Countess, Rose was prepared to believe that what she said was so, even more than the parson on Sundays, or her mother, but she wondered how it were possible for anything to have a value above money? Money bought everything, if you didn't have enough money, you couldn't have anything, even if you were the Talbot-Careys. Even people like them needed money so that they could feed themselves and their servants, and buy things for their houses. And if people like her father and mother didn't have any money, they couldn't eat.

"When I was young I spent a lot of time in Moscow," the old lady beckoned impatiently to Lucy for another cup of tea, and then went on, "Do you know where Moscow is?"

Rose shook her head.

"It is where I come from, where I was born, Moscow is in Russia, which is very far away. Alors, when I was in Moscow I was seventeen. You cannot imagine this old lady being seventeen, but I once was that age, and I loved to dance. Mon Dieu—how I loved dancing! I could dance longer and better than most other girls of my age and it was one day when I was dancing at a great ball that Lord Charles Talbot-Carey saw me and fell in love with me, but he could never get near me to dance with me because I had so many partners. I believe it was a whole week before he could have the honour, and then it was that it happened."

The old lady fell silent. And Rose settled her eyes on the floor waiting until the Countess would see fit to tell her what it was that happened. She would have loved to say as she did with her father, 'what happened?,' but of course she never would. The old lady looked down at her eventually, "did you know child

that when it happens it happens. Did you know
that?"

Rose shook her head.

"Never forget it. If one day when you are a woman,
you wonder how you will ever know love, remember
what I say—you will know it, because when it comes
it cannot be denied. Unless you are blind and deaf
and dumb and even then I believe it cannot be denied,
because you would feel it in your bones, even if you
could not smell it, or hear it, or see it. When Lord
Charles saw me he knew, and when eventually I
danced with him—I knew. And the next day he
gave me this—" they all looked at the emerald, Rose
and Lucy and the old lady, imagining back in their
different ways to that time when the old lady's waist
was as slim as a wand, and her hands were as smooth
as silk. Rose couldn't quite imagine what sort of dress
she would have been wearing when Lord Charles saw
her, but she thought it was most probably like the
one in the picture in the room next door which showed
the old Countess in a beautiful thin gold dress, with
a white bosom and hair as red brown and shiny as
a chestnut when you first pick it out of its prickly case.

"He gave me this ring, and he left me to follow him
to England, which I did, leaving behind my beloved
Russia, family, everything I knew. Everyone knew me
to be mad, except my mother. But, you understand,
it was the ring that told me I was right, when everyone else was telling me I was not. It was my ring
looking at me with its big green eye which led me
to this great house and this damp land. I could not
speak a word of English, only Russian and French,
and that was terrible because I could not even tell a
servant how to make my tea and even Vilanova was of
no use, because all she would do was to cry. Mon
Dieu, I have never seen so many tears as Vilanova
shed in those first months that I was married. And
as for Lord Charles, he frightened her nearly to death.
He had only to come in one door and she would fly
out of another. Imaginez-vous such a situation, like

something in a play. Husband here, maid out there, maid in here, husband out there. Terrible. And now Vilanova is an old woman like me, we are old women together. Only the ring is not old. The hand yes, but not the ring."

There was silence.

And then the old lady looked sharply at Rose and said, "Do you now understand why this ring is without value, priceless?"

"I think so, Your Ladyship," said Rose a little frightened, because the old woman was frowning at her quite fiercely.

"Why, then?"

"Because you would never, never sell it?" Rose ventured.

The old lady cackled with laughter, and muttered to Lucy something about Rose being 'peasant'. Rose was glad to go home to Tim and Tatty. Sometimes there were things about the old Countess that she did not understand at all.

Going home to Tatty was one of the great joys. He was a small dog, but not so small that you couldn't imagine him to be bigger. Sometimes she and Tim would put him on the end of a long piece of string and run round the garden after him pretending that he was a horse and they were riding behind him in their carriage, just like all the fine ladies and gentlemen that they saw passing through the Lodge gates. Other days they would run across the fields, jumping over the long grass and making Tatty jump with them. They had as much fun as the colts that raced round the meadows at the back of the stables, and as spring crept into summer they looked forward to the longer evenings and the pleasant thought that soon there would be no more learning to do, but days spent in helping to gather in the harvest and other pleasurable pursuits.

Tim never went up to the big house with Rose, nor did the old Countess seem to be interested in meeting him, even on his birthday.

"Perhaps she doesn't like boys, Rose," said Tim wistfully.

"Maybe," said Rose, and then after a great deal of thought told Tim that it might be something to do with the old Countess having her first little boy go and die on her. "Perhaps seeing you would remind her, Tim. I mean perhaps seeing a little boy like yourself would remind her that she once had a little boy like yourself, and then she wouldn't like that, because older people don't like being reminded of things that make them sad, Tim. They like to talk about things that make them happy. Except for Grandmother, she only likes to talk about sad things because she's such a sad thing herself."

"Grandmother doesn't like us, Rose."

"Of course she does, Tim. Everybody's relations *like* each other, they just have a different way of saying it, that's all."

"No, she don't, Rose, really she don't. She says we're too fine for her, and why can't we speak like her and Father, and why do we have to call her fangled things like 'Grandmother' like gentry or something, and why do we talk more like gentry than normal folk, and she says Mother's bringing us up to be like cuckoos, and that Mother's the cuckoo, and that you going up to the big house will give you more airs and graces than is good for you, and that soon it'll be a halfpenny to talk to you, and if you say anything to her direction she'll whip you for being so cheeky. And things like that. Anyway, it don't matter, Rose, because I bit her."

"*Tim*. You didn't."

"Yes, I did, Rose," said Tim proudly, "and then I ran."

"We daren't go home now. Not till Mother gets back," Rose sat up and brushed some strands of grass out of her hair. "We daren't go back," she said again, and then looked at Tatty. "I'm glad we've got Tatty with us, Tim. She might have whipped Tatty because she couldn't find us."

"She won't whip us if Mother's there, will she, Rose?"

"No, but she'll say to Mother about you biting her, Tim, she'll say that all right."

"And Mother'll say that she's sure I'm sorry, and I won't do it again."

"And then Grandmother will say 'ye don't whip 'em enow, ye don't whip enow, 'een gentry'd whip 'em.'" Rose fell back into the long grass laughing.

"Say it again, Rose, say it again," Tim begged, "that was just like Grandmother."

But Rose was too busy stroking Tatty, and besides that the sun was so fine and warm it made her feel as lazy as a cow.

"Rose?"

"Yes, Tim."

"Rose, do you think our real Grandmother got eaten up?"

"Tim, what *do* you mean?"

"Like in the story, Rose, you know. When Teacher said the other day that the wolf ate the Grandmother up and then got into the Grandmother's clothes. Do you think our Grandmother is the wolf, and our *real* Grandmother, the one God meant us to have, do you think she's really in the nasty Grandmother's tummy, and Grandmother's really a wolf all the time, and if Father chopped her down, our real nice Grandmother would step out? Do you think that's how it really is, Rose?"

Rose didn't think she'd better answer that. After all if God wanted you to honour your mother and father, as it said in the Bible, then He probably meant you to honour grandmothers as well.

Since Tatty had arrived, Rose had become more aware of sin. The thought that God had sent her a dog for her birthday necessarily filled her with gratitude towards Him, but lying alongside that sense of gratitude was the fear that if she didn't keep on the right side of Him, He would take him away again. Life without Tatty would be unbearable. It was because of him that she now woke up ahead of even Grandmother, and because of him she was always so willing to run any errand that anyone wanted. Running errands were nothing but joy when you had a dog running alongside of you, as he was doing now.

Sometimes when he was running beside her on a fine morning like this morning had been, Rose would wonder why it was that they ever had to stop running, she and Tim and Tatty, and as she did when she was sitting in the old Countess' room, she imagined herself running away with Tim and Tatty, perhaps to find the young man in the picture—running towards what Mother called the 'horizon'. The 'horizon' didn't look like Southwold, it didn't even look as if there were any other villages there, it just looked blue and misty, and the hills that filled it before it became blue and misty were as curved and green as apples.

Once they could see their mother was back in the Lodge the children crept out from behind the neat hedge that surrounded their garden, and feigning innocence of Tim's offence, they walked into the kitchen. To their mutual relief everyone seemed to have forgotten about Tim's offence in the excitement of a parcel having arrived from London for Grandmother —with her name on it—and a great deal of expensive postage.

Rose stared at the wrapping in awe. Imagine that that parcel had come all that way. That parcel had been touched by people who lived in that great city called London. It was unimaginable. Not even Mother had been to London. For about the hundredth time that year Rose wished she had been born a boy like Tim. If she had been born a boy she could go to London and become Lord Mayor, or become a soldier and fight for the Queen. Girls could never do anything exciting.

Grandmother was enjoying her hour of triumph to the full. Rose thought she had never seen anyone unwrap a parcel so slowly, and then again it didn't seem possible that a parcel could have so many wrappings. At last Grandmother reached inside and pulled out the contents. It was a blue shawl made of silk with long fringes. Grandmother's eyes glittered. This was a shawl that would set everyone back on their heels. This was a shawl that would turn every head in church on Sunday. This was a shawl to twitch and pull, and affect to be unconcerned by. This was indeed a shawl.

Rose watched her father's eyes running slowly over the shawl, taking in all its fine details; the hand embroidery at the corners, the lovely colour of the silk and length of the fringes, and she knew that he was wishing that he could buy Mother a shawl like this. She knew that he was thinking how much better the shawl would look round Mother's fine shoulders instead of draped round Grandmother's hefty frame. Rose felt, along with her father, that if things were as they should be it would be Mother who would be walking to church in that shawl, not Grandmother. Her mother appeared to have no such thoughts. She smiled at Grandmother's delight and re-arranged the shawl for her so that it sat better round her, standing back to admire its effect, and then as she always did, she went back to the stove, happy that someone else was happy.

"I'll warrant that Mabel Burrows'd give every bit of her fine china, and not less, to have a shawl as dainty as this," said Grandmother, and then because the shawl's former owner was on old friend of hers, who had died leaving it to her, Grandmother gave a small sigh and said, "Poor Agnes, she must have looked a treat in this, except I always did say she'd not the strength of a fledgling, let alone enough to make a good, strong body."

"It be beautiful all right, that shawl," said John Buck still looking at it wistfully.

"Fit for the Countess herself," agreed Grandmother.

"Yup, that be a lady's shawl all right," said her son, and Rose sitting next to him at the table could almost feel him wishing and wishing for a shawl like that for Lucy. As for herself, she wanted to go and pull it off Grandmother and give it to her mother, but she didn't. Instead she ate up her supper in silence, while planning one day to be as rich as rich could be.

She told her mother this later that night when she came up to kiss her and Tim goodnight.

"Those aren't the important things in life, Rose."

"But I want you to have beautiful things, and I want you to be able to wear a silk shawl in church."

"So—and so do I," said Tim fervently.

"Children—God does not send us into the world to covet others' property, or to have fine shawls, but to do His will."

Lucy looked at her children sitting up in their bed, and wondered if they could understand the importance of what she was saying.

"We must accept God's will for us, and we must be quiet so we can hear God's will, and if we covet the property of others we are not being quiet in our hearts, but noisy in our greed. Do you understand?"

They thought, a little doubtfully, that perhaps they did.

She kissed them both, and after hearing them repeat the Lord's Prayer, she went quietly back down the wooden stairs to fetch her cloak, and make her way back to the big house. There was still a long night's work ahead, helping out in the kitchens, and seeing to the old Countess and her maid, Madame Vilanova.

"Only Lucy makes the tea as we like it—eh, Vilanova?"

Vilanova nodded, and stared into the bottom of her cup, as if she could read all about her necessarily short future there. Now in old age, the two old ladies sitting with their lace caps and their cups of tea, were more like two old friends than mistress and maid. Their long association, and their mutual sense of exile had given them a similarity, so that they could almost have been two old sisters, and Vilanova's voice and speech mannerisms, as happens with servants who

have been a long time with the same family, were very
much modelled on her mistress, only she had a dis-
concerting habit of bursting into tears if anyone mentioned Russia, or even something that reminded her of
Russia. This habit annoyed the old Countess. It not
only annoyed her, but it had obviously been a source
of contention between them for more than half a
century. The length of time had done nothing to
spoil either the freshness of the old Countess's irrita-
tion or the intensity of Vilanova's outbursts.

Tonight it needed only a mention of the inclement
summer weather, and tears began to drip down old
Vilanova's face, weakening her tea and causing the
old Countess to bang on the polished wood floor with
her stick.

"Stop that, you peasant."

Vilanova did not stop, nor could she be frightened
into holding back her tears.

"In Russia, the summers are summers, the sun
shines, and the sky is blue, not like here," she sobbed,
"when I remember my mother, I remember summer."

"You are a foolish peasant, Vilanova, your mother
was a foolish peasant, and as ugly as toads."

"My mother was as beautiful as a summer in Russia."

"Her mother was as ugly as toads," the old Countess
told Lucy, "she was such an ugly peasant my father
would run when he saw her. My father hated ugly
people. I hate ugly people, that is why I hate Vilanova.
She is an ugly old woman like me."

"I loved my beautiful mother."

"You hated your mother, you ran away from her.
Every time she saw her mother she ran away," the
old Countess reaffirmed to Lucy, and then turning
back to old Vilanova she said, "you are a silly old
woman, you hated your mother, she whipped you every
day. I used to hide you in my bedroom so you could
not be found by your ugly old mother. If I had not
hidden you—you would have died from the beatings
your ugly old mother gave you. If I had not asked

for you to be my maid you would have been killed by your mother's beatings."

But Vilanova appeared not to have heard the Countess' version of her fearsome childhood, and she continued to cry effortlessly into her tea, now and then wiping her nose with a small lace handkerchief.

The old Countess frowned. "The old peasant has got my handkerchief," she said à propos of nothing in particular, and then turning to Lucy she said, "more tea for an old woman, Lucy."

Lucy held out the cup of tea for her, and then stood by her chair waiting to hear some story, or some old memory that the Countess liked to mull over when she was drinking her tea last thing at night.

But tonight she refrained from reminiscing, perhaps afraid that Vilanova's sobs would become louder if she touched on some story from their past, or mentioned Russia. Instead she looked up at Lucy and said, "Lucy—Vilanova is peasant—Rose, your daughter is peasant, but you, you are not peasant. What do you remember from when you were young? Why do you think you speak French like Vilanova and me?"

"I can remember very little from when I was a child, mi'lady."

"You remember your French," said the old lady sharply.

"Yes, mi'lady, but I can't remember learning it."

"So—you are a mystery, Lucy?" The old lady frowned. She didn't like mysteries and she suspected Lucy was keeping something from her.

Lucy was silent, and then sensing the old lady's displeasure, she said, "I remember a large garden, and trees where I used to walk every day."

"Who with? Who did you walk with?"

"A lady who always spoke to me in French."

"And who was this lady who always spoke to you in French?"

"I do not know, mi'lady, but I know that after the large garden I can't remember very much except going in a boat, and then I remember being with nuns, and there was a young nun who was very kind to me."

Lucy stopped here instinctively sensitive to the fact that she might be talking too long, or too much, and thus would give displeasure to the old lady.

"Go on, go on," said the old lady impatiently, "I knew you were not peasant, Lucy."

"I remember the young nun was called Sister Emmanuel. She had a lovely skin, and pink cheeks, and she would give me hot milk, and she taught me English I think, because I don't remember speaking French after that, which leads me to think that perhaps I might then have been in England."

"And after that?"

Lucy looked at the old lady, and a closed expression came into her large grey eyes.

"After that was the orphanage."

"Ah, yes the orphanage, from which you ran away. And then you met the good John Buck, who is peasant, and does not speak French like you."

Lucy said nothing. She was in no position to defend her husband. The old lady patted her hand.

"He is very good, your peasant. You know the day I wondered about you, Lucy—the day I wondered about you was when I heard you speaking French to Vilanova. I taught Vilanova her French so she has a very pretty accent like me, but you, who taught you your pretty accent, Lucy? Your accent is not peasant—so from where, I ask myself? Not from the back streets of Marseilles, no, not from the gutters of Paris. If only we knew where it was, that large garden—then we would solve the mystery that is Lucy, n'est ce pas?"

The old lady patted Lucy's hand again and very soon it was time for Lucy to help the two old ladies to bed. Poor Vilanova was no longer very adept at arranging things for the old Countess, and it was Lucy who had to help them both, while pretending that Vilanova was really doing it; something very necessary for the pride of both mistress and maid.

It was as Lucy made her way down from the back

staircase from the old Countess' rooms that Widgery, the butler, stepped out of the darkness and confronted her. No-one at Southwold liked Widgery, that is no-one *below stairs* at Southwold liked Widgery—although the Earl and Countess professed to be very satisfied with him. So far Lucy had had very little to do with him, since her duties mostly took her to the old Countess' rooms, and the old Countess was an eccentric law unto herself; but now he was standing at the bottom of the stairs waiting for her and there was no way Lucy could avoid him.

"Good evening, Lucy, and how is Mrs. Buck tonight?"

"Quite well, thank you, Mr. Widgery."

"Been looking after the old Countess' interests as is your wont, no doubt?"

"Her Ladyship has just now retired to bed," said Lucy firmly.

"I noticed that you looked a little pale tonight in the kitchens, Lucy. Nothing the matter I hope?"

"I hope not, Mr. Widgery."

"We wouldn't like anything to affect your work would we, Lucy? I mean we wouldn't wish to disturb our interests with the old lady by going and having ill health. Ill health is not tolerated below stairs, is it, Mrs. Buck?"

"No doubt it is not, Mr. Widgery."

"No it is not, Lucy, it is not tolerated at all. Just remember that, and be so good as to make up your mind to look a little healthier tomorrow. I should hate to have to report anything untoward to the Countess—really I would."

"Yes, Mr. Widgery."

"Goodnight, Lucy."

"Goodnight, Mr. Widgery."

It was late now, and the moon was up as Rose watched her mother's lantern threading its way through the trees and down the little lane to the Lodge. Grandmother was asleep and snoring, and Father had gone out night fishing with one of the coachmen, so Rose

knew that it was safe to creep downstairs and see her
mother, even though it was so late, and she just might
be cross. She pushed open the kitchen door and saw
her mother sitting at the heavy wooden table, but as
she saw her she immediately wished that she hadn't—
her mother was crying.

To Rose the sight of her mother crying was so
terrible that it was almost shocking, as if she had suddenly found out that she wore a wig, or didn't really
love her father. She wished ardently that she hadn't
made a noise pushing open the door, but she had,
and her mother looked up, and it was as she looked
up that Rose saw that her mother was not a saint,
nor a goddess, but a woman in a grey dress with tear
stains and blotches, and a nose that was shining a
little too much, and fingers that tore at her poor,
much-mended handkerchief.

"Why, Mother—what's the matter?" Rose crept up
to her, feeling dreadfully embarrassed, but she managed to put a clumsy arm round her.

"Nothing, Rose dear, nothing at all. At least it's
nothing that need concern you—yet."

Lucy began to sob a little more for having said
that, and then she suddenly looked up at Rose, and
in a way that Rose would never forget she said, "God
help us for having been born women Rose, God help
us."

Rose shivered. She didn't know why but her mother's words sounded terrible, like blasphemy. Why did
her mother want God's help so much? From the way
she was looking she knew that it couldn't be for anything very nice.

"I must wash my face before your father comes in,"
Lucy got up and went to the sink, "you're to say
nothing of this to your father, Rose dear, promise?"

Rose nodded, all the time wishing that she hadn't
had the idea of coming downstairs in the first place.
She didn't want her mother to cry, and she didn't
want to keep a secret from her father, that wasn't the
sort of thing that happened in their family. In their

family—Father was kind and laughed, and Mother was quiet and beautiful—and they never kept secrets against each other, and most of all, Mother never cried.

Lucy patted her face dry, and then sipped a cup of water, and very soon Rose could see the mother that she knew, the only mother that she wanted to know, coming back to life.

"Up to bed now, Rose."

"Yes, Mother."

Rose kissed her, and ran back up the stairs. She hoped that she would soon be asleep, and that when she woke up in the morning what she had seen would turn out to be a dream. Outside, Tatty barked a greeting to Father back from his fishing. Rose closed her eyes. Soon it would be morning.

And soon it was morning, but Rose had to reluctantly admit to herself that what had happened was true and wasn't a dream. She felt embarrassed to go down to the kitchen. She didn't know how to look her father in the face, even to say good morning to him, now that she had a secret against him, although she couldn't think exactly what the secret was. She hoped it was only that her mother had been crying, but somehow she felt that it couldn't just be that. She envied Tim for not knowing anything about secrets.

"Hurry, Rose, we'll soon be off for the haymaking."

Tim peered anxiously round the door at her. Rose threw off the blanket she'd been huddling under and sprang out of bed. At least the morning was fine, and secret or no secret, there was Tim waiting for her, and Tatty outside. She wouldn't think any more, thinking was bad for you. The sort of thing to do in winter, not in summer when the sun was up and the hay was ready to be tossed.

"There's the Fiddys ahead of us," said Tim, matter of factly, as they set off towards the fields clutching some bread for their dinner and a bottle of water. "Yes, them's the Fiddys all right. And there's the Brownlows. Charlie's got an apple. Now he's dropped it. I expect his sister says to him what a fool he is for dropping it. She says that a lot to him, Rose."

"You're an old woman, Tim, you and your gossip, anyone would think you were an old woman."

Tim ignored this criticism.

"There's Mary Brownlow giving Tom a kick," he said with some satisfaction, "there he go giving her a kick back. He can give a good kick can Tom. He kicked teacher the other day, and she went hopping round the room, and then he had to go and stand in the corner. That were the day you were staying behind to help Grandmother, Rose."

"She didn't need any help," Rose remembered with some scorn, "she just don't like us learning to read and write when she can't."

She tied the strings of her sun bonnet under her chin a little more firmly. Haymaking could be a vigorous business, and a girl needed to keep her sun bonnet straight. Once she'd dropped a bonnet in the fields, and someone had taken it. That had been terrible. If the sun got up high you could give yourself a fine headache for a week with no bonnet on.

"Come on," said Tim, "let's get started before them Fiddys."

If they all sang in the fields while they worked, it wasn't because they wanted to make the time go quicker, but rather because this season of the year was for them a time of celebration, and they knew it. Gathering in the harvest, picking the fruit, all the numerous tasks that needed to be done on the Southwold estate, meant that for a time they would become like one family. So they sang to celebrate their sense of community, and the songs they sang were the old songs, songs they'd heard their fathers and their grandfathers sing—although none the worse for that. And whereas, in winter, they would hurry by each other, huddled into their jackets against the weather, now neighbour smiled at neighbour as they pitched into both song and hay, and when they stopped for their midday dinner they showed each other their provisions and swopped a small piece of bacon with a piece of cheese, or passed a water bottle round from one to the other, those that had manners carefully wiping the top before they took a swig.

By evening the children were half asleep and as it was getting dusk they scrambled aboard the last wagon of hay, Rose still determinedly clutching her bonnet. She looked at the tops of the trees as they passed overhead of them and thought how wonderful it was that it was summer. And then she thought that the noise of the horse's hooves on the road, and the smell of the hay, were the two things which she loved next to Tim and Tatty and Mother and Father.

Grandmother stood at the entrance to the Lodge.

"Quick, Rose, fool girl, quick, your Mother's now fainted and I can do nothing with her."

Rose stumbled into the kitchen, her heart beating. Tim started to cry.

"Hush that noise, boy," snapped Grandmother. And then she said to Rose, "I've been and thrown water and goodness knows all down her, and she still lies there like a fish after a stone."

"Mother," Rose bent over her mother shouting, "Mother wake up, please." But mother lay grey and still, and Tim's sobs became more pronounced.

Rose put her head down to her mother's heart as she had once seen her father do when old Burrows collapsed at the fair.

"That's the wrong side, child," snapped her grandmother, "anyway her heart still beats for sure."

"Tim, quick run and get Father, he'll be with Mr. Coombe in the vegetable garden."

Tim ran, tears still dripping down his hot face. He hardly thought he would have any breath for running after a day in the fields, but fear helps to hasten things, and to his surprise he found his legs seemed to be moving even quicker than when he ran a hot potato race the week before.

Seeing her father bending over her mother and crying out to her was like her mother's tears the night before—something that Rose did not want to witness. She didn't want to see her parents as human beings, or as weak and tearful as Tim and she. She wanted them to be as she saw them, as she wanted them to be. And yet she couldn't help noticing how tenderly her father took her mother in his arms, and how he wiped her forehead and smoothed her hair, and then lifted her up the Lodge stairs to their bedroom. And in doing all these things, she saw how much it was possible for a man to love a woman.

"I've never seen anyone faint out for so long as that before," grumbled her grandmother, "but then your poor mother has not more strength than a goat, and I can't say that I didn't say as much to your poor father when he brought her home. John, say I, marry one of your own kind, marry one who'll bear you good strong children, bring you a good brood into the world. Have nought to do with these weak and watery women. They'll bring you nought but bad luck, mark my words. And so I have said to him, but he bore no more attention to me than if I was the wind blowing through the eaves, and he married her, and now look."

Rose frowned at Tim because he seemed about to repeat his offence against the old lady and bite her again, but when he saw Rose's frown he contented himself with pulling a face at her back. Then a hush settled over the house, and the children sitting opposite their grandmother couldn't hear anything except the silence and the clock ticking, and Grandmother breathing somewhat heavily after her outburst against their mother. Because they had had no previous experience of sickness, the children could not imagine what was going on in their parents' room, but as they were poor people's children they knew that if their mother was ill it was bad—bad for her, and bad for the house. If a mother could not work the children went short. Rose knew this because the girl next to her at school had had no dinner, because of her mother being ill and not working, and she could only eat when she got home at night, not like Rose and Tim who could take something with them to school, and have something when they got home.

By the time her father came downstairs Rose's imagination had extended itself to nursing her mother back to health, and then taking her on a trip, although how she would pay for it she hadn't thought. When she saw her father's face however, she knew suddenly that her mother had fainted because of something last night, because of the secret.

"I told you, John Buck, as much as ten years ago I told you, that no good would come of this marriage, that a strange woman speaking fangled languages, born away from your own village, would bring you no luck. I told you that, but you thought I was a fool when it was John Buck was the fool. I told you about that, but you knew better as sons will always know better than their poor mothers."

"I think we should make her a hot drink to steady her," John looked wearily away from his mother.

"Hot drinks will never make her into a fine strong woman who could bear you sons, and still be up to go gleaning in the morning," snapped the old lady who, it seemed to Rose, had overmuch respect for 'gleaning'.

Rose knew that the reference to the sons was a slight to her, because her grandmother didn't like girls, even though she was one herself. She said that no-one thought Father was a man after Rose was born, and that it was a good thing that young Tim had followed on eventually, even after all that time, because young Tim had proved that Father was a man.

"Rose will take her mother a drink won't you, Rose?" her father looked pleadingly at Rose, and Rose nodded. "I have to go back to finish off my bit of work."

"I told you to marry your own kind, I told you if you'd married your own kind there'd be none of this hot drinks, and fainting like gentry," Grandmother daubed her eyes with the corner of her apron as was her custom when she thought she wasn't getting every ear in the room. "I'd have had a dozen fine strong grandsons afore now if you'd heard what I'd said and taken to one of the village girls like any folk with sense."

John turned by the door and looked at his mother. "Well," he said, "happen by next spring you'll have one more grandson, if all goes right, anyway."

Chapter 3

If the state of the weather was important to the Earl
and Countess of Southwold, in that it begged the
question as to whether or not the Countess needed
to wear her furs, it was considerably more important
to their tenants. A bad harvest meant a thin winter,
and although they did not run the risk of starvation
as some small-holders and tenants did, nevertheless the
Harvest Supper was considerably gayer if there was
a good reason to give thanks.

This year there was every reason to give praise in
both church and hall, because the harvest had been
good. All was safely gathered in, and the tenants of
Southwold gave vociferous thanks for this great mercy,
and if the praise that rose to the heavens was louder
for the realisation of the feast that was to come, there
was no reason to think that the Lord thought any the
less of it.

As far as their temporal lord, the Earl of Southwold,
was concerned, the fact that there was a good harvest
and that therefore the books would balance up nicely
for his estate manager, was of considerably less interest than the fact that one of his mother's maids
had got herself pregnant—albeit in wedlock. The
harvest concerned him in a very distant way, but the
maid affected him directly.

The Earl was a peace-loving man. He liked his estate better than he liked London or anywhere fashionable, which was very proper in an earl, except that

49

he didn't like his estate or its acres or its beauties but because it contained the one place where he wanted to be—his library. If Southwold had consisted only of his library he would have been perfectly happy, a fact that his wife was aware of, but which she found hard to accept, particularly when she was feeling irritated by him, which was fairly frequently since the old Countess' maid had become pregnant.

However well run even the largest household, however smooth its workings, it takes only one cog to stick and the whole machine can become, if not exactly ineffectual, at least less efficient. Southwold had become less efficient since Lucy Buck had become pregnant, because she had been frequently unable to come to the house, and the infrequency of her visits made the old Countess cross, and the fact that the old Countess was cross made old Madame Vilanova weep, and that affected Daisy, the maid delegated by Widgery to replace Lucy, and the fact that Daisy got affected made the old Countess even crosser, so that she was extremely short tempered with her daughter-in-law, and consequently the Countess took the Earl to task for his mother's rude manners.

"I can't understand your mother at all. Widgery says that Daisy is most efficient, really most efficient."

The Earl did not answer, hoping perhaps by not answering to make his wife go away and leave him. It had no such effect.

"And I wish she wouldn't speak French to Daisy all the time, Daisy does not understand French, Widgery says. Really Russians are most peculiar. I do hope nothing of your mother has rubbed off on Hugo or Marjorie, really I do."

The Earl moved his finger along the top of the book he was holding in a definitely anticipatory kind of way, as if his finger and not he was dying to get to work and open the book. His wife paid no attention.

"I can't understand this maid getting herself in this condition, she just doesn't seem the type, and then

John Buck is such a good gardener," the Countess sighed heavily.

For a second the Earl wondered how John Buck's gardening was going to be affected by his wife's condition, but not knowing very much about these things, he thought it was probably most possible. There was no doubt about it that women's conditions appeared to affect everything. Sometimes he wondered whether they didn't even affect the angle of the sun. He had read somewhere of a very interesting theory to do with women being affected by the moon, and if this was so, there didn't seem to be very much reason why they couldn't also be affected by the sun, and if they were affected by the sun it would appear that they could equally easily affect *it*.

"You haven't heard a word I've just said," the Countess was looking at him crossly. The Earl sighed inwardly. Ever since the maid's condition had been discovered everyone appeared to be looking at him crossly. Except for Widgery, of course. Thank goodness for Widgery. Widgery was the sort of fellow that you could really lean on. Widgery knew when a person did not wish to be disturbed, and what was better, Widgery was a man and therefore on his side. It appeared that Widgery had even warned this maid against the evils of falling ill, and the consequent effect on the family economy. He had, it appeared, even begged her to consider the soundness of his advice, but she had gone ahead with her foolishness, which was probably how John Buck's gardening had become affected.

The Earl looked up to find the Countess had disappeared. He rang the bell for Widgery.

"Widgery—I wonder if you could assist me on one point?"

"Mi'lord?"

"Why do they always call for hot water when women are having babies? Why, Widgery? For what reason is there this constant need for hot water?"

Widgery gave the matter his consideration, and then

after a lengthy pause, he said, "I'm afraid I do not know the answer to that particular question, mi'lord, but I will endeavour to find out for Your Lordship."

"Will you, Widgery? Good. Nothing indiscreet, mind, but please make some enquiries. It is, if I may say so, something that has caused me considerable puzzlement."

The Earl opened his book and lovingly smoothed the first page, much as a tired man runs his hand over a crisply laundered sheet before stepping into bed. Widgery, knowing the signs, withdrew.

Outside it was beginning to snow. He checked that the fire in the music room was burning well. The Countess liked to take tea in the music room during the winter. As he drew the strings of the heavy velvet curtains he noticed a small figure hurrying towards the house, dwarfed by the great cedar trees on the lawns, and looking against the blue light of the snowy evening, like a small grey animal struggling against the elements. Widgery frowned. Lucy Buck getting herself into a condition had caused enough trouble without her children coming up to the big house to bother people.

"Be off with you, child, we don't want to see you here," Widgery stood in the entrance to the doorway and gestured to Rose to go away. "Be off I tell you, your family's caused enough trouble here, go away."

Snowflakes formed on Rose's eyelashes, and settled on her nose, but she was so cold already she barely felt them. Grandmother's grey shawl was nice and long on her, but it had holes in it and wasn't really very warm against the snow.

"Please, Mr. Widgery, Daisy said I was to come and see the old Countess, sir, I mean Her Ladyship that is. Daisy said to come," she finished lamely.

"Daisy has no business sending you messages," Widgery frowned, and half-closed the door, as if he were rationing how much warm air he would let out into Rose's path. He thought for a moment, and then quickly realising that if Daisy had sent for the child, then it must be on orders from the old Countess, he opened the door again, and Rose stepped thankfully into the shelter of the house.

"Wipe those feet of yours and make sure that you make no dirty marks on the floor, or you'll be down on your knees cleaning up after yourself, see if you won't."

Widgery stalked off in the direction of the kitchens, leaving Rose to carefully wipe her feet, removing every vestige of snow and dirt on the mat. It was only when she looked up from this task that she realised that she hardly knew the way to the old Countess' rooms. Possibly because on her previous visits she had been so impressed by her surroundings she had kept her eyes down, but for whatever reason she now felt quite lost. She tried to stem the panic that was rising in her throat, but it was difficult. She knew that the old Countess would be waiting for her, and therefore there was no going back, but on the other hand it was very difficult to see how she could go forward, when the house was so very dark, and she did not know the way.

Eventually she inched forward trying to remember the feel of the walk that she had taken with her mother so many times. She remembered that for most of the way the floor was stone, and that eventually it turned to polished wood, and then it turned to stairs, lots of stairs, and so finally to the big oak doors that led to the old Countess' apartments.

"What in heavens name are you doing here? Widgery, what on earth is this creature doing in here?"

Rose shrank against the wall.

"I thought I heard something, and indeed I was right. What on earth is this creature doing in here?"

Widgery cleared his throat, and when he spoke his tones suggested as much regret as if he had found one of the family portraits slashed, or a piece of Meissen china broken.

"Your Ladyship," he said, "This is, I'm afraid, one of the maid's children. It appears Her Ladyship, the Dowager Countess, sent for her." Widgery's inflection conveyed exactly what he felt about the Dowager's foolishness in sending for the offspring of a maid.

"Yes, Widgery that's all very well, but what is one of the maid's children doing in the State Rooms. If I hadn't by chance heard something moving around—damage could have been done, Widgery, extensive damage."

"Yes, mi'lady."

"Were you trying to steal something, child, were you hoping to steal something? the Countess tapped her foot inpatiently, a characteristic of hers which together with her habit of repeating herself, made the Earl spend even more time in his library than he might perhaps have done had he been married to someone a little calmer.

"No, mi'lady," Rose felt tears were not very far away, but she knew that tears would only serve to make her look guiltier. "Excuse me mi'lady, but I was trying to find my way to the rooms of the old Countess, and I'm afraid I got lost."

"Well you mustn't get lost must you, child? It's a bad habit to get into. Widgery, see this child does not get lost again."

"Yes, mi'lady."

The Countess withdrew into the music room again. Although she knew she was fortunate in having married an Earl, she sometimes wished that she had married someone who liked London a little better. She found her temper was a trifle shorter when she was at Southwold. The days could seem very long, and it was difficult to keep warm unless you spent most of your time in one of the smaller rooms.

Widgery's hand pinched Rose's arm as he pushed her up the stairs in front of him.

"You take good care you never get lost again, you heard Her Ladyship. You've no business getting lost in this house, do you hear? It's a pity your mother didn't lose you. There——" He pushed her in front of the now familiar carved oak door, and left her. Rose wished she could have bitten him like Tim had bitten

Grandmother, but biting butlers was not in the general scheme of things. Not that is, if you wanted your father to keep his job. A good butler was not easy to come by, and everyone knew that Mr. Widgery was a great favourite with the Earl and Countess, and however much the Countess might admire Father's display of flowers, and however much the Head Gardener might value his way with roses, John Buck was easily replaceable. There was no doubt about that. Father often reminded Rose and Tim of this fact himself, just to make sure they were appreciating his luck in being the Earl's Lodge Keeper, and allowed to garden on the estate.

"We'd be out like that," Father would say snapping his fingers, "and we'd have no home, and no fire and nothing, that's what would happen if we caused offence."

Rose shut her eyes. She hoped, goodness she hoped, that she had not caused offence. If she had caused offence and Father got his dismissal because of her, she'd kill herself. Throw herself into the river like a girl years ago that Grandmother had told her of.

She knocked gently on the door, and stood waiting. She knocked again eventually, remembering that the two old ladies inside were a little deaf and possibly couldn't hear her inoffensive little tap.

"Ah, there you are, Lucy's little peasant child. Come here and sit by an old woman."

Rose sat on the little embroidered stool that had been so familiar in the days when she came up to the house with her mother. She found the heat of the fire, and the kind look in the old lady's eyes almost unbearable. Somehow everything had been so wonderful before Mother had got herself into a condition, and now nothing was wonderful.

"How is your mother, little one?" asked the old lady in her funny accent.

"She is not well, Your Ladyship."

"What does she say?" asked Vilanova.

"She says she is not well, you old fool," snapped

the Dowager Countess. "She has the baby soon, I think?"

"Yes, I think so," agreed Rose.

"Is there an old woman to be with her, to help with the baby coming?"

Rose nodded. The midwife in the village was coming up to help Grandmother. Rose remembered her coming when Tim was born. She had no teeth at all, and she had slapped Rose for getting in her way.

"Vilanova—bring the child a biscuit."

Vilanova extended Rose a box of biscuits, and Rose very politely bit into it. The walk through the snow had made her even hungrier, and she would have liked to have stuffed it into her mouth, but she was determined never to let her mother down. Her mother always ate delicately, like a lady, not like Grandmother and Father who gobbled their food.

"You look thin, child," the Countess peered at Rose. "That shawl is too thin for this weather, and you are too thin."

Rose said nothing. There was very little to say. She knew she was thinner, and so was Tim, but then without Mother's wage there was bound to be less to go round.

"Have you a pocket?"

Rose nodded, and the old lady gave her some biscuits to put in it.

"Thank you, Your Ladyship."

"That's all right, little peasant. And here, something for your mother," she handed Rose a basket, "women do not feel good when the babies are coming, so I have made them put some delicacies in there for her. She will not feel like heavy English puddings. Tell her to get better soon, there is an old woman who misses her. Now go quickly, before Vilanova starts crying."

Rose knelt quietly by her mother's bedside. She knew that she should leave her sleeping, but she was so excited about the Countess' gifts that she couldn't wait to see her mother's face. Perhaps when she saw the contents of the basket, perhaps she would wake up and look like she used to do before she had her condition?

"Look, Mother, just look, chicken and bread and all sorts. The old Countess said it would help to make you feel better, and she gave me a shawl instead of Grandmother's old one because it had so many holes, and this one has no holes at all. Look, it's so warm you hardly notice the cold. You can have it when you feel better, because I don't really need it."

Lucy opened her eyes, and looked at her daughter. Something of the despair she felt left her when she saw Rose's little pale face so happy and excited. She sat up and looked into the basket. The old lady had made Cook pack up what to her was merely a light snack, something that might fill a small corner just before you retired, or carry you through from breakfast until lunch, but to the Bucks, and to Rose feeling very hungry after her walk, it was a feast.

"Eat, Mother, please. You haven't eaten anything for so long," Rose pleaded, and her mother ate a little chicken.

"You and Tim have the rest," said Lucy.

"Yes, we will, don't worry," Rose pulled the blanket round her mother, and wished for the hundredth time that she would get better. Although she had a bump where the baby was, she looked so thin, as thin as the thinnest stick, and as white as when you peeled it.

Rose put the basket of provisions on the kitchen table, and gave her grandmother as fierce a look as she dared.

"This is for Tim and Father," she said warningly, "the old Countess sent it for Mother. Now she's eaten what she wants—Tim and Father are to have what's left."

"Who says who is going to have what food now? Airs and graces, that's what you're made of, like your poor mother. Happen they've not got her very far, eh?" Grandmother snatched the basket and delved into it.

Rose sighed. It was awful to see how greedy Grand-

mother was, but then she was very old and perhaps
old people got hungrier. Lately she herself hadn't had
much appetite for what little there was. Like her father
she just wanted everything to be over. Soon. The possibility that any minute now there would be a baby to
look after never occurred to her. She could only think
of her mother getting better and everything being like
it was before, with her and Tim and Tatty waiting by
the hedge to see her coming across the lawn. She heard
Tatty barking and knew her father was back. As usual
he didn't want to take his hat off, but went straight up
to her mother. It seemed all he wanted to do at the
moment—just come in and go straight up to be with
Lucy. And then Rose would take him something up
to eat, and he would sit with Lucy all evening. Sometimes when Rose came to get his plate, he would be
sitting holding her hand while she slept, and sometimes he would be reading bits aloud to her from her
Bible.

Tonight he went up to the bedroom as usual, but
was quickly down again.

"Mother—Rose—quickly, something's happening,
she's having pains."

Grandmother dropped her chicken leg and stared
at her son, "But son, baby's not meant to be here for
another while yet."

"It's coming, I tell you, it's coming."

"I told you nought good would come of this marriage John, no strong baby be early."

"Rose, run for Granny Page, quick, Rose."

Rose snatched up her new wool shawl and ran out
into the snow. It was over a mile to the village and
the snow was getting thicker on the ground, but she
was running as if it was spring and she was a colt
trying out her legs. Occasionally she stumbled because
parts of the road to the village were uneven. By the
time she found herself outside Granny Page's door
her dress and shawl were soaked.

Granny Page peered round the door at her.

"Yes?" she said, only it didn't sound like 'Yes' when she said it, because she had so few teeth.

"Mother's started," said Rose, "Father says can you come quickly."

"Tsh, it's always come quickly when there's a baby on the way," mumbled the old lady, and shuffled back into her kitchen for her old cloak hanging behind the door.

Her little cottage smelt strongly of broth, and as if she was in the habit of staying in bed a great deal and not changing the linen. She took such a long time fetching her cloak that Rose peered into the kitchen doorway to see if she was really coming, or perhaps had forgotten that Rose was there. The old lady turned quickly when she saw Rose.

"Be off," she snarled, "be off."

Rose withdrew into the snowy street. Granny Page was hiding her money.

When she eventually ventured through her front door, Rose realised that she would be lucky if she got her to the Lodge at all. Granny had no boots on, and her feet were so swollen that even the slippers she was wearing had difficulty fitting her feet. The only good thing about her was that she was so stooped and old she had a natural protection from the snow that drove at them. Rose gripped her firmly by the arm, if she could only get her to the Lodge before her slippers gave out, all would be well.

They struggled together against the snow storm. There was no running now, because the wind was so strong even a carthorse would have had to push against it. As it was, Rose and Granny struggled together against the weather like two small animals, only unlike the animals they could not shelter under a hedge, or find refuge down a burrow, they had to keep going. Ever after, when Rose looked back on that night, she often wondered how she did keep going, because Granny seemed to grow heavier and heavier, and slower and slower, with each small step, until they seemed in the end to be moving along in matters of inches, not yards.

Indeed if the road from the village had not led past the Lodge, she doubted whether she would have been able to find her way back, so snow-covered had the landscape become, and so crouched against the weather were the two of them, that even when the Lodge did eventually come into view, it was only when they were practically upon it, that they could look up and see it.

Grandmother opened the door. She and Granny were old acquaintances. Granny had delivered every baby in the village.

"The water's boiling, Granny," said Grandmother, who had put on her best apron to make it seem that she always wore an apron with lace in the house, but for the first ten minutes of her arrival Granny appeared impervious to either aprons or anything else, and sat perched on a kitchen chair like a squirrel, occasionally blowing on her fingertips that stuck out of her mittens like claws.

Rose and her grandmother gazed at Granny. They knew they couldn't hurry her upstairs, and what was worse they knew she wouldn't be hurried. There was a saying in the village—"two things be not hurried, spring nor a midwife." Granny said 'Tsh' several times as was her habit. From the way her grandmother reacted to this Rose thought that perhaps this was a good sign.

After some minutes the old lady looked at them. "I'll be up then," she said, and then when the other two brightened visibly at this statement, she added, "when I've had a cup of soup."

Rose watched her sipping the bowl of soup, and wanted to tip it over her. Although she had no teeth, she appeared to chew the soup as if it was bread, and the chewing process took a long time, a very long time. It seemed impossible that anyone could take so long to drink a cup of soup, when someone was upstairs having a baby.

Eventually Granny eased herself off the wooden chair, and like a caterpillar unfurled herself slowly.

Rose hoped that, like a caterpillar, she wouldn't quickly curl up again. By the look of her she could easily—but she didn't. Instead she crept forward towards the door that led to the stairs, her sodden slippers making a scraping noise along the flagged floor. Grandmother followed her, carrying the first of the buckets of hot water that were to make their way up the stairs throughout the night.

Rose went in search of Tim. She knew his nature, and that she would find him hiding somewhere. He had become so quiet since their mother had been ill. Sometimes she would find him sitting with Tatty in his kennel, sometimes he'd be in the little box room with some of his snails. Tonight he was in the box room, with Tatty.

"Tim, you shouldn't have Tatty in the house," Rose whispered to him, because she was afraid someone might hear, and come up and throw Tatty out into the snow again.

"He was so cold outside, Rose," Tim looked at her pleadingly, and went on stroking Tatty. "You were cold, weren't you, Tatty?"

Tatty looked from one to the other of them, and gave a nervous yawn.

"He's afraid you're going to put him outside, Rose," Tim translated, "he's afraid you're going to put him back in his kennel—where he's so cold."

"Tim, what's this?" Rose held up a crust of bread, "you've not been feeding the dog bread, Tim?"

"Yes, I have, Rose," said Tim almost proudly, "he can't catch so many rats when there's snow, and he keeps getting hungry at the moment."

"I know, Tim, but you can't give him our bread, Father'd whip you if he found out."

"I don't care, I like Tatty better than anyone—except Mother," said Tim defiantly, "and he hasn't been having much to eat. And that was my bit of bread I gave him, so it don't make much difference."

Rose stroked Tatty. The way he looked at you, you'd almost think he understood every word you said.

It had been a hard winter for the poor little dog, and yet he seemed just as cheerful as ever. Still ready to play at a moment's notice, and Tim was right, if they gave him their bread it was all right. She stiffened suddenly, and Tatty pricked his ears.

"What was that Rose?" Tim had gone quite white.

"I don't know, Tim," said Rose quickly, although she did know.

"There it goes again, Rose."

"Block your ears, Tim." Rose pushed Tim's head down, and she blocked her own ears.

It was terrible to hear a woman groaning like that. She'd once heard it before when Tim was born, but that had been during the day so she could run outside and hide until it was all over. Tonight there was no-where where you could get away from the noise. She felt trapped by it, just like the time when she got trapped in the hay loft when they were playing near the stables, and they'd brought a stallion in to visit the mares. She hadn't seen anything, only heard him squealing, and the grooms shouting, and just like at this moment, not even blocking her ears had kept the noise away.

"I wish she'd stop," Tim started to cry, and Rose put her arm around him.

They stayed up in the box room all night, huddled together with their dog, and being children they eventually fell asleep. When they woke it was morning, although still dark, and they were stiff and cold. Downstairs they could hear a cry which even they knew to be a baby.

Rose looked at Tim and for the first time it came to her that this was what it was all about, having a baby meant—having a baby! About the same time that this realisation was making itself known to her, Tim appeared to be having the same idea.

"That's a baby, Rose, Mother's had her baby."

They pushed each other in their eagerness to get down the stairs, and even forgot to smuggle Tatty out again, so that they all ran into the kitchen at the same time. Their father was sitting at the table. He looked up as they came in, no expression of joy or celebration on his face, only a grey, unshaved look that made him seem unfamiliar.

"What's that dog doing in here?" He pointed accusingly at Tatty, "get it out of here. Get it out, I'm telling you."

He picked up Tatty, opened the back door and threw him out into the snow.

Rose and Tim stared at him, and then Tim went to the back door and let himself out.

"Where are you going?" shouted his father, "come back in here."

Tim stayed outside. Rose knew that he would be sitting with Tatty in the kennel.

"Shall I make you something, Father?"

She hardly spoke above a whisper, because she felt so frightened. She didn't know why, but she knew something terrible had happened, because Father loved Tatty, and he was never cruel and he never drank anything, and now that she was standing near him she could smell that he had been drinking and smelt like the grooms did on a Saturday night.

"What's the matter?" Her father stared at her, "stop looking at me like that. You should be happy you've a little brother, that should make you happy."

Rose said nothing, and perhaps because she was silent, her father suddenly took her hand and pulled her near. He looked at her so desperately she wanted to run away.

"It's Mother, isn't it?" she asked.

Her father nodded, and his large hand wrapped round hers felt as if he was about to break her fingers, so tightly was he holding on to her.

"I'll go up to her, shall I?"

Her father shook his head. Rose thought for a minute, and then she knew that the best way to deal with this moment was to pretend that she was her mother. At a moment like this Mother always moved calmly, and thought about other people. She might not be quite eleven yet but she could pretend she was. She let her father's hand go with difficulty.

"You sit there, Father, and I'll go and see if I can do something."

Her mother's room was dark, because the two old ladies were too busy cleaning up the baby to notice Rose slipping into the room. She knelt beside her parents' bed, and when she saw how pale her mother was, as pale and white as the snow outside, Rose wanted to scream. She didn't want her mother to be pale and white, she wanted her to be walking across the lawn towards her on a spring day, or asking her the names of flowers, she didn't want her to be lying there like something carved on a tomb. Rose slipped her hand into the one that lay on the patchwork quilt. She hoped that her mother would turn and smile at her and get her colour back if she felt one of her children's hands in hers. But she didn't turn or smile, and Rose felt that she didn't even know that it was Rose holding her hand, or even that anyone else was in the room, or even that there was a room that she was in.

"What will you be doing here, child?"

Grandmother frowned at her from above the bundle of shawls that was holding the baby.

"I'm being with Mother," said Rose.

"This is no place for children," Her grandmother looked at her uncomfortably, "you'll do best to take Granny Page home now it's getting lighter."

"Well, you've a fine grandson there," Granny Page mumbled as the old ladies went down the stairs, "but by the look of the mother you'll be needing someone to feed him for you."

"Mother, it's Rose—please wake up Mother," Rose shook her mother's hand as strongly as she dared. "Please don't die, Mother, please."

As if to encourage her hopes Rose suddenly noticed her mother's lips were moving, although her eyes were shut. She couldn't understand what she was whispering. She thought it must be something in French. She didn't want her to know that she couldn't understand what she was saying, so she stroked her hand as if she did.

Her grandmother came back up the stairs, and shook her by the shoulder, "I told you this was no place for children," she whispered to Rose, "now be off and take Granny Page home"

Rose turned on her grandmother.

"You or Father take Granny Page home," she said so fiercely that even her grandmother took a step backwards.

"Your father's not well, and I'm old," grumbled Grandmother.

"Father's been drinking, let him take Granny Page home, it'll do him good. I'm staying here with Mother, and you mind Tim and the baby."

Rose turned back to her mother, but not before she saw that Grandmother was looking at her oddly, as if she had suddenly changed, or as if she had only just seen her.

Rose stayed holding her mother's hand, until her father came back from the village. Then she went to fetch him.

"I think you should shave yourself Father," she told him, "Mother wouldn't like to see you like that."

Her father didn't appear to hear what she had said, but sat down at the table.

"Give Father some water to shave himself, Grandmother," said Rose, and then she said to him a little louder, "where are Mother's beads with the cross on them?"

Grandmother looked up from nursing the baby on her lap. "What do you want with that Popish nonsense?"

"Mother would want them," said Rose.

"They're under my mattress," Tim had crept into the kitchen and was crouching by the stove, "she lent them me when I was frightened in the storm last summer."

Tim's eyes filled with tears at the memory.

Rose threaded the beads through her mother's fingers, and then knelt beside her parents' bed again. Nothing would make her leave her mother now, but she knew that she would want to have her beads. Mother always held her beads when something happened—no matter what Grandmother said about popery or heathen ways.

When her father joined her beside the bed, Rose noticed with detachment that he had shaved, and no longer smelt of drink. He felt her mother's wrist, and Rose knew this was to make sure her heart was still beating. It obviously was, because he seemed to look a little better after that.

"There's gates to open," Grandmother hissed through the door, and her son got dutifully to his feet. "Is she still with us?" she asked Rose, but Rose didn't reply, and she went down to the baby again.

The snow was beginning to melt as John opened the gates to allow Lady Marjorie's carriage to pass through. Perhaps because the sun was coming out, and she was pleased to be back at Southwold, in spite of the weather, Lady Marjorie leant out of window and called to John, "How's your wife John?" She liked John Buck, ever since years ago when he had given Hugo a black eye for pushing her in the pond.

She looked out of her carriage window, her cheeks pink and healthy against the white of her furs. "I said, 'How's your wife John?'" He appeared not to have heard her.

"Sorry, Lady Marjorie?"

"How's Lucy?"

The poor man said nothing, but his face, usually so broad and smiling, crumpled suddenly. "She's dying, Lady Marjorie."

Rose didn't turn as Lady Marjorie tiptoed into the little room. Nevertheless, she knew there was gentry in the room because she could smell perfume, and hear the swish of skirts. Lady Marjorie knelt beside her.

Death is a solemn business, and how long they knelt before it, none of them knew, but eventually

Rose felt Lady Marjorie's hands guiding her down the stairs to the kitchen.

"Your mother is dead, Rose dear, you must be a comfort to your father now." The young girl's face looked down at the little girl in front of her, deeply troubled. She looked from the little girl to the old woman who was holding the baby. "That baby will need to be fed," she said quickly, "I'll tell the carriage to take it to the village. Is there someone there who can nurse it for you? Never mind—Mrs. Petifor will know. I will take the children up to the house for a meal, they've had a terrible shock, and then I will send the carriage back for you and the baby."

Upstairs they could hear their father sobbing, downstairs the baby cried. The children followed the young girl into her carriage, and although she would have liked to have hugged them to her, she didn't because her furs were very white.

Chapter 4

The arrival in the hall at Southwold of two of the
Lodge Keeper's children was not what the Countess
expected. It was not only not what she expected, but
she was extremely put out, not to say peeved, by her
daughter's manner of return.

Marjorie was not, on the whole, given to whims or
acts of emotion, but plucking up children from the
Lodge and depositing them at Southwold, was quite
obviously not only a whim but also an act of emotion.
The Countess didn't like acts of emotion, any more
than she liked tenants' children. 'Self control' was one
of her favourite words. She always felt that if 'self control' was observed by the masses, which it quite obviously wasn't, then all would be well and they would
overcome their difficulties. The case of the maid dying
in childbirth was quite obviously a clear example of
a lack of self control and looking into her daughter's
face she realised that not only was the maid guilty
of this—but any moment now it was quite obvious
that her daughter was going to be guilty of it too.
Marjorie was on the verge of tears, something that
the Countess felt she could not appreciate in a returning daughter. However—even though her husband
could rarely find a subject upon which to converse
with her—she was not altogether stupid, and, after
'self control,' 'dealing with situations' was another of
her virtues. She set about 'dealing with the situation'
she saw before her.

"Of course the children shall have a hot bath and a meal, dear, I shall ring for Widgery and tell him myself. No, dear, there's no need for you to ring for Widgery—oh very well."

She pursed her lips slightly as Marjorie pulled the bell pull for the butler. Marjorie was becoming a trifle independent lately, no doubt that was how all young ladies became nowadays as soon as they became engaged. The Countess liked her future son-in-law, even though he wasn't as brilliant a match as a mother could wish for. Hugo said he was very bright, and he certainly had charm, of that there was no doubt— it was just that she hoped that he wasn't filling Marjorie's head with the sort of ideas that she and her father wouldn't like. Sometimes she suspected he was a little bit too liberal to make her quite easy, but then all young men had a few silly ideas about reforming the world and such like matters, when they were young. Happily, when they matured a little they usually found out just how silly these ideas were, and if they didn't—well they just didn't get on in life, and that was that.

When Widgery appeared the Countess noticed that his eyes strayed to the dirty marks the children's feet had made on the marble floor of the hall. The Countess' eyes had also taken in this unsavoury fact.

"You had better send one of the maids to clean up this mess," she said to Widgery, and tried not to betray any emotion when Marjorie interrupted her, and implored Widgery to hurry to fetch Mrs. Petifor so that they could comfort the children by giving them a meal, and perhaps a hot bath and some clothes.

"Marjorie," her mother took her aside, "I don't think you should go too far in this matter."

"Mamma—these children have just lost their mother," Marjorie had flung her furs aside and was preparing to follow Widgery, "they have had a terrible shock and need to be comforted."

The Countess watched her only daughter disappearing in the wake of Widgery, and sighed. Sometimes she suspected that Marjorie had inherited more of the old Countess' Russian blood than she actually cared to think about. Giving tenants' children meals, and things like this, were actions that the old lady would be perfectly capable of. It seemed that only a few months ago she had given a perfectly good Sèvres box to someone or another. In fact, when the Countess had inquired after it (since it had been a Christmas present from herself a few years back) the old Countess had merely shrugged her shoulders, and said she had given it away, as if everyone gave away Sèvres boxes on any day of the week.

Lady Marjorie watched the young children eating, and wished she could do something more definite to help poor John Buck's children. She knew that he had worshipped his dark and slender wife, and she wondered what would happen to the poor little family now that she was gone. Certainly the grandmother was a dreadful woman, forever hanging about as if she wanted to do something—she wouldn't do much to cheer the poor children's lives, and with the father working so much, their future didn't look very bright. Still at least no-one at Southwold was allowed to starve, and at least their father was a favourite with Mamma, thanks to his extraordinary way with roses. His improvements to the Countess' rose garden had definitely done much to protect him when his wife had been found to be indisposed.

"Have we any clothes and things we could lend the children, Mrs. Petifor?" Lady Marjorie looked at Mrs. Petifor with the firm eye of one who knew that Mrs. Petifor would most definitely find some clothes for the children, that is if she didn't want a certain young lady getting very cross with her.

Mrs. Petifor recognised the look on Lady Marjorie's face, and quickly replied that there were some old children's clothes that were in quite a good state of repair at the back of one of the linen cupboards.

"There," Lady Marjorie spun Rose round, "how do you feel now? Better? And Tim? How's little Tim?"

Tim stared at her gravely, he felt uncomfortable in velvet, but obviously the young lady thought he looked nice, and obviously she wanted him to smile—so he smiled.

They climbed back into the carriage again, a forlorn little couple in their second-hand clothes. They were tired now, and the new clothes were uncomfortable, but they tried to look pleased because the gentry seemed pleased, so they knew they must be right.

"I hope you're not going to make a practice of bringing home young persons to be dressed and fed, Marjorie?" Her mother looked at Marjorie as sternly as she dared. It was difficult to risk angering Marjorie, young girls did such silly things nowadays. Poor Sarah's girl had eloped to Florence with a painter. The Countess could only thank the Almighty for preserving Marjorie from the attentions of painters.

"Of course I shan't make a *practice* of bringing children home, Mamma," said Lady Marjorie a trifle petulantly, "those are John Buck's children, and his poor wife is dead."

The Countess thought the less said about the matter was probably by far the better. Girls who were engaged were inclined to be emotional.

"I wonder where Papa is?" she said, to change the subject.

The children climbed out of the carriage and ran into the Lodge. Just for a minute they had forgotten what had happened, and that their mother was dead. But when they saw their father sitting at the table staring in front of him, they knew that she was and that this was not a bad dream from which they would wake, and then shake themselves like Tatty, but cold day, and the house was as cold as your own bed when you climbed back into it after a nightmare.

Tim began to cry. He looked so pathetic in his funny velvet clothes that Rose almost felt inclined to laugh, but then she didn't. Her mother was dead, and she didn't think she would ever laugh again.

Ted, the undertaker, knocked on the door, and

when their father opened it and saw him, it was too much for him to bear, and he ran past him and down the garden. Rose looked at Ted. He was a kind man, in spite of being an undertaker.

"Are you going to take Mother away with you now?" she asked him, as he measured her up.

"No," Ted shook his head, "not yet, not till coffin arrives. Think I've got one that will suit—don't reckon it'll be too much," he added hopefully.

Rose shook her head.

"No, Ted, it mustn't be too much. Father hasn't any money, on account of Mother not being able to work lately." She looked down at her mother. She was glad they weren't taking her away yet.

"I'll come tomorrow. And I'll be telling the Vicar for you, Rose. The lads will dig for you. Hope the weather holds off. And by the way, Dorothy says to tell you that the baby is fine."

Rose looked at him. Of course—the baby.

Ted looked at Rose looking up at him. She was a reflection of the dead woman he had just measured. You'd swear it was her come to life if you hadn't just seen her laid out. Poor John, it must make it worse to see the poor woman's face all around you. Ted shook his head sadly and closed the Lodge door behind him. He had lost his first wife, and in just such a way. It had taken him a couple of years before he could hold his head up and see what was around him, but when he had—by fortune it was Dorothy's eye that he had caught. Women and babies, he thought as he walked back along the road to the village, they were hard to hold onto, no doubt of that.

The following day they buried Lucy Buck, and the weather kept off. The sun even shone as they lowered her into the grave. John's face was rigid and grey with tiredness and grief. Rose held Tim's hand and that kept him from crying, and Grandmother wore her blue shawl, in spite of the cold wind, because she was determined to show it off to Mabel Burrows and the

women of the village who had gathered in the graveyard to see the coffin lowered.

Rose looked back at the mound of freshly dug earth,
and wondered what they would do for a headstone.
She knew that they were expensive, but she didn't
dare think how much they might cost. All she knew
was that Mother must have a gravestone, with her
name on it, and the day she died, because no one
knew the day she had been born. Not even Mother had
known that.

"We were lucky it kept from snowing," Grandmother said taking off her shawl.

Rose ignored her, and took Tim up to their bedroom.

"I think you'd better rest, Tim. Mother would say
you'd better, you know."

"Yes, Rose."

"I'm going to be Mother now Tim, and I want you
to remember that. I'm going to be very quiet in my
heart, like she used to tell us to be, so that I can
hear her telling me what to do, from heaven."

"Yes, Rose."

"So have a little sleep now, Tim, and then I'm
going to find a way to get a headstone for Mother.
Mother must have a headstone," she added half to
herself.

"Yes, she must, mustn't she, Rose, otherwise we
won't know where to find her, will we, Rose?"

"No, we won't."

Rose closed the door.

She sat down on one of the wooden stairs outside
the bedroom, and thought for a long time. She had
to have a headstone for her mother soon, or as Tim
said they wouldn't be able to find her. The flowers
on her grave would die, and the earth would get flat-
tened, and she would get lost.

She couldn't believe that she would never see her
mother again. It seemed too easy just to bury someone, and then never see them again. If everything in
life was so difficult, as she knew that it was, it just

didn't seem possible that death could be so easy. She remembered how often her mother had prayed with them for people who were dead, and she wondered if she should pray for her now? But somehow the thought repelled her. It didn't seem possible that someone so good and beautiful should need prayers. She made up her mind to pray *to,* not for her.

She went down to the kitchen, and found her father and grandmother in the same positions as she had left them. Father just staring in front of him, looking down the oak table to mother's chair as if he expected her to be sitting there sewing, as she always had done. And Grandmother sitting in the rocking chair in the corner not paying attention to anything.

Now that the funeral was over and Grandmother had worn the blue shawl for all to admire, she seemed listless, as if there was nothing around the house that needed doing. This puzzled Rose. Grandmother hadn't liked Mother, Grandmother hadn't wanted Mother or Father to get married to each other, so why didn't she get around and do all the things that Mother would be doing, instead of just sitting in the rocking chair and paying no attention?

"Shall I cut some bread?" Rose asked, but receiving no reply, she too sat down, and eventually fell asleep to the sound of the clock ticking, and her silent family.

An hour or two later Rose woke to her grandmother's voice.

"Gates, John," she nodded towards the window, and John stopped staring, and hurried out into the evening to open the gates.

It was the gates that finally seemed to pump life back into the Lodge again. If neither Rose, nor Tim, nor their father, felt like eating, and if their grandmother didn't feel like cooking, and if the house began to look dusty and neglected because no-one felt like polishing it, then at least the gates still needed attending. The gates could not be ignored like meals and housework, they had a life of their own, letting in the gentry in their carriages, and the tradesmen from the village, and callers from neighbouring houses. The gates were a witness to the fact that life would go on, inexorably, no matter how you were feeling. It was the gates that prevented John from following his wife, although lying on his side staring at the wall in his empty bed, he was often tempted to run across the lawn and jump into the river, and oblivion.

Rose didn't know that what her father was suffering was not only grief and despair, but terrible remorse. Although she knew, if a little roughly, what the basic mechanics of procreation amounted to, she couldn't associate her mother's death from childbirth with the bitter lines that appeared in his face over the following months. In a way she wasn't interested by the effect that her mother's death had had on the two older members of the family, so obsessed was she by two, to her more important issues—looking after Tim, and finding a way to buy her mother a headstone.

Her grandmother did nothing to help Tim. She seemed to be incapable of looking after him, now that she no longer had a daughter-in-law to grumble at. Now that Lucy had gone, Rose realised what she had always only dimly appreciated, that her mother had run the house single-handed. But she had done it so quietly and efficiently, and so unobtrusively, that half the time she had made it seem as if Grandmother was doing it, whereas now that Lucy was no longer there, it was perfectly apparent to Rose that Grandmother was useless.

Besides dressing herself, and baking the bread, her grandmother did nothing, and, Rose realised, had never done anything. She had been vociferous in her complaint on every subject, loud in her condemnations of humanity in general, while idling away every day that had been given to her. She was one of those people who had made a genius out of doing nothing and making it seem as if it was something; so, every day Rose tried to get a little more done before she went to school. She tried to remember what Lucy would do before she went up to the big house every day. She tried to remember the sequence in which she had performed all her household duties, and she tried to do them as well as she thought she would have wanted, because Rose felt that her mother was with her and would always be with her. She knew that Tim, because he was younger, had no such feeling, and she knew how much he missed her from the way he cried in his sleep, or would suddenly, for no particular reason, throw himself on the ground and burst into tears.

Sometimes Rose wished that she could cry, but somehow she couldn't. Crying would take up time, and she didn't seem to have very much of that. And then her thoughts were so taken up with worrying about everything. She wondered once or twice if this was what being a grown-up meant? Worrying about whether or not the baby was getting enough, and whether they would be able to save enough to pay the woman in the village who was feeding him. Worrying whether Father's trousers would keep from getting any thinner round the knees, and whether the darns would hold, and whether the embrocation was having any effect on his bad chest. When she went to bed at nights she often found she couldn't sleep because of these problems, but when she did eventually fall asleep it was always in the middle of wondering if they would ever have enough money to buy the headstone.

Possibly, just as the need for the gates to be opened and shut kept her father going, so the thought that her mother lay buried without a headstone kept Rose going. She felt determined that once the headstone was in place there would be an end to her worries and therefore she managed to ignore everyday problems, looking ahead only to the great day when they would see the piece of marble put into place.

When she realised, quite suddenly, how it would be possible to achieve her aim, it was almost a shock. And then, because she didn't want to do what she knew was obviously the solution, she ignored the fact that she had indeed found the solution and pretended that it wasn't really, because it seemed so hard to give up what in her heart she knew she must give up, what she knew could be sold for the price of the precious headstone—her little china box.

She traced the outline of the little blue flowers on the box with her finger, remembering the day of her birthday. The feel of the cold porcelain, the outline of the decoration, brought back that day as exactly as if she had suddenly rounded a corner and seen it painted in pictures before her eyes. She remembered how much her shoes had pinched on the walk up to the house, and how she had suddenly forgotten all about them in the excitement of actually treading the stairs and walking into the rooms of that unknown species—the gentry.

"Father, you must take this box and sell it in town, and then we can buy Mother a headstone."

"I wonder, would it be your Mother's thought, Rose?" her father looked from her to the box and back again. He knew that his wife had thought of the box as a dowry for Rose. "Besides," he added quickly, "there'll be no-one for the gates."

Rose could see that her father did not realise how important it was to purchase that headstone. She could see that he didn't realise that if they didn't buy Mother a headstone, they would lose her forever, never to find her again.

"Tim and I will do the gate," she heard herself say.

"You can't manage the gates, Rose." Her father shook his head.

"I can't, Father, but both of us could. He could do one, and I could do the other."

"You'd never shift them."

"Yes we would, Father."

"You mind your tongue, girl," grumbled her grandmother, "ideas the like of that, and what would gentry say to children opening gates? Do you want to get your father wrong? Ideas like yours'll get him wrong, and then where'll it get us?"

"Father—how long would it take you—into town and back?" Rose stared at her father anxiously.

"Now, Rose, I'd say half a day—there and back, if I hurried and didn't stop for left or right."

"And how many carriages go through in half a day, Father? One or two, and they're tradesmen. If you went early, Father, you could be back for noon, and no-one would know better. They couldn't know if they didn't see, could they?"

Rose saw that the idea was catching her father's imagination.

"I suppose I could leave before light, be there for opening, and still be back. There'd be no-one in the village with money for this, no doubt of that. You'd have to be in town to get money for this."

"And then we could buy Mother a headstone, such as the gentry have."

"They cost more than an old box," said Grandmother, not liking to see her daughter-in-law doing well—even in death.

"This box is French, Father. French things fetch a lot of money—Mother told me once."

"That's true, Rose, and we could get her something that would make her proud, couldn't we, Rose? So that she could look down and say 'John'—she'd say 'John'—what would she say, Rose?" John looked helplessly at his daughter.

"She'd say 'thank you, John', wouldn't she, Father? The way she always said it."

"Yes, that's what she'd say."

"You'll go, won't you, Father?"

"I'll go, Rose, I'll go, even if it costs us more than we could give, we should do this for your mother."

Rose knew that he was thinking it might cost them their home, that if he was found out he might be asked to leave the Lodge and they might have to go away from Southwold, but she knew that even this thought wouldn't stop him from going now. She wondered if he realised just why the headstone was so important, and thought he probably didn't. Her mother had once told her that it was up to women to think of things, that men didn't find it so easy to think of things. And she thought this was most likely to be true, because men never seemed to realise when they had holes in their clothes, or if they did they just waited for women to sew them, and very few of them could bake a loaf, or even pick up a baby, although they were strong. It seemed that God had made women to be in the house and think, and men to be strong for lifting and working.

John had little difficulty in rising earlier next morning, since he slept only a few hours at a time. He pulled on his coat and his breeches and crept downstairs.

"Rose, what'll you be doing here?" He stared at his daughter in astonishment. She was the colour of a white wall.

"I was waiting for you, Father, to give you your bread and see you were off."

"I can cut bread, Rose, you should be sleeping. How will you manage the gates on no sleep?"

Rose looked as if she thought this was irrelevant. She gave him the little box, wrapped in a piece of cloth, and watched him put it carefully into his pocket.

"Get the best price you can, won't you, Father? Remember, the best price will buy the best headstone."

Her father nodded. He looked almost forlorn, like Tim when he couldn't think of an answer at school.

"I'll do my best, Rose."

He turned at the door and put one of his large hands on her shoulder, almost weighing her down. "You'll go to your bed now, won't you, girl?"

Rose didn't answer. She couldn't tell him that she couldn't sleep, wouldn't sleep, until she saw the money for the box safe in the hands of the stone cutter. She had waited up all night to see her father off, dozing in front of the stove with her head on the kitchen table, determined that she should see him walking off towards the town with the little box safe in his pocket.

John turned back along the road and unaccountably he found his eyes filling with tears as the little girl waved to him from the Lodge Gates. He thought most probably that the sight of her waiting downstairs for him as her mother used to do had affected him, and that her likeness to her mother most likely always would affect him. Nowadays she seemed to be more like her than when Lucy was alive. Sometimes it made him wish himself to the devil just to see her dusting, or taking care of Tim—doing up his buttons or some such.

He cleared his throat, and quickened his pace. His lantern threw shadows in front of him as he walked. He must walk as fast as he could, walk out, stride out, to bring himself back in time, to bring himself back to the gates and the Lodge before anyone found out and got him wrong. This walk could cost them everything they had, but he knew he must make it, if only for the memory of his love.

"My love is like a red, red rose."

Lucy had once taught him a poem that went like that, and he had learnt it to please her, although now he remembered only that first line. His love had not been like a red rose. He liked red roses—and Her Ladyship had some beauties—but his favourites were always the white ones. If you looked at a white rose that had just opened, just for a moment you saw something perfect, and then it would quickly become yellow, because it was too perfect to last, and that was like Lucy. Lucy had been too perfect to last. She had been a white rose all right. Her skin so white against her black hair, and that black hair so heavy that when she let it down it covered her down to her waist, and her waist still so trim that you could swear you would span it between just the two of your hands put together.

He frowned and stared at the road in front of him, keeping up the pace he had set himself, and his thoughts swerving away from the direction that they looked as if they might lead him to. There were many things best not remembered. Nowadays it seemed as if most things were best not remembered. He knew that Rose was right about the headstone. If he got that headstone

for Lucy, perhaps she would forgive him for what he
had done to her. Not that she had once said anything,
his white and perfect rose, not once. But perhaps once
that headstone was laid in place he could learn to
forgive himself a little, although he doubted it.

When he arrived in the town it was light and the
shutters were being removed from the shop fronts.
He sat on a bench in the main square, waiting for the
time to pass. He had some idea of doing business, from
watching horse sales and the like, and he knew that
should he arrive in the shop as it opened, his price
would look low. He must arrive in the shop some time
after it had opened, as long as he dared to leave it.
In view of the children being in charge of the gates
while he was away it couldn't be very long, but it
mustn't be obvious to the man that he *needed* to sell
the box, only that he *wanted* to sell it.

"Where did you come by this?"

John found his neck reddening, and his fists tighten-
ing. Town people had a way of putting things that could
get you angered quicker than anyone swearing at you
to your face. He knew the question meant 'where did
you steal this?' and he found it hard to answer.

"It rightly belongs to my daughter," he said slowly,
"she say to me to bring it to town and sell it for her."

"Yes? And where did she come by it, may I ask?"

"She was given it sir, for her birthday sir, her tenth
birthday as it was, by a very generous lady."

"I can believe that."

John's blood raced even quicker when he heard that
reply. Why even the very look of this man made you
want to floor him. He took a deep breath, but then
after he had taken a step or two backwards he thought
of how much the headstone meant, and then he thought
that folk most like *would* wonder how a man like
him came by anything so delicate and lady-like, so
he waited for his eyes to see less red and then he
said, "I see you are thinking this box might not belong to my daughter, sir. Well it does, it was given

to her by the old Countess herself, a great lady, the old Dowager Countess Southwold herself."

The effect this statement had on the man in front of John was ultimately satisfying. For, while at first he thought John was not telling the truth, he finally realised that it would be too easy to check up on a story of this nature. If the farmer, or whatever he was, wanted to lie to him, he wouldn't need to fabricate such a story. Something much simpler would have satisfied.

"Why did the Dowager give your daughter this box?"

"It was her tenth birthday," said John.

The shop owner picked up the box, and looked at it thoughtfully. Such shining simplicity pointed to a very good sale.

Inwardly John heaved a sigh of relief. Now it was up to him to get the best price.

When next he saw his gates again, for knowing them as he did—every shining, twisted, curving wrought iron curlecue—he thought of them as his, his pockets were heavy and his heart was considerably lighter. This evening he would walk down to the village and give over the money to Ted for the tombstone, and soon his beloved would have a monument fit for gentry.

Rose looked at him from the other side of the kitchen. He didn't need to ask her what he wanted to know.

"Only one carriage, Father, and that was a tradesman," she said triumphantly.

John sat down heavily in his chair, and if he could have admitted it to himself, he would have realised that he felt like bursting into tears. All the way back from the town his fear had been that the Earl or Countess would have seen his children dragging those heavy iron gates open, and that they would have demanded his dismissal. Now he was home he could hardly believe his good fortune had held out.

"Someone at the gates, John," said Grandmother.

John got up, and went thankfully out into the cold again.

Rose watched him opening the gates from the window, and she felt a strange excitement at the thought that they now had the money to get the headstone. The feeling she had was not like the excitement before a birthday, nor even like the kind you got when you were on your way to school, but a feeling as if you knew that any minute now, quite soon, you might be going to burst into tears, but not because you felt sad.

"Father—we'll have to write the letters for Ted, he always needs to have the letters written for him."

Rose watched her father eating his supper with some impatience. Somehow he didn't seem very good at thinking for himself. He would have walked off to the village to see Ted and give him the money, and never thought of writing anything out first. Not that he could write, not having been to school like her and Tim.

"Can *you* write what we require, Rose?"

"I might be able to, Father, if you think of what to say."

John stopped eating for a minute, and stared past Rose. There were so many things he wanted to say, if he had the words. If he could write words like 'My love is like a red, red rose', those were the kind of words that Lucy would appreciate. He looked at his daughter. Rose had been to school, perhaps she would know of words that would look good? She had a good way of forming her letters, the teacher had said.

"I don't know if I could write well enough for Ted to copy. I don't know that I could do it well enough, Father."

"You make good letters, Rose, your mother said so, and teacher say so."

"But not good enough for a headstone, Father. I wouldn't know how to set it out."

"What shall we do, Rose?"

Rose felt everyone was suddenly looking at her, as if she knew the answer, as if they were *sure* that she would know the answer. She knew she must find the answer; after all the trouble they had been to, they mustn't now make a mistake in the letters on Mother's headstone. They could never hold their heads up in the village if they made a mistake. Not that many in the village could read or write, but things got about in a village and it wouldn't be long before someone found out, and then folk might gossip. Rose felt her cheeks going pink at the thought of folk gossiping.

"I know, Father, let's go to teacher, she'll help us. She always says she'll help us, doesn't she, Tim?"

Tim nodded, "Yes, Father, teacher always says she'll help us when we want."

"I daren't, Rose. What'll folk say if I go knocking on teacher's door?"

"What will they say, John?" Grandmother looked grim at the thought of what she knew they would say. Teacher was not young, but she was a woman, a lady most folk would say, and she had no husband.

"I'll come, then?"

"You'll come, Rose?" Her father looked at her puzzled.

"If I come with you, Father, teacher will do the letters for Ted, and no-one can say anything, because I'll be with you."

Rose didn't know why it was important for her father not to be seen knocking on the teacher's door at night, but she knew that no-one did do that kind of thing in their village. Her father was very shy of going on this walk to the teacher's cottage, Rose could tell that by the way he had whistled all the way to her front door. Lamps were lit in the windows of the cottage round them, and Rose stamped her feet up and down to stop them from getting cold, and also to make sure that if anyone in the other cottages had seen them walking up to the teacher's door, they couldn't fail to notice that Rose was with her father and that he was not alone.

"Good evening, ma'am," John removed his cap.

Mrs. Dickinson stared at the man and his daughter.

She thought she recognised the Lodge Keeper from Southwold. She looked at the little girl beside him a little closer.

"Rose Buck—my goodness—I didn't recognise you in the dark."

"Good evening, ma'am," John began again.

"Good evening," replied Mrs. Dickinson at last, realising that she was facing something in the nature of a deputation, and that being so she must observe the conventions.

"Myself and my daughter, ma'am were wondering if you could be of some assistance to us?" John had rehearsed his opening phrase on the walk, carefully adopting the style of speech that he knew gentry appreciated.

"I will certainly be glad to give you any assistance that I can," said Mrs. Dickinson, much to John's relief, because he had somewhat counted on her replying in this way, and if she hadn't, it would have upset his next statement.

"That is very kind of you, ma'am, and myself and my daughter much appreciate your kindliness—the assistance we require is for the writing out of a headstone, for my wife, Rose's mother."

"Come in," said Mrs. Dickinson, opening the cottage door wider for them to follow her into her little sitting room. As she closed the door she thought of how much she had wanted to be a missionary when she was young, and how dull being a teacher had seemed to be in comparison, but now she realised that there was very little difference. After all, it was just as important to bring the Word to the natives of England as it was to the natives of Africa. "What kind of inscription had you in mind?"

John looked down at Rose.

"Father wanted to do the inscription properly," said Rose, speaking for both of them, "with Mother's name, and the date of her death, because she never knew when she was born."

Mrs. Dickinson busied herself at her desk and eventually found a nice, white piece of paper and dipping her pen in black ink, she waited for instructions.

"Name goes first, doesn't it, ma'am?"

"Yes, that's right, Mr. Buck."

"Well that'll be 'Lucy Buck'—and if you wouldn't mind putting it in big letters ma'am, then Ted can copy what he sees. His reading isn't up to much I'm afraid, ma'am."

Mrs. Dickinson wrote out Lucy's name and the date of her death, and then she waited patiently for John to tell her what he would like to put at the bottom of the headstone.

"Perhaps a piece out of the Bible?" Rose suggested.

"But, Rose, lying there near the church she can hear the Bible every Sunday, I was thinking on something more like—poetry."

"That's a very good idea Mr. Buck, poetry is most suitable for a headstone. If I may make a few suggestions?" Mrs. Dickinson bustled to her bookshelves, and took down one or two items from it. "How about something from Shakespeare? He can be most appropriate."

"Whatever you suggest, ma'am, I should be most grateful."

Valiantly Mrs. Dickinson read from her volumes lines here and lines there that she thought might be a fitting tribute to the poor man's wife, but it was perfectly apparent that neither father nor daughter could find satisfaction in the lines she suggested, and were becoming minute by minute more embarrassed by the situation in which they found themselves.

"How about something in your own words?" she suggested eventually.

"Yes, Father, how about something in your words?"

John turned away from the teacher and said in half-whisper to Rose, "what does she mean?"

"Something you might put in a letter," Rose explained.

"I never yet wrote a letter, Rose."

"Well, how about something that you used to say to her. Something she liked to hear you say."

John thought about this, and then he said doubtfully, "I used to say to her she was a great lady, which she was, but then I'm not sure as that would do for a headstone."

Rose looked at Mrs. Dickinson, and knew their time was running out. Mrs. Dickinson couldn't spend all evening trying to think of poetry for Father to put on the headstone. She had books to look at and lessons to prepare. Mrs. Dickinson didn't only teach them how to read and write and add up. She taught them about kings and queens from olden days, and about far away places where the Empire was, and where the Queen ruled and the flag flew. Mrs. Dickinson had been abroad. She had once been to France and eaten snails.

"Let's put something French, Father."

"Rose is thinking my wife would like that, because she spoke French, ma'am," John looked at Mrs. Dickinson apologetically. He thought that like the rest of the village, she would probably take a poor view of a man who had married someone who could speak French.

"An excellent idea, Rose, and how about the words, what words would you like in French?"

"The same as Father used to say—'A great lady'."

"How about 'She was a great lady'?"

"Yes, Mother would like that. She liked French almost as much as she liked English, although she never did know how she came to speak it."

Mrs. Dickinson dipped her pen in the ink again and wrote "C'était une grande dame."

Ted stared at her piece of paper. Rose and her father looked at each other, and knew with relief that it wouldn't make any difference to Ted whether it was writing in French, or any other language.

"That looks nice all right, John, most nice. I'll do that for you all right, shouldn't take long, once we get going that is."

John and Rose handed him the money with a great feeling of relief. They had almost accomplished their goal. Soon the headstone would be in place.

"Now we shan't lose Mother, shall we, Rose?" Tim looked down at his mother's grave.

"No, Tim, we shan't ever lose Mother now."

Out of the corner of her eye Rose saw that several women from the village were standing gossiping at the gate of the churchyard. She knew they were busy saying that Mother was a foreigner and only a foreigner would have strange words on their headstone, because Ted's wife who could read would have told them. She took Tim firmly by the hand. "Come on, Tim, we must catch up Father," she said.

"It looks like a nice bed now, Rose, don't it?" said Tim looking back over his shoulder.

Rose didn't reply, but walked quickly past the little knot of women, pulling Tim behind her. Even the Earl himself had stopped and stared at Mother's headstone before the service, and then turned and said something to the Countess. She hoped there wouldn't be trouble for Father because of it. Poor Father, he hadn't been able to keep from crying when he saw that headstone in place. Up till then, in the excitement of being able to afford it, he had forgotten that his great and wonderful lady lay beneath the ground, but now, this morning, he had seen for himself what he had forgotten was true, and he had walked away from them and wept. And Tim had wept, and she had found it difficult not to cry with him. Only Grandmother had been unmoved, too concerned about everyone seeing her shawl to take in what was written on the headstone.

LUCY BUCK. DIED 1883.
"C'ETAIT UNE GRANDE DAME"

The Earl settled himself among his books again. He was satisfied that the new vicar was the kind of fellow he liked. The sermon had been exactly ten minutes long, just as he had ordered. Ten minutes was long enough for anyone's taste, and in his opinion ten minutes was the exact time it took for people to begin fidgeting. Admittedly his wife was an exception, it took her only about two minutes, but then she tended to be an exception in most things.

Widgery coughed from the doorway.

"Yes, Widgery?"

"About the matter you asked me to enquire about, Your Lordship? The matter of the boiling water?"

"Yes, Widgery?"

"It is used for a great many purposes I believe, sir, including the brewing of tea."

"Really, Widgery. Well, thank you very much, I've always wondered. Seen a calf born you know, never seen a baby. Thank goodness," he added after some thought.

Widgery withdrew. He was glad to see that the Earl did not take an over personal interest in his servants. Not like his daughter, bringing tenants' children in for meals, or his mother, who appeared to be quite happy to sit and gossip with the maids, in spite of being, so he understood—a Princess in her own country. But then being a Princess abroad was not equal to being even an Honourable in England, everyone knew that. Widgery was glad he had been born British, and he was glad that the matter of the maid had sorted itself out. Just for a minute he remembered how pretty she was, and then he put the thought out of his mind. What was done was done. He sniffed the air. It was gammon and parsley sauce in the servants' hall today—his favourite.

Chapter 5

Rose stood by the window and watched the carriage passing through the gates, albeit a little slowly, because a carriage drawn by a dozen healthy tenants will not go at the same speed as one drawn by horses.

The celebrations for Lady Marjorie Talbot-Carey's marriage to Richard Bellamy Esq. were about to begin, but first the carriage was to be drawn up the drive by the tenants, and then there was to be a garden party where all were invited. The young couple had been married in London. There had been a large society wedding, and hundreds invited to the reception, but now Lady Marjorie was bringing her husband home to be introduced to the tenants of her father's estate, and there was to be dancing and fireworks.

It didn't seem to matter very much that Rose's frock was a little too much on the small side to be quite as pretty as she would have wished, or that Tim had a patch in his shirt that showed more than a little —on account of Rose's sewing being no great shakes. Nothing like that seemed to matter. This was a great day for Southwold and everyone knew it.

Rose straightened her ribbon in the looking glass above the kitchen basin and then went upstairs to look at the baby. She looked at him lying asleep on his back. She loved to squeeze him, and kiss him even more than she liked running about with Tatty and Tim. She hadn't run about with Tatty and Tim very much since young John had arrived home, nor had she been able to go to school as much as she had wished, on account of the fact that there was so much to do in the house and Grandmother couldn't be trusted to be left with the baby very often, except if Rose had just fed him and he was sleeping. She tried to feed him just before she left for school so that he might sleep without waking until she got home. And so often she would run home as fast as she could with Tim and Tatty trailing behind her, because she was so afraid that young John would wake and Grandmother would give him 'something to make him sleep'. Rose knew that you should never give babies 'something to make them sleep', because her mother had told her that it was bad for them.

Young John was just beginning to walk and so the pace at which they set off towards the celebrations was necessarily slow. Rose looked at her two brothers. They were as unlike as they could be. Tim, like her, was as thin as the thinnest stick, and the baby was as fat as Tim was thin. When her father had got the baby and brought him home, they had all stared at him. No-one wanted him. It was enough to manage without there being a baby to look after. Grandmother said so, often.

The reason Father had taken it into his head to suddenly go off down to the village and fetch him, was because he had heard from Ben at Southwold Arms that you could leave a baby too long. Ben had told Father that he had been left too long with the woman who was nursing him, and so when his father and a new wife came to fetch him—why he had screamed for days, thinking they had taken him from his own mother. Father was afraid that this might happen to their baby and so he had gone to fetch him.

Young John was ten months old when Father walked in the kitchen door with him. Father, of course, looking as worried as a man could be because he hated to see a woman cry, and Margaret had cried her eyes out when he had taken the baby from her, even though she had two of her own and another on the

way. Of course, Father had given her what he could,
but she was different from some, and if his last name
hadn't been Buck, Father said she would have kept
John for her own. But in Father's opinion a child belonged with his family, and with no-one else. He said
this several times while Grandmother just sniffed and
said several times back to him, that in her opinion
she had already too much on her hands without a
baby crying for her all day long. And all the while
they were talking, poor young John just sat on a chair
and looked sleepily at everyone, because it was already
dark, and he should have been in bed.

"You had better left him with Margaret," Grandmother rocked herself viciously in her chair, "a baby
is no good for an old woman and a child."

John looked at Rose helplessly. He wanted her to
say she wanted the baby, and that she thought as he
did, but she couldn't. She couldn't even look at the
creature. She didn't want him in the house. She felt
the same as Grandmother, he'd have been better left
with Margaret.

He started to cry. They all stared at him, but no-
one made a sound. Eventually because it was a loud
noise and young John seemed quite capable of sus-
taining it for some time to come, Tim went up to him,
and shook his hand up and down. Miraculously the
tears stopped, and he smiled at Tim.

"He's smiling, Rose," said Tim, a little unneces-
sarily.

"He can smile, it's us that'll soon have no smiles,"
grumbled Grandmother.

"I think he's tired, Rose."

"And what would a bit of a boy know about that?"

"He just now yawned, Rose."

Rose picked up the baby. He was very heavy. She
had made a bed out of some blankets and a box to
put beside hers and Tim's bed.

"I'll put him upstairs," she told her father, but
she wanted to throw him downstairs. She hated babies.
They killed women.

Perhaps because he slept through the night beside her bed without stirring, in the morning Rose looked down at her small brother with slightly less resentment than she had felt when she saw him coming through the door in their father's arms. She didn't know what to give him for breakfast, but she thought she would soak some bread in a cup of milk.

"He likes that, Rose," said Tim watching the baby supping up his bread.

Rose looked at the baby thoughtfully. Although she hated to admit it, the fact that he had eaten his breakfast with such relish pleased her. She wondered now whether he would stay on the chair long enough for her to get the house swept, or whether he would cry and make it difficult for her. She knew that there was no point in asking Grandmother to look after him. It was all she could do to bake the bread nowadays. She no longer rose at dawn to be the first down in the morning, her incentive for doing so having been taken away. There was no point in competing to be mistress of the house, when there was no mistress to compete with. She did nothing except the baking, and even then she made sure that Rose kneaded the dough for her, telling her that her hands were no longer what they were, and the pain got her if she pressed down too hard. Sometimes when she felt very tired Rose would have liked to have bitten her grandmother as Tim had once done.

How she got through that first day with the baby at home was something that Rose could only wonder at. It was as if everything was against her. The washing dropped off the line, and had to be done again. Grandmother burnt herself on the stove, and sat nursing her arm all day and making remarks. Tim didn't come in for his dinner, because Tatty got himself lost chasing rats in the stable yard; and so she worried that he'd hurt himself, and when he arrived home he had—he'd cut his knee and grazed his face, and torn his good shirt that she'd asked him to keep for best. And then just as Father came in, and she thought she had everything to rights, the baby fell off his chair and banged his head on the stone floor, and lay there.

"He'll be all right," said John uneasily as Rose picked him up from the floor, "babies are all right more times than you can say, Rose."

Rose looked down at the baby.

"He's not all right, Father, he's not moving," she announced presently, "quickly bring some cold water, Tim."

She splashed cold water over him, but the head remained very still on her lap. She felt his pulse.

"He's still alive," she told Tim who was standing very close as if he could help her just from standing near.

"Perhaps you'd better take him upstairs, Rose," said Tim anxiously.

"Yes, I'll take him upstairs, Tim. You bring some cold water."

"He'll be all right," said their father again, but he didn't move from the table where he was sitting, and Rose knew it was because he had been drinking and he didn't want her to smell the ale on his breath. She knew that her mother had hated him drinking, and he was ashamed to say that he did in front of Rose. But Rose knew that he now spent every evening at the Southwold Arms and that was why he sometimes forgot to eat his meal, or fell asleep very early still sitting at the table.

The two children bent over the box that held their brother, and splashed water over him liberally, but the baby didn't wake.

"You keep splashing, Tim, I'll go and warm a blanket, like Mother did once when you fell off the hayrick."

She snatched a blanket from their bed and hurried downstairs, so quickly that she was in time to see her father passing Grandmother a bottle of gin. She pretended not to notice, and went straight to the stove to warm the blanket. Grandmother hid the bottle under her apron and went on rocking her chair, only a little faster.

"I'll stay awake, Tim, you go to sleep."

"I'll wake up when you want me to, Rose," said Tim, but she could see that his eyelids were drooping and he was already nearly fast asleep.

"May the angels keep you safe until morning," said Rose, because that's what their mother used to say.

She looked down at the baby and felt his pulse again. She didn't know how to make him better, but she thought that if she kept him warm, and watched over him, it would help. If water didn't wake him then she would just have to leave him.

"Is he still alive, Rose?" Tim looked at her. It was dawn and he had woken to find Rose feeling the baby's pulse.

"Yes, he is Tim, he's still alive. I've been praying to Mother, and I think she's going to keep him alive for us."

Tim took in this thought for a few moments, and then he said, "you don't think she wants to take the baby to heaven with her, do you, Rose?"

Rose shook her head. "You'd better go downstairs and light the fire, Tim. Father will be up soon."

Tim padded obediently downstairs. He laid the fire very carefully, almost extra carefully, because he was so worried about the baby. It was like a superstition with him. If he laid the fire very well, and drank his milk well, and ate his bread well, and remembered to do all his buttons up in the right order, and brushed his hair, then whatever he was hoping at that moment would be all right, but if he did one thing wrong then it wouldn't happen.

He went upstairs again.

"The fire's lit, Rose. I'll stay with the baby while you get Father's breakfast."

Because she had seen her father passing Grandmother the bottle of gin, Rose now watched him while he ate. She noticed that he looked older than he used to, and that his hands shook when he drank, only very slightly, but they shook. She knew that when people drank their hands shook in the morning, because one of Ted's brothers had drunk himself to death, and his hands had shaken all the time. So much so that neither Ted nor his brothers would now touch a drop. They were a large family, so that the matter of their giving up ale somewhat affected the Southwold Arms, and Ben would grumble to anyone that would listen that the profit he made from that one brother had been washed away by his death. Ben had had his eye on one of Ted's sisters for a long while now, so that it was thought that it would have been wiser for him not to grumble. But it was not in Ben's character to keep quiet. Any more than it was in her father's character to lie, as he was doing now.

"I might have to go to the village for a new pair of boots some time today, Rose. Will you and Tim be able to watch the gates—with the baby as he is?"

"Yes, Father."

Rose watched him going out of the door. He had brought the baby home. He had given him to her to look after and now young John was ill, all he wanted to think about was 'going out'. She washed up his dishes and laid out breakfast for Tim. It was the way things were. She remembered her mother's face when she had said 'God help us for having been born women', and shivered as she had done then. It was terrible to be a woman, not just because you had to do everything in the house as well as your work or because you had to have babies and die, but because it was terrible. The Bible said it was because Eve had tempted Adam with the apple, and Rose knew that this must be true. Women suffered because the first woman had been wicked. Men could be as wicked as they wished, but they would never suffer as women did because Adam had not been wicked like Eve, and, Rose suspected, because God was a man.

Rose and Tim took it in turns to sit with the baby all that day. Grandmother slept late, and when she awoke she was extremely cross, and it was all they could do to keep her from bothering them with the least thing. She, who had always said she would be so proud to have grandsons, seemed unmoved by the fact that young John had not woken since his fall. She grumbled to Tim that Rose hadn't cooked the potatoes properly, and she wished that they could have cream on their fruit every day of the week the way that farmers' wives did.

"I wish that Grandmother had fallen off the chair, Rose," said Tim.

Rose didn't reply. Although the baby was still alive, now that it was getting late and it was a full day since he had hurt himself, they both felt that there couldn't be much hope.

"Wouldn't you like to go to sleep now, Tim?"

Tim didn't appear to have heard.

"Where's Father, Rose? Why does he go to the village so often?"

Rose thought for a while, and then she whispered, "I think he's drinking, Tim. I saw him give Grandmother a bottle of gin only last night."

Rose saw that Tim was too young to appreciate the significance of this remark, so she pulled the blanket over his shoulders and settled him down. Outside the latticed window she could hear an owl hooting. Inside the baby breathed regularly. That at least was something.

"Tim! He's woken! Tim! He's crying!"

Rose cried too.

Tim looked so frightened at her sobs, she tried to calm herself. She rocked the baby. She hadn't cried since her mother had died, that had been something that she'd been proud of. Even Grandmother had cried at the funeral, but Rose hadn't.

"Look, Rose, he's smiling."

They stared at their little brother lying on the pillow in the candlelight. He had stuck his fingers in his mouth.

"Perhaps he's hungry."

Tim crept back up the stairs with a cup of milk and some bread for the baby, and a piece of cake each for them, "I brought something for us too, Rose, something to stop us feeling so hungry. Grandmother's eaten what we left at supper. She says old folk need it."

They fed the baby, and they ate their cake, and then too happy to move him, they fell asleep beside the baby, and in the morning Rose realised that she did like babies after all.

"I'll whip who took the cake," said Grandmother.

"No, you won't, Grandmother," said Rose, "You won't whip anyone."

"See if I don't."

"Tim and I ate the cake, because we were hungry from watching over the baby."

"I'll whip the pair of you."

"No, you won't," said Rose again, and quickly picked up the baby because her grandmother looked as if she was going to hit her. Tim ran behind the table. "If you touch Tim, I'll tell Mrs. Petifor that you drink gin," Rose heard herself say.

When she saw the effect it had on her grandmother, she wished she hadn't heard herself say it. She went quite white, and picked up a spoon to hit Rose with. Rose joined Tim behind the table, still clutching the baby.

She knew that her grandmother was immensely proud of her growing friendship with Mrs. Petifor, and that the housekeeper was a person who never touched alcohol, as she had heard her remark this to Father once.

Just as suddenly as their grandmother had seized the wooden spoon, Rose and Tim watched her drop it. She started to cry, dabbing her eyes with the corner of her apron. She cried because she said she missed 'their dear mother', and then as the children remained where they were, she cried because she said an old woman needed a little comfort in the evenings, and then she cried, very loudly, about the fact that her friendship with Mrs. Petifor was only for Rose's good.

"Why Grandmother, whatever do you mean?" Rose came up to her still clutching the baby.

"For your good, so there'll be a post for you at the house, when you're ready." Grandmother renewed her sobs, and Rose put the baby down, and turned to comfort her.

At that moment the wooden spoon came down so hard against the side of her face that Rose nearly fainted with the suddenness of the pain. Then as she felt the spoon come crashing against her head again and again, Rose knew that her grandmother was wicked, as wicked as the devil. More wicked than the devil. She resolved to hate her forever.

It was surprising how effective that resolution was. Even Rose had been surprised at how deep her despite for her grandmother became, and how much Rose's emotion affected the old lady. Today Grandmother had gone to the village to fetch her friend, Mrs. Burrows, for the celebrations. Mrs. Burrows' legs not being what they were she was better walking with someone to lean on. But even today Rose was glad to say she had managed to make Grandmother uneasy by merely polishing the kitchen floors so hard, and making it so shiny, that Grandmother had been forced to walk about in her stockinged feet all morning. A fact that she hated because she was afraid that someone might glimpse her shoeless feet from outside.

With the amount of traffic that had been through their gates since early morning, it was highly possible that someone, if only a coachman, had glimpsed her feet through the open doorway. For Father left their door open in order that he might run out as he heard a new arrival and open the gates and bow as the Countess liked him to do, and then close them again; and of course no sooner had he closed them than he had to run out again, but the Countess insisted that everyone arriving at Southwold should be accorded the same welcome. 'Southwold starts at the gates' she was in the habit of remarking to John, and John, because he loved his gates as much as he was currently prone to loving his ale, heartily agreed with her. And of course he liked to see who it was that was arriving as much as anyone. He had helped to pull Lady Marjorie's coach on its nuptial ropes, he and Ted and all Ted's brothers, except the one who had died.

When they rounded the corner of the hedge, the sight of the marquees and the tables on the big lawns, with the cedar trees towering over them, was no surprise. All week they, and especially Tim, had watched the preparations for the great event. The footmen raising the tents under the supervision of Mr. Widgery, the maids hurrying to and fro in their white hats and aprons bobbing in and out between the trees, the labourers banging posts into the soft green turf, and everyone hoping for as fine a day as they had got.

"Here they come!"

The cry went up, and the assembly of people gave a great cheer as they saw the young couple make their way across the terrace and down the wide stone steps, preparatory to shaking hands with everyone. Mr. Widgery gave a sign, and the Earl's farm manager stepped forward and read an address.

"Your Lordship, Your Ladyship, Mr. Bellamy, sir," he began, and then stopped. He was so pleased to have managed this first sentence, that he looked over the top of the bound and illuminated address, and smiled for no reason other than the satisfaction of having effected this first difficult sentence without mishap.

There was a shuffle among the audience. A general settling into the substance of what he was about to say. And approval, albeit silent, that he had managed to cope with this first difficult sentence without letting the village down.

"He'll be all right now," said Ben, the landlord of the Southwold Arms, to no-one in particular.

"It was with the humblest and greatest of gratitude that we heard of Her Ladyship's betrothal to the honourable gentleman present, Mr. Richard Bellamy, Esquire. The villagers and members of Your Ladyship's parish could not have been more overjoyed that

Her Ladyship had chosen to become united in marriage to such a fine and honourable gentleman."

"He's taking the long route round, to be sure."
This was Ben again, and no-one cared to disagree
with him.

"Your Lordship well knows that your humble tenants and parishioners hold the good health and happiness of Your Lordship's family before all else, and
Your Lordship must know that this—" he hesitated
here because he had to turn the page, "Your Lordship must know that this before all else is the subject
of Your Lordship's humble tenants, and parishioners'
dearest concern. And—"

There was not a person present, including the Earl
and Countess and the bride and groom, who had not
by now noticed that the manager's address was only
just begun. Thoughts flew off in all directions, and
returned with relief when he finally stepped back and
bowed, and everybody realised it was over. Much
as they all felt many of the sentiments expressed in
the address quite fervently, and perhaps a little more
fervently than was their wont because everyone could
smell the ox that was roasting on an open fire somewhere to the side of one of the marquees, nevertheless
being forced to stand and listen to an address is a very
dull business at the best of times, smacking too much
of the Sunday sermon, and too little of the sense of
celebration that they all undoubtedly felt at the sight of
two such fine young people having been joined in wedlock.

On occasions like these every child, and every man
and woman, felt that what happened to the Talbot-
Careys happened to them, and of course it was true.
However big the estate, and Southwold was not small,
nevertheless the sense of belonging to each other was
very strong. If Lady Marjorie looked radiant, there
was not a farmer, nor a labourer, who wasn't feeling
that it was 'his' Lady Marjorie, 'their' Lady Marjorie,
who was looking radiant. She was as much theirs as
their own daughters, and she belonged to them as

much as their farms and their cottages belonged to her family. Many of them felt, like the Countess, that she could have made a more brilliant match. But like the Countess also, they were thankful that she had married such an evidently charming and handsome man, who would go far and no doubt carve out a name for himself, notwithstanding the fact that he was not as well-born as his wife.

The preparations for the wedding celebrations had caused Mr. Widgery some headaches, although he would not have admitted it to his dearest friend, if he had one. The question of the clemency of the weather had caused him to toss and turn at nights more than somewhat and he had prepared his two plans of campaign according to the state of the elements. The first plan had been to enclose the terrace in tenting so that in the event of its raining, Lady Marjorie and Mr. Bellamy could have made their appearance and listened to the address in the safety of a covered place. And yet there could have been no question of the tenants penetrating the main house, so the marquees would have had to have been linked and the enclosure on the terraces could have been kept for the gentry, while below the steps the farmers and labourers and their families could have enjoyed themselves, while staying at a safe distance from the quality.

Mr. Widgery had been very glad that the weather had turned out to what it was, sunshine, and not a cloud in the sky, because he had had not a few nightmares about 'plan one'. Being the kind of person who disdained to court favour among the lower ranks, he naturally had an overriding fear that one day they would 'get the better of him'. People 'getting the better of him' was one of Mr. Widgery's dreads, together with finding a spider in his bed. The trouble to his mind about 'plan one' was that it brought the common people too near the steps of Southwold for his peace of mind. It brought them almost within breathing distance, and that had been one of his nightmares, that they would become uncontrollable, and rush the steps of Southwold, like all those common people during the French Revolution. In his nightmares he saw them dressed like revolutionaries rushing through the corridors of Southwold. The landlord of the Southwold Arms would be sitting in His Lordship's chair and the dairyman from the village would be sprawled about the Throne Room with the carpenter, and all the time Mr. Widgery would be clapping his hands for order. But no-one would hear him, except the maids, who would point at him and laugh. Mr. Widgery couldn't stand laughter.

"There's Mr. Widgery strutting about like a turkey cock. Anyone would think he was paying for the party," said one of the maids to Rose.

Rose didn't reply. She knew that if the day ever came that she went to work at the big house like her mother had done, she would need to know that she had stayed on the right side of Mr. Widgery, whenever possible. Already she had committed a crime, the day that she got lost on the way to the old Countess' rooms, and she wanted to make amends for that somehow. Joining in with Daisy's gossip would not have been her idea of making amends. Rose knew already that the last person you could trust to keep a still tongue in her head was one of your own sex. She knew this from watching Grandmother gossiping with the old ladies who called at the Lodge, and she knew it from school, where everyone was so anxious to be teacher's special pupil that they would say anything, or do anything, to make you wrong with her. You had to tread your way carefully, the same as if you were speaking with gentry. That was another time that you had to tread your way carefully, the same as Mother had done.

The baby had fallen asleep on her shoulder. She had fed him as much meat and as much cake as he could take, and now satiated, he had fallen asleep, his cheeks flushed from the sun and his hat tipped forward on his eyes. She loved the weight of him on her lap, even though it made it difficult for her to eat what she had chosen for herself. And that again had been difficult. How difficult to know what to choose when there was a choice of so much! Rose didn't think in her whole life that human beings could have seen so much food everywhere. Why there must have been at least a hundred-weight of strawberries alone. And that was to say nothing of the cakes and the trifles and the cream. The cream was a mountain, a real mountain of cream, so yellow and luscious that you were afraid to dip your spoon into such a wonderful construction.

And then there were pheasants and hams and legs of mutton, and capons stuffed to bursting. And there were baskets of red and shiny cherries, and apples and pears polished and then sugared to make them look as if they had snow on them, and there were lobsters with bright pink shells, and tomatoes and peaches from the greenhouses. There were tongues and pressed beef and grouse, and there were large green fruits which Daisy said were called 'melons'. And raspberries, Rose's favourite. Large bowls of raspberries ready to be spooned in heaps onto the shiny white plates provided.

Of course everyone had been a little hesitant to be the first to begin. No-one wished to look greedy, just as no-one wished anyone else to point him or her out as the person who had made a pig of himself at the party. It had taken Ben, more free and easy in his ways than most by nature of his profession, to start in with a good big helping, because up until then everyone had been taking little tiny dolls' portions and watching each other's plates to see what was the polite amount. But old Ben had no such inhibitions. He pulled a whole grouse to pieces in front of Mr. Widgery and ate it with relish, all the time asking Mr. Widgery why didn't he join him? And then he gulped a large tankard of ale and started in again, this time on the beef, which he pronounced to be the best that he had eaten since the spring.

"Food is for eating," he said looking around for

someone to agree with him, and no sooner had he said that when everyone fell on the tables as if they hadn't eaten anything for weeks and piled their plates nearly as high as the mountain of cream. And some of the maids giggled behind Mr. Widgery's back because they could see that Mr. Widgery thought Ben had been impertinent, but he couldn't say anything, on account of the fact that even the Earl had pronounced Ben's ale to be the best kept in the country.

Tim had disappeared and Rose guessed that he had taken Tatty some beef. And that wouldn't have been all he had taken Tatty. He loved his dog so much that now the warm nights were here it was all she could do to stop him going to sleep in the kennel with the little terrier. Not that you could blame him. Tatty was no ordinary dog. He was as gay as a lark, and he could jump higher than a dog twice his size. And as for catching rats—well, he was the stable boy's best friend. There wasn't a rat that dared to show his face when Tatty was around, old James the coachman had told her. James liked Tim. He didn't like many, but he liked Tim, there was no doubt of that. Tim was a funny boy. So quiet and so good for his age.

"There's Grandmother overdoing it," he said matter of factly to Rose when he returned. "She'll be letting out her belt pretty quick by the looks of it. Mrs. Burrows' had enough. Soon she say to Grandmother 'quick, I be having the palps'—she always say that when she's eaten her fill, and then Grandmother has to undo her bodice."

"Hush up, Tim," Rose pushed him with her foot. She didn't think that boys of Tim's age should be saying words like 'bodice'. It wasn't proper. And Mother wouldn't have liked it. Mother never liked to hear them saying words that weren't right for their age, same as she never liked to hear them having too much of an accent. She liked them to speak as she spoke, different from Father and the rest of the village. It was difficult for Tim, though. He sometimes got bullied by the village boys for the way he spoke. That's why he had more accent sometimes now than when Mother was alive. It was natural really.

"There's them Fiddys tucking in," Tim nodded his head in their direction, "they like their food all right. Mary Brownlow's dropped her strawberries, and look at Jim, Rose—he's more cream on his plate than anyone. He likes cream, Jim."

"You're an old woman, Tim," said Rose, as she always did, but she never stopped him from gossiping. He had a way of saying things that made her want to laugh.

"There's going to be dancing later, Rose, and they're going to light all the lanterns."

It was like fairyland, Rose was quite sure of that. When all the tables had been cleared away, and all the food taken back to the kitchen—all the food there was left that is—because what people hadn't eaten they had put in their pockets, or hidden under bushes to collect later when they were going home. Even the fountain had been illuminated, and in the light of the candles the water looked as bright and as sparkling as jewellery in the sunshine.

Lady Marjorie and her husband led off the dancing, because that was how things should be, and the musicians played a waltz so that for a few minutes everyone was very quiet at the sight of such a beautiful pair circling in the light of the candles. And then, of course, no-one felt like dancing, even though the Earl and Countess and the young Viscount Ashby, Lady Marjorie's brother, and all the house guests who were staying with them, even though they were all waltzing, not one person from the village or the estate dared to join them. Because no-one knew how to waltz, or if they did they were afraid to, and then it might not have looked right to dance with gentry already dancing.

Of course everyone clapped when the dance was over, because it had been such a fine and pretty sight, but no-one knew how to get on with it and start dancing themselves, so they just talked among themselves and pretended that they knew it wasn't right to dance with gentry about.

"Will you have this dance? I'm sorry, will you do me the honour of dancing this one with me?"

Rose felt quite faint at the sight of the young man bowing in front of her. Why on earth would the young Viscount want to dance with a little girl not yet twelve? She looked about her for help, but only Tim was sitting near her on the grass, with the baby asleep beside him. She felt her legs moving forward, and wanted to stop them.

"You dance very nicely," said the young Viscount, "but I wish you would stop watching your feet. What's that?"

"I'm trying to see the step," Rose whispered.

"You don't want to bother about steps," he said gaily, "just do anything, like everyone else."

And everyone else *was* doing anything, anything at all. Rose saw that, when she managed to screw up her courage and glance around the lawn. All the guests from the big house were dancing with the tenants, and there were other children dancing too. Mary Brownlow was dancing with the Earl. It made Rose want to laugh.

After that it was very jolly. Everyone swopping partners after each dance and no-one minding whether they knew the steps or not, and of course there was quite a bit drunk, because dancing is a hot and thirsty business, and when there's free ale, and lemonade for the children, people tend to feel thirstier than they might have done had they been paying for it out of their own pockets.

Tim came up to her.

"I've just danced with Mrs. Petifor," he announced proudly, "and she trod on my foot. She's very heavy, Rose."

"Look at Ben, Tim, he's dancing with the Countess. She won't like it if he treads on her toes, will she?"

"Last time Ben trod on someone they didn't walk for a few days," agreed Tim. "James says—" most of Tim's conversation was littered with 'James says'. He was very fond of James. "James say that's why Ted's sister won't wed him. He say that Ted's sister don't like big men, and Ben's too big for her. But James say that Ted's sister will be a spinster if she go on being so choosy. Father's dancing with her now. Do you think she's pretty, Rose? James says she's not bad for a woman."

Rose looked across to where she could see her father dancing. He was dancing with Ted's sister, and what's more he was looking as if he was enjoying it. She suddenly felt angry. What was Father doing dancing with Ted's sister. It wasn't proper. It wasn't right for him to be dancing with Ted's sister, and enjoying it too. She hoped they would stop dancing now that the music had stopped, and that they would change partners, as almost everyone else was doing, but they didn't. They stood talking. Father talking as he never did normally, half laughing, and bending over Ted's sister as if she was one of his best plants. In fact it looked to Rose as if she might as well be one of his plants, the look he had on his face. Father was in the habit of talking to his plants. He was not in the habit of talking to ladies.

"Here come Albert," said Tim. "Hallo, Albert. Do you want to dance with my sister? She's very dear to dance with. The Viscount danced with her, so now I'm charging a farthing a dance."

Albert smiled uncertainly.

"Rose—Albert wants to dance with you," said Tim a little more loudly, because Rose looked as if she hadn't heard what they'd been saying. "Albert wants to dance with you, and I say a farthing a dance, do you agree, Rose?"

"I haven't got a farthing, Tim," Albert smiled uncertainly.

Albert was the son of a farmer. Rose looked at him. Poor Albert, he was so skinny. He was always getting the worst of it. Hardly a day went by during the winter when they went to school when Albert didn't appear

in the school room with a cut or a bruise, because
someone had given him a beating. He was so thin that
he didn't seem able to defend himself against other
boys. Tim said he had no weight to put behind his
punches, and that made it difficult for him.

"James say if you haven't got no weight behind
your punch, you may as well not worry, and Albert's
got no weight you see, Rose. James say he's a bit of
a weakling, not like his father and his brother who are
built like trees."

"Would you, Rose?"

"What did you say, Albert?"

"Would you have this dance with me?"

"Very well. Tim keep an eye on the baby."

"That's a farthing, Albert," shouted Tim, but they
were well into the Posthorn Gallop by then.

They all dashed round and round in time to the
music, and Rose quite forgot to keep an eye on her
father and Ted's sister as she had meant to do. Albert
had thin long fingers, like his long thin body, and he
was as dark and pale as she was. She fell against him
laughing. Everyone was laughing and falling against
each other. The musicians had speeded up the Gallop
so much, that there wasn't a person there who wasn't
as breathless as they'd ever been.

"Goodness, that was funny."

"Let's go and fetch a lemonade."

"Yes, let's."

It was only standing there by the drinks table that
Rose realised that her father had disappeared.
Grandmother was still there, and Mrs. Burrows, and
all the old ladies from the village in their best caps
and black dresses. And there was Ted and Ben, and
she could even see Albert's father enjoying a joke
with another farmer as burly and as red-faced as he
was, but nowhere could she see Father, or Ted's sister,
Mary.

Chapter 6

The village mourned the passing of the old Countess as heartily as they mourned anyone's passing. Almost as if she was their own mother. True it was that the lady had been of a great age and that everyone must go when they're called, but nevertheless she was missed. She was missed as much as if someone had suddenly forbidden the eating of roast beef on Sunday. They said that it was when her old maid Vilanova passed on that the heart went out of her. Vilanova was the spark that she still needed to keep her going, the necessary sense of impatience that can keep life ticking over when it is, in truth, waning. Vilanova was her childhood, her adolescence and her marriage, and when she died, it was as if the album had finally closed its pages, and that being so, she felt no more need to linger.

It was not customary for the women of the village to go to funerals. Rose watched the cortège passing through the Lodge gates, and thought about how much the old Countess had been to her, and that now she was dead they would no longer see her sledge being pulled through the snow by a little grey pony as they had used to do. The Countess had loved her sledge, although she called it something different, and she would always insist on going in it once or twice a winter if there was the least suggestion of snow.

It was the old Countess who had given her the little box and who had loved her mother to read to her.

In her imagination Rose wished that the old Countess was her grandmother, instead of the one she had. She wished that she could have gone and helped look after her when she was ill instead of silly Daisy. Rose knew that she would have looked after her well, the way her mother used to, because she had watched her mother so often. She knew that the old lady liked to be read to from the right hand side, because that was her better ear, and that she liked sugar in her tea and a glass of port in a little crystal glass before she went to bed (Mother had told her that). She knew also that she didn't think much of her daughter-in-law, and that after the Countess had been to tea with her, she very often got in a bad temper and told Vilanova she was an old fool, even more times than she normally did.

Now she was dead, and watching the horses with their black plumes, the coachman in his black cloak and hat, the carriages with the passengers clothed in black, and the women with long black veils and only the occasional mourning brooch gleaming in the winter's sunlight, Rose thought that she felt sad.

"She was a great lady, a great lady," said her father drowsily at supper that night.

Rose looked round from the sink where she was washing the dishes. Her father was full of ale as usual. He wore a black armband as did all the men in the village, but he didn't know what he was talking about, because he never knew what he was talking about nowadays. She said nothing, because there was very little point in talking to a man who had taken too much drink, of that she was certain. Grandmother snored in her chair. Rose sighed. The Lodge was very dull and quiet when Tim was out, which he was more and more recently. He was only a lad still, but already he had a passion for horses, and to get him to leave the stables, even to go to school, was all she could do. No-one else appeared to care. Father was too preoccupied with trying to pretend he wasn't down at the Southwold Arms, or courting Ted's sister, and Grandmother was too old and silly to even get herself up the stairs on her own.

Rose had only young John for company. But she loved his company, so it was no hardship really. He was a beautiful boy, as round as an apple with rosy cheeks like an apple and a lovely shiny skin like an apple. He was beautiful. She was lucky with his clothes because Mother had been given so many by the old Countess. Some of them had been worn by the young Viscount when he was little and some hadn't been worn at all. She must have been given them when Tim was born, and of course Rose hadn't taken much notice, not being older then. But some months back she had found them stored in the attic, all neat and tidy as Mother left everything, with little bags of lavender pressed between them.

Rose had almost cried when she discovered them. Somehow it was as if her mother had just gone out of the room. Just finished tidying them and pressing the lavender bags between each garment and then gone quietly out, so much were they still in place from when she had last touched them with her pretty hands. And how pretty her hands had been! She'd had hands as soft and delicate as if she had just been born, as soft and as delicate as young John's feet before he began to walk.

"Rose?"

Her father looked at her as she sat stitching one of young John's buttons back into place.

"Rose, do you think—?"

Rose looked at him the way she looked at her grandmother, not with dislike but without emotion, which within a family amounts to dislike. Every evening her father seemed to be about to try to tell her something, and every evening she looked at him and thought how much less he was without her mother, and how much a grown man had to have done for him, even though he pretended to be the head of the house.

"What do I think, Father?"

"Do you think it might be wicked in a man to take a wife again?"

"What does the Bible say, Father?"

"I don't know what the Bible says, Rose. My reading's not up to much. Your mother was teaching me to—" he stopped because he knew instinctively that he was going to get in a muddle if he pursued first one line of conversation, and then after a few words, another. That was all right for Rose. She was quick thinking like her mother had been, but he couldn't do that.

He started again.

"You remember when we went to the Brownlows' wedding? That was what I'm talking about, Rose, that was a second wife. The first wife had died, and that was the second wife. You see, Rose, there are certain things a man has need of, and he needs a woman to have those needs with."

Rose put her sewing down.

"This is to do with Ted's sister, isn't it, Father?"

Her father looked at her astonished. If children imagine that they easily deceive their parents, parents are more often fooled by the same thought. He had no idea that Rose knew of his courting of Ted's sister, no idea at all.

"You are right, Rose," he said quietly, "it is to do with Ted's sister. She and I have reached an understanding, but I want you and Tim to be right in your minds about it too, as we are."

Hearing her father saying 'we', and not meaning her mother, Rose felt angry, so angry that if she hadn't been afraid of her father's strength she would have flown at him.

"You can bring another woman into this house, Father, but don't expect Tim to welcome her, and don't expect me to welcome her. And don't think that I will want to see her scrubbing my floors and caring for young John, because I will hate her. I will hate her as much as I love the memory of Mother."

Her father paled, and at that moment Rose realised

triumphantly that her father was afraid of her. She might be only a strip of a girl still, and she might be only the daughter of the house, but her father was as afraid of her as if she was his own wife. He was afraid because she now did what Mother had done, nearly as well as Mother had done it, and she looked after Grandmother the way Mother would have done, and she cared for young John the way her mother would have done. She couldn't sew as neatly as her or read as quickly, but she could bake and clean and sweep, and young John looked as well-kept and as well looked after as gentry's children, and her father knew it. Once or twice lately when she had looked in the mirror she had even thought she might look a little like her mother, and she felt proud of that thought.

She picked up her sewing and went up to bed. Young John still slept beside her, although Tim now slept in the box room. She sat down on the end of her bed and stared ahead of her. It was a lonely and sometimes frightening process, growing up without a mother. Rose knew that she would soon be an adult, but her discovery of her impending maturity had both frightened and embittered her. She wished she could be a woman as beautiful and gracious as her mother had been, but she hated what she had to go through to become like that. So although she ran the house and was mother to her brothers, she still wanted to be a child, as they were. She wanted to be able to crawl on someone's lap the way young John crawled on hers, or spend her days in the stables with Tatty the way Tim did. She thought of the days when her mother was alive, and it seemed to her that she had only been a child for a few minutes.

Soon, too, she would no longer go to school, and would be going up to the big house to start her training as an underhousemaid. She hated the thought of leaving young John, and at night she lay awake listening to his sleeping and wondering who would look after him once she went to work? She knew that Margaret

in the village would take him for her, and that once
she started earning she could afford to pay her, but
that would mean that young John would no longer be
around the Lodge. No toys to trip over, no muddy
footsteps, no sturdy legs running in and out of the
kitchen door pulling up daisies to give her. It was
an unbearable thought. And then—Margaret was an
untidy woman, her hair always sprouting out in all
directions, and more times than not a dirty old apron
tied around her. And the inside of her cottage was
like last year's birds' nests, with stuff hanging from
the dressers, and everything so higgledy piggledy that
you wouldn't be able to find a place to sit down if
you had wanted to. If Margaret looked after him
it wouldn't be long before young John looked like
any village child, with his mouth covered in yesterday's
dinner and clothes hanging off his back which needed
mending, and goodness knows what. She didn't want
her young John going around looking like any village
child, not when she had managed to make him look
so good. Not when she had kept him so clean and
so neat.

And now there was a worse threat than leaving him
with Margaret. There was the thought of Ted's sister.
Ted's sister, with her large red hands and her whispy
blonde hair, and her face as round as a moon and
her large brown eyes, like a cow. Ted's sister might
think she was the village beauty now that Lucy was
dead, but everyone knew that she was as plain as a
pikestaff, and she spoke like a village woman. Not like
Lucy, who had spoken like a lady. The very thought
of seeing her standing in the Lodge kitchen, perhaps
trying to bake bread or trying to polish the floor—the
very thought of that woman doing all those things in
her Mother's kitchen, repulsed Rose. No doubt at all
but that a woman with large hands like hers would
bake bread so leaden and heavy that father would
be forever getting indigestion, and Grandmother with
her few teeth wouldn't be able to chew it. Rose smiled
at the thought. Let her father try to marry again, or

let him try to bring another woman to the Lodge, and he would regret it.

She brushed her hair a hundred times, while repeating the Lord's Prayer ten times. Tomorrow, she resolved, she would go down to the village and speak to Margaret. She thought that perhaps between the two of them they could make a plan so that Rose could collect young John in the evenings when she had finished work, and then bring him back to Margaret in the mornings. It would mean getting up early and going to bed late, but he was her brother, and no matter what, she was determined to try to keep him with her as much as she could.

She turned sideways and looked in the mirror. Her hair was getting really quite long.

Rose trod carefully over the cobblestoned alleyway that led to Margaret's cottage. She had just passed Albert in the main street. He looked as if he might be in trouble, as usual. A crowd of boys from another village had passed by and seeing Albert sitting on a wall reading, they had surrounded him. At the moment that she had passed by Albert had been employed in talking at them so fast that they hadn't yet had time to set upon him.

She had just knocked on Margaret's door, and stepped inside at her call, when Albert himself pushed past her, slammed the door, and leant against it. The hounds were after him.

"Quick, push the table!"

Rose and Margaret ran behind Margaret's heavy old table, and pushed as hard as they could, just in time to stop the door from giving way. Gangs from other villages often caused trouble. Boys that should be busy working the land, or helping their fathers, would take pleasure in causing trouble to their neighbours.

"Pests they are, but they'll be off soon." Margaret drew her front room curtains to shut out the grinning faces.

Even her curtains had saggy, untidy hems, Rose

noticed, and sighed at the thought that young John might soon be in her charge. She was a good woman, Margaret, but a dreadful muddler.

"I did nothing," Albert looked at the two women hopelessly. "I was sitting doing some of my reading, on the church wall."

"Reading's enough to bother some," said Margaret significantly, and pushed some sewing on to the floor so that Rose could sit down. "Some people don't hold with reading at all, but just you find a place to sit, Albert, and I'll make us a cup of tea. You'll be wanting a cup of tea, after an experience."

To Margaret, who rarely saw the outside of her cottage except to walk to church on Sundays, everything was 'an experience'. Her lazy attitude towards life was offset by her intense interest in anyone's 'experiences'. If any one of her many children hurt themselves or were ill, they were always told 'my, you have had an experience', and there was no doubt that her amiable attitude went a long way to healing them quicker than any medicine. The children weren't often ill, although they were always out in all weathers, possibly because their mother's muddle was too much, even for them, and it was a source of astonishment to Rose that they all fitted into the one, small cottage when the weather was too much for them to venture out. There were only two bedrooms in the cottage and no box room like the Lodge, and now Margaret was in a condition once more, and that would make six, not counting the baby that she was nursing for the poor girl who died last January.

Albert ventured to peep through one of the curtains when they had all finished their tea.

"They've gone," he said with relief.

"Poor lad, you could have been no match for all of them," Margaret looked at him affectionately.

Albert's colour had returned little by little listening to the girls chatting while they drank their tea, but now it deepened, and he looked at the floor, "I'm no match for anyone," he mumbled, "not anyone."

"That's because you're young yet, you'll soon broaden out," said Margaret encouragingly, "why, my brother Will, he never was more than a bit of a lad until he got to sixteen, and then he filled out, and he got so large he'd give people who'd not seen him for some time a real experience. Rose will know that I'm saying the truth. She remembers Will who used to carry her on his shoulders when she was a little thing, don't you, Rose?"

Rose nodded. "It's true, Will was a big man, Albert, as big as Father, bigger almost I should have said."

"You see, Albert, there's no saying that being as thin as you are is all you will experience." Margaret settled herself more comfortably into her chair, from whence, Rose suspected, she would not be moving for the rest of the afternoon. Margaret liked sitting almost as much as she liked having company in her cottage. Being married to the farrier meant that you were on your own a good deal, while he journeyed to outlying farms and places as much as fifteen miles away.

"Now, Rose, say why you've come to visit me. Tell me why you're here. We all know why Albert's here," she added somewhat tactlessly, and again Albert blushed so hot and red that Rose could have sworn that you could have warmed your hands just by holding them up to his face.

Rose had no such shyness. Perhaps because she had taken her mother's place for as much as nearly four years now, everyone in the village tended to treat her as the mistress of the Lodge. They forgot that she was only coming up fourteen and would not have been considered if her mother had been alive. But so quick was she in her ways, and so tidy was the Lodge, and so well-kept the child, that no-one now thought of her as 'Rose' that they knew only a few years back. Rose, with her dog Tatty running barefoot through the village, and Rose with her young brother Tim. Now she was 'Rose of the Lodge', and they

stopped to chat with her when they saw her and asked
after the children, just as if they were her sons and
not her brothers.

Of course everyone in the village knew how long
poor John had come courting Ted's sister, and naturally
there had been endless speculation as to the outcome.
It was now a long time that John had come up to
Ted's house and sat in the backroom with the family,
and it was considered that the poor man had served
his time and that he should be allowed to take a
second wife, same as any man would who'd lost his
first in childbirth. There was even a ripple of pleasant
anticipation at the thought that there might be a good
wedding to dance at—Ted being a generous man.
Even so, everyone knew also that poor John was in
the habit of respecting his daughter the way he had
once been ruled by his strange, foreign wife, and no-
one dared advise him to his face, this way or that,
although there was no-one to be found who hadn't
had a theory which they had voiced in private.

"If it was me, I'd belt her, and that would be that,"
Mr. Brownlow had said one night in the Southwold
Arms.

Although there wasn't a man in the place who
didn't sympathise with this idea, nevertheless the company looked uneasy at the thought. Rose was a slip of
a girl it was true, but she had a sharp tongue, as
all women tended to who had been taught to read,
and she was moreover a pet to the school teacher and
no-one would like to be answerable to the school
teacher. The school teacher had been appointed by
the vicar, and the vicar had been appointed by the
Earl, and it therefore didn't take much imagination to
think that to be in disfavour with teacher might mean
that you would end up being in disfavour with the Earl
of Southwold himself.

So no-one raised his voice in agreement with Mr.
Brownlow and only Ben behind the bar saw fit to
disagree with him, because he was that sore at not
being able to court Ted's sister himself that he was

prepared to defend Rose against all-comers, so long as she was known to be against the marriage and even though she was a woman.

Because she had an assumed maturity, Rose could approach the subject of Margaret looking after young John once she went into service, with no embarrassment. She did not blush to look Margaret in the face the way Albert had done, and she sat upright on her chair as her Mother had taught her, and didn't fidget and fiddle the way most girls her age would. Margaret observed this, and listened to Rose, but what she had to say in return to Rose's enquiry wasn't what Rose expected, nor was it what she wanted to hear, and at the end, when Margaret had quite finished saying what was on her mind, Rose was blushing as red as Albert had just done, and she was looking only just her fourteen years and as vulnerable as a kitten.

"Rose, I'm as fond of young John as if he was my own, but no child should be shuttled backward and forward from Lodge to cottage like a basket on market day. It wouldn't be right, Rose. No sooner had you left him than he'd start setting up because he'd miss you, and then when he's settled in with me, why it would be dark and you'd be back fetching him and he'd set up because he wouldn't want to leave here. And so it would be Rose, and it's not right for a child. He's your brother and you've brought him up since he was a baby, but it wouldn't be right. And all for what, Rose? So that you could see him sleeping beside your bed at night? You're young to have these feelings put upon you, Rose, but every mother knows that if she doesn't learn that she'll know nothing but heartbreak all her days, and now you have to learn it although you're hardly more than a child. Let poor John marry Ted's sister! She's a good woman, she'll do you no harm, and come the autumn you'll be working at the big house, and you'll not worry about her sooner than you think. Why, you'll be so tired when you get back each night when they've finished with you, it'll be all you'll be able to do to keep awake to climb the stairs to your bed. And that'll be no good to young John. Let your father marry and be in peace, Rose, and let your mother's memory be likewise."

Rose burst out of Margaret's cottage like a bull charging through a gate, and for no reason that he knew, Albert followed her. She was so angry with Margaret, and what she had said, that if she could have she would have hit her with her hand. But she knew that should she, Margaret would clap her one so hard about the ears that Rose wouldn't have heard properly for a while. Margaret was gentle, and Margaret was lazy, but Margaret had an arm on her that could clout as well as her husband could shoe a horse. It was said that the first time he got drunk, she had thrown first his clothes out of the window and then his bed linen and that he had had to run for his life to escape following them.

Rose stopped by the churchyard wall to catch her breath, and then, quite suddenly, she burst into tears.

"Don't cry, Rose," Albert put his hand on her arm, and Rose nearly jumped out of her skin. She hadn't noticed him running after her, nor seen that he was beside her.

"My, you gave me a fright, Albert," she jumped backwards from him, and her tears stopped as suddenly as they had come on.

"I don't like to see you cry, Rose," said Albert, and his concern was so evident, and he looked so thin and as vulnerable as she felt, that she didn't mind him taking her hand and patting it, although normally she'd have told him off, especially since they were so near the church.

"My mother's buried here, Albert, and now all they can talk about is Father marrying again," Rose looked down at her mother's headstone, and her pale face looked pinched from crying. She tossed her head. "It's not right, Albert, it's not right at all. And what will happen when Father gets to heaven. Which wife will then be his, may I ask?"

Albert looked as puzzled by this question as any man would.

"I don't know much about that, I'm afraid, Rose, but we could go for a walk and talk about the Bible, if you'd like to."

"No, I can't do that, Albert. I've got to go home and give young John his milk, and then there's the washing to be brought in, because Grandmother can't be trusted with anything now. And if she tries and drops it, it'll mean another day's scrubbing tomorrow, and I can't scrub tomorrow because tomorrow's baking day, and if you do washing on baking day, then not one thing gets properly done in the rush."

"Can I walk with you, back to the Lodge?"

"Yes, you may, Albert, but don't let's talk any more or I might start crying again, and women who cry deserve what they get. Crying never got you anywhere."

The way she said that, and the determined manner in which she walked beside him, impressed Albert. He felt that if only he had something of Rose's character he would possibly grow big and strong like Margaret's brother, Will, and that he would no longer live in fear of his father. He would have liked to have talked to Rose about his father, and how much he was afraid of him, because he had a feeling that she might understand, but he couldn't because he was a little afraid of Rose too.

That night Rose sat and watched young John asleep. She knew that what Margaret had said was true. She knew it in her heart, and she knew it in her mind, but the thought of sharing her kitchen with another woman was more than she could bear. And yet how else would young John be looked after? It had long ago been arranged between her grandmother and Mrs. Petifor that she should go to work in the big house once autumn came and the harvest was over, and now the time was coming and Rose knew that young John could never be cared for by her grandmother. Margaret was right in knowing that they

couldn't tear a young boy between two places. He was
his father's son and he belonged in the Lodge, and
whatever Ted's sister was or was not, Rose would
not be seeing her all day, nor until late in the evening.
Yet if she was here—then young John would be there,
and Rose would still see him.

"I think you should marry, Father."

Rose had waited up for her father to come home,
and now he paused in the doorway with his hat still on
his head and looked at her astounded. Rose found
it difficult to keep an expression of repulsion from her
face. She could almost hear the ale swilling about in
his stomach and he looked so red in the face, like a
turkey.

"Did I hear you, Rose?"

"I don't know, Father. I said I thought you should
marry. Like Mr. Brownlow, take a wife, or you might
get lonely."

Rose heard her voice sounding so prim and like
gentry against her father's thickened voice and heavier
accent. Sometimes she felt so distant from him, like
she did now. But on other days he would suddenly
do something, or suddenly say something, that would
make her feel that it was something she would have
said at that moment or something she was in the habit
of doing. Such moments were like a pain in her chest
and she would suddenly remember how much she had
loved him when her mother was alive and how happy
they had been.

"I don't need your advice, young Rose," said John,
but Rose could tell by the way that he had sat down
so suddenly, that he was as surprised and pleased
as if it was Christmas Day and he'd forgotten it. "Of
course, as you know, Rose, Ted's sister and I have
been giving it some thought for some time, but we
would—" he suddenly stopped, and to Rose's horror,
drunken tears started to drip down his cheeks.

"Why, Father, you mustn't cry," she knelt beside his
chair, and then she too cried, because now that she had
said what she had said she knew that nothing would

ever be the same again, and soon there would be someone else to be in the house in her stead, and someone
else would pick up young John when he fell over,
and there would be someone else in her father's bed.

"Mind, Father, I don't think it would be good to
have the wedding until after the harvest." She knew
that he would agree to anything while he had drunk
so much and while he was so happy at the idea that he
could marry. "Not until after the harvest," she said
again.

Naturally the news of the impending wedding was
greeted with relief by most of the village.

"I didn't think I could take the sight of John going
up to Ted's place one more time," Mrs. Burrows remarked to anyone who would listen, and the whiskers
on her face twitched with pleasant anticipation at the
thought of the food and drink to be enjoyed at the
feast.

"Does Father want to get married because he feels
lonely?" Tim asked Rose.

"Yes, Tim," said Rose, "and then men like having
wives, so they can do the work. And that's important,
now I'm going up to work at the big house."

"Jim likes Ted's sister. He says she's a woman
who knows where she should be, and butter won't turn
at the sight of her neither."

"Well, that's as may be," said Rose.

She was concerned that not only she should look
proper for the wedding, but Tim and young John and
of course the groom, who was so excited nowadays
that it was all he could do to manage to remember
his duties. Grandmother was taken care of, because
she had her shawl, and that was all right. But Tim
and young John weren't so easy to fit with something.
Tim grew every minute of the day, so that sometimes
she thought he must have been living on oats like the
horses, so leggy had he become. And then Rose had
finally grown out of everything but the one dress that
she had worn at Lady Marjorie's wedding celebrations,
and even that was too small if she was honest.

Like all her problems, Rose regarded the question of the family wedding attire as one that she should work out on her own. She pondered for days how she could turn every one of them into something special for the great day, and how to make them all from sow's ears into silk purses, and eventually she came up with the solution.

"Well, I never did in all my born days," said Grandmother when Rose passed her the hat she had trimmed for her. "Is that what you were doing that day you went to town?"

Rose nodded excitedly, and watched Grandmother peering blindly at herself in the looking glass above the kitchen sink. A slow smile spread across her face as she gradually saw herself revealed in the splendour of the trimmed hat. Ribbons and roses might not be quite the thing for an old lady in some people's eyes, but to Mrs. Buck her day had come. It might be late, but it had come.

"How did you come by all this?" Grandmother half-whispered. She was so astonished, not just by her hat, but by the sight of every one of them in fine new clothes, right down to young John in a suit of blue and a wonderfully cut pair of knickerbockers.

"We're not having Ted's family saying we looked poor for the wedding," said Rose crisply, and patted her own hat proudly. It had a saucy bow.

"She spent her dowry, Mother," John looked across at his mother. "What was left from her box."

His mother said nothing. She couldn't wait to see Mabel Burrows. The ribbons on her hat exactly matched her shawl. It would be enough to turn Mabel quite sour, she was glad to say. And then what a turn out they were going to be for the village to gossip over! Mrs. Buck's heart swelled with pride. Rose might not be a soft girl, she might bully and chivvy, and look too much like her mother to make you feel comfortable, but she knew what was wanted, when it was wanted. And that was a good thing, especially at a wedding.

There were more people in the church than Rose
would have thought possible. Everyone arranged themselves on either side of the aisle as best they could,
though some were in a great confusion because they
felt themselves to be friends of both sides. Poor Ben,
who had had such a soft spot for Ted's sister, sat at
the back, as if by doing so he could absolve himself
from the proceedings and yet show willing because
he had at least turned up.

"Brethren, we are gathered here today—"

The vicar looked at the couple before him with some
sympathy. John was a good man, and quite a favourite with the Countess because of his gardening.
Now he was taking a new wife and one from the village—he knew that everyone felt that it was a day
for rejoicing. Even the vicar felt a trifle thirsty.

It was a fine day when they all wandered out into
the churchyard. A little breezy, but sunny. The wom-
en's dresses billowed becomingly and the ribbons on
their hats fluttered. There wasn't one person present
who hadn't noticed that the Bucks were sporting new
clothes, including the bridegroom in a new jacket of
lovat green. Not that anyone saw fit to make a comment, yet. Now they all shook hands and exchanged
greetings as they were accustomed to do on Sundays,
and as if they hadn't already seen each other only
too recently.

"I'll help Grandmother," Rose told Tim. "You
go with Mrs. Burrows."

Tim sighed. He hated going with Mrs. Burrows.
She leant so hard on his shoulder, and she smelt of
camphor.

Ted and his brothers had hurried back after the
ceremony to put the finishing touches to the house.
Now that the guests had started to arrive, they were
all standing in a straight line next to the bride and
groom, like skittles in a row.

"I don't suppose you'll be drinking, then," said
Ben to Ted, as he shook his hand at the door. "It's
not the custom in this house, I hear."

He looked wry, or he attempted to look wry, but failed and succeeded only in looking embarrassed. The largeness of his face and figure prevented him from being able to register any great subtlety of expression, just as it is difficult for a thin man to look jovial.

"We're making today an exception," said Ted, speaking for himself and his brothers. He looked as embarrassed as any man would who had failed to bring business to the Southwold Arms for so much time. "It's not every day our sister gets married, I hope, and that being so, it's an exception. A fine thing it would be if her brothers never drank her health. You wouldn't but agree with that would you, Ben?"

By this time Ben was half way down the line of brothers, so he hadn't heard, but he had seen the spread that the brothers had provided, and feeling heartened by the sight of it, he had quite forgotten any bitterness he might have felt about the brothers' desertion of his good inn.

Rose too looked at the tables with the food laid out on it, and her eyes widened. If she had spent all her dowry on their clothes, then Ted and his brothers had surely spent all their savings on the wedding feast. It was a most wonderful display. Perhaps Lady Marjorie's wedding celebrations had given the brothers an incentive, set them a target at which to aim, and that being so, they had not missed their mark by very much.

"She kissed me, Rose," said Tim thickly through his clotted cream and fruit pie. "I don't like people kissing me, Rose. And then she said, 'I'll be a mother to you.' I don't want her being a mother to me, Rose."

"That's your third helping, Tim, you'll be sick," said Rose, and wished her grandmother wouldn't make noises when she had finished eating. It was somehow so odd, particularly when she was wearing such a smart hat.

A drowsiness set over the company once they had eaten their fill. The men grouped in one corner re-filled their glasses and drank ale and cider, but the women and children at the other end lay about like cats in the sunshine, and if they could have stretched out they would have done. As it was their heads nodded sideways a little, and several of the old ladies forgot all about company manners and let their chins droop on to their fronts and snored as heartily as they had eaten.

"Come outside, come outside," Tim burst into the room waking them all from their dozy state. "There's a fiddler and his boy, and they've got a dog that does tricks."

"Bless me, it's years since I saw a fiddler," said Grandmother, and followed the rest of the company outside into the sunshine. "Why, there he is, I would have said Tim was 'een now deceiving us with one of his stories if I hadn't seen for myself."

"Come on," shouted Ted. "Let's dance then."

Since it was his land, and his garden, the villagers needed no second urging. Within moments jackets were taken off and hats flung unceremoniously on the grass, and everyone began to dance in any fashion that took them. It was as if they all sensed that this was one of the remaining days of sunshine, now the harvest was gathered and autumn upon them, and they wanted to dance to celebrate the day, and the marriage, and then to dance while they still could—outside in the air and feeling the soft green grass under their feet.

It is debatable whether more happiness is found by refinement. The sophisticated man seems always to be seeking to find what the peasant takes for granted. A sense of carelessness, an inhibition, a whole-hearted enjoyment. Certainly no-one dancing to the fiddler outside Ted's house would have envied the performers at a debutante ball, and yet there might have been more than a number of people at any Society event that year who would have given a great deal to be dancing with the same gaiety as Ted's guests.

"I hope Ted takes care not to ask them in," said Mrs. Burrows, watching from the porch. "They're

Irish those fiddlers, and you can't be too careful with Irish. I once knew of a man who got left for dead by an Irishman."

The music grew faster and faster and soon it had found out who had eaten too much and who had drunk too much and who was not getting any younger, until finally only the young ones were left, dancing and dancing as if their lives depended on it or they were going to be paid at the end. Rose changed hands and looked over her shoulder at Albert as they passed each other. He danced lightly, Albert, and his thin hand felt cool beside everyone else's. He saw her looking at him, and blushed. She shut her eyes, and for a minute tried to pretend she was dancing in a ballroom, not with Albert and the children, but with a young man who was nobly born and thought Rose the most beautiful girl in the room.

Dusk fell. The fiddlers were paid, given a glass of ale, and sent on their way. Rose looked round for her father. He had gone. Home to the Lodge with his new bride.

"I call that a downright thing to do," grumbled Ben, "going off in secret like that before we could clout them, or wish them well."

"Don't worry, I've put things in their bed as you wouldn't want to find at any time," Grandmother laughed, and the rest of the company laughed with her. Rose didn't. She didn't like to think about that sort of thing.

Chapter 7

Mrs. Dickinson looked at Rose. She was getting to be, if not a pretty girl, at least quite striking. Her hair needed tidying up a trifle, and she was very thin, but nevertheless you could see she could be attractive. Having thought that, she then felt a sense of regret. An attractive face could not, in her mind, be anything but a drawback if you were about to start training as an under-housemaid. Goodness knows what indignities she would have to suffer from other members of the staff. Mrs. Dickinson had once had a cousin who was a knight's wife, so she felt she knew something of the kind of life that Rose was about to enter. Staff were always bickering, her cousin had told her, and the larger the staff the more they seemed to take it out of each other.

Of course, some of the regret she felt at Rose leaving her school was professional. She knew that if she had had the time, she could have really made something of Rose Buck. She knew it because of the attention that Rose paid to detail. Nothing seemed to escape her observation. And knowing how she was responsible for her brothers had often made Mrs. Dickinson wonder how she had had any enthusiasm left for reading or writing. Now all that quickness and ability would go towards blacking fires and making beds and emptying night chambers.

Mrs. Dickinson sighed at the thought. It was really so primitive the way girls like Rose were put to work so young, but then it was only a few years ago that politicians had put a stop to the number of hours that children could work.

"I've read all this book, Mrs. Dickinson," Rose put the book she had been lent on the school teacher's desk, "and I understood most of it."

"That's very good, Rose. Now don't forget to come and see me, even now you'll be working. And practise that writing of yours whenever you can. A good hand takes particular practice."

"Yes, Mrs. Dickinson."

"Work hard now, Rose, but don't abandon the three R's. It's just as important for a housemaid to be literate as it is for a duchess, never forget that."

"No, Mrs. Dickinson."

Rose shook hands, and bobbed a curtsy, and then she walked down the school room. No more sitting in the white-painted room learning about all those wonderful things. She did hope she'd remember some of them. And that Mrs. Dickinson would be proud of her.

Mrs. Dickinson watched her go. One of her best pupils, gone to be a housemaid. Still, at least she had Albert Smith. One day he might live to make Southwold School famous. Or if not Albert, then someone else. It was Mrs. Dickinson's ambition to have a famous pupil. Great men so often had humble beginnings, she only hoped that one of them would one day come under her guiding hand. Teaching had its own rewards of course, but she did hope that one day she would earn that final accolade. She wondered why she felt low in herself. It wasn't as if she wouldn't be seeing Rose, and she'd still be in the village.

And it wasn't far for Rose to go to work. But the way she felt that morning when she set off from the Lodge to arrive promptly after the staff had breakfasted, it might have been France. She hardly ate anything, although Mary and her father tried to coax her to fill her tummy.

"You'll be needing it, Rose," said Mary gently.

But Rose could only look at her, and say nothing.

She felt so nervous she really could not swallow anything, not even a cup of tea. She looked at young John happily chewing his bacon. Already he was beginning to show signs of attachment to Mary, and she was very gentle with him, it had to be admitted, not like Grandmother. In Rose's eyes she still looked like a friendly cow, with her round placid face and her brown eyes, but she was not someone to be forever whipping a child. She might not know how to dress him and she might not know exactly how he should look, but she kept him clean and tidy nevertheless. Naturally, Rose had been able to give her advice on many points, and she was glad to say that Mary had taken them to heart, and what's more put them into practice too.

"Behave yourself, girl," said Grandmother from the corner of the kitchen.

If Rose had had her hair loose, she would have tossed her head at Grandmother's remark, but it was pinned up underneath the little white hat that was her uniform. At first it had been exciting trying on a new uniform. Black dress and white cap, thick black stockings, and a pair of new shoes that squeaked when you walked because the leather was so stiff and new. But this morning the uniform felt strange and unfriendly, and the shoes were tight as she crunched up the drive. She didn't know why, but now she was actually going into service at the big house, and it was her first day, she didn't think it was quite proper to walk across the lawns but more appropriate to walk up the drive and circle round to the staff entrance.

The house looked immense. Perhaps because she was going into its service. It seemed as large as something in a dream, and it stared down at her, watching her like a big dog watches an ant approaching one of its paws. Its perfect proportions were already like a challenge to her own inadequacies and in the early morning autumn air the fabric of the building appeared to be alive, a cool moulded brick that when you touched it would be as soft as its colour.

Standing in the servants' hall, Rose felt quite lost. Lost in her clothes, which were too big for her thin frame. Lost in this new, bustling, noisy, incomprehensible world.

There was no-one who seemed to be still. And yet everyone appeared to know exactly where they should be going, and what they should be doing. They were clearing, sweeping, putting away, coming in, or going out, as if directed by unseen voices. Occasionally someone spoke to someone else and there was a suppressed giggle, and an unsuppressed frown from Mr. Widgery, but otherwise no-one appeared to notice each other, so concentrated were they on the tasks they had in hand.

This was a scene that Rose would grow used to, eventually not even notice, so familiar was it to become; but on that first day she wanted to run away. She wanted to go home.

Mr. Widgery beckoned to a girl who was dressed much the same as Rose, only her hat was a little taller, with slightly more lace on it, and her dress fitted her.

"Anne!"

"Yes, Mr. Widgery."

"This is Rose, the new under-housemaid. She will be sharing duties with Lottie." He looked at Rose. "Work hard, girl, learn your duties, and you will find that no-one bothers you, not even me. Right, be off, don't hang around with your mouths falling open! Can't stand my staff being dawdlers, we don't tolerate dawdlers at Southwold. I should say not."

Rose followed Anne up the backstairs.

"When you walk through the house, Rose, you must never make a noise and you must walk to the side of the stairs, and if anyone passes you, you pause, and let them go by. Do you understand?"

Rose nodded. She felt just like that day when Lucy had brought her to the house, and then again when she had come to see the old Countess, and got lost.

Everything she did that first week, she did to the sound of Anne's voice instructing her. She thought she

had known how to run a house, and how to be a cook.
She learnt in only one hour at Southwold that she knew
nothing.

"Staff do not raise their voices in the house."

"Should you ever catch sight of the Earl and Countess, you bob a curtsy."

"Never put your brushes away in a dirty state."

"Never talk at table until the vegetables have been
served."

If she had worked hard running the Lodge since
her mother's death, if she had worked hard at her reading and writing, now she slaved. It was just as Margaret had said. When she got back to the Lodge at
night, when she crawled back down the drive, her feet
swollen in their tight black shoes and her arms aching
from twelve hours non-stop duties, she could hardly
pull herself up the stairs to her little bedroom. And
in the morning she was gone before she had time to
exchange more than a word with anyone.

It took time to sort out the staff at the house. And
if she had thought she had known a little about the
structure of Southwold from being the Lodge Keeper's
daughter, she now realised that she had glimpsed from
the Lodge windows only a little of the grandeur that
made up Southwold. She had seen the greenhouses,
but not the fruit. Now she saw it being piled up in
silver baskets. Peaches, pears, apples, grapes. She had
seen the butcher's cart swaying through the gates. Now
she saw the carcases being dragged through the kitchen.
She saw crystal glass, silver and gold plate, china and
porcelain of every description, and for the first time
the reality of Southwold frightened her, and then it
won her.

Quite suddenly she knew that more than anything
she wanted to be part of this life, this extraordinary,
magnificent awe-inspiring existence. She didn't want
to marry someone in the village, as Margaret had done,
and bring up a mob of children. She wanted to be like
Anne in her crisp uniform. Anne, bossing her and
Lottie about, or Mrs. Petifor bossing Anne. She wanted

to be somebody in the awe-inspiring hierachy in which she was at present nobody.

Rose knew that nothing could change the fact that she was the Lodge Keeper's daughter, just as nothing could change the fact that Lottie was Big Jim the coachman's daughter. They both had the same advantage in that, by dint of their birth, they had both been admitted to Southwold. But Rose was not like Lottie. She didn't dream of marrying a farmer and going to market in her best bonnet. She dreamt of becoming a personal maid, like Miss Hodges. She didn't want to find a way out of Southwold, she wanted to find a way up Southwold.

Lottie was a plump little creature, and she cried a great deal, which Rose found embarrassing. She felt that Lottie was letting down the under-housemaids by crying every time something went wrong or Anne scolded her, but Lottie was impervious to Rose's embarrassment. If she felt hurt, she cried.

"What is it, Lottie?"

"It's Mrs. Petifor, she says I'm to have no dinner because of the chip in that plate last night. And I'm so hungry, Rose."

Rose looked at Lottie. She was so plump and pathetic, like a fat puppy whimpering in the dark of the corridor.

"I'll put some of mine in my pocket for you," she said comfortingly, "but do hurry, Lottie. If we're found here neither of us will have dinner."

"Will you really keep something for me, Rose? I get so hungry, and when I go home, there's nothing left."

"Yes, I'll keep something for you."

Rose managed to slip a piece of tart into her pocket. It lay wrapped in her handkerchief, until she and Lottie were sent to draw the curtains in the steward's room and lay the table for tea. Mrs. Petifor and Mrs. Amey liked to have tea together. Mrs. Amey was Southwold's treasured cook. She made the madeira cakes that Mrs.

Petifor doted on, so their friendship was based on something pretty solid.

It wasn't until Lottie saw the cake lying out upon the table surrounded by all the other little delicacies that Mrs. Petifor particularly liked to see on a tea table that she remembered just how hungry she was, and that Rose remembered the tart lying in her handkerchief at the bottom of her pocket. She gave it to Lottie who crammed it into her mouth as fast as she could, but not fast enough, and being Lottie she managed to leave a large display of crumbs all around her mouth.

"Mr. Widgery!"

"Mrs. Petifor?"

In Rose's eyes the room appeared to darken as Mr. Widgery entered.

"Mr. Widgery," Mrs. Petifor was triumphant as she looked from Lottie to the butler, and back again. "Mr. Widgery, would you believe your eyes? Would you, Mr. Widgery? Here is an under-housemaid, a person little higher than a scully, and she is eating, Mr. Widgery, eating a piece of tart in the steward's room! Can you believe your eyes, Mr. Widgery, if you had not been called to witness this scene of abandon, this orgy of eating, this complete abnegation of all that an under-housemaid should be engaged in?"

Mrs. Petifor had had the benefit of a good education by virtue of a father who had been doing rather better earlier on in his life than he eventually did towards its end, and by her literate use of words she could subtly, and constantly, remind the rest of the staff of this.

Mr. Widgery had absolutely no idea what 'abnegation' meant, but he had absolutely no intention of letting Mrs. Petifor realise this. He thought it might be to do with the Bible, and then he thought it might not; but he made a little note in the back of his mind to look it up in an old volume of Debrett's when he got a chance. He felt sure that Debrett's, being the kind of volume that it was, would carry such words as "abnegation'. In fact, he would dare swear it was something

to do with kings coming and going, although what that
had to do with housemaids, under or over, had him
beaten.

He blinked several times to allow himself time to
form his words. Mrs. Petifor's magnificent use of the
Queen's English irritated him intensely, if he was to be
completely honest, which he was not in the habit of
being for the most part of the day He was fond of
calling this habit 'protecting others'. And he was *very*
fond of 'protecting others'. He 'protected' the Earl
and Countess from things below stairs, and he 'protected' persons below stairs from themselves; that, in
his opinion, was a butler's main task. However, protection apart, at this very moment he sensed that he
was about to do something very dramatic, something
he had not the pleasure of doing for some time, and
something that he secretly enjoyed doing more than
anything in the world. He was about to wield his power.

He might not have Mrs. Petifor's power over words,
but he had complete power below stairs. His word
was law, and although it was his duty to treat Mrs.
Amey with the reverence due to a superb cook, and
Nanny with the respect due to one who had brought
up the Heir, and Mrs. Petifor with the right degree of
manners and authority, nevertheless he was king of his
underworld. He was the emperor of the darkness of
the silver cupboards, ruler over all glass and porcelain,
the never sleeping conscience of the domestic nation
contained in the servants' hall, the steward's room,
and in every pantry and scullery that Southwold
boasted.

Mr. Widgery advanced a step. Rose felt that she
could scream, if she had dared. She knew that her
career was already in ruins, after only one week. She
knew it from the way that Mr. Widgery had drawn
himself up to his full height. She knew it from the time
he took to speak, and she knew it from the way that
Lottie was cowering against the wall.

"You have been eating have you not?"

Lottie nodded.

"You have been eating, here in the steward's room, without a by your leave, or a word from anyone. You have had the impudence, the impudence——" he repeated this word in the hope that Mrs. Petifor might be impressed by it, even though it didn't quite reach the giddy heights of 'abnegation', "to eat a tart here, within sight of Mrs. Petifor, in front of Mrs. Amey, and this after having been forbidden dinner because you had disgraced yourself earlier."

Tears started to drip down Lottie's cheeks, where they had been frozen in terror behind her eyelids before.

"I am going to dismiss you, Lottie Freston. I'm going to dismiss you without reference, and without character. I am going to send you back to your poor sire, and let him make of you what he will."

Lottie started to scream. It was horrible.

"Please, Mr. Widgery sir, please, don't send me home. My father will beat me, sir, he will, sir. He beats me, he wouldn't touch a horse but he beats me. Please, sir, don't, sir."

Not even Mr. Widgery was prepared for this terrible outburst. Rose felt herself go white as Mr. Widgery pulled Lottie away from his feet. And she remembered that Tim had told terrible tales of the beatings that Big Jim was in the habit of giving his nine children. And how thankful they had been that their own father had never touched them—although Rose knew that sometimes he might have liked to—but he never did, because Mother would never stand for violence, the way she would never stand for bad manners, and anyway, one look from her grey eyes would be enough to quieten anyone.

"Out, girl, out!" ordered Mr. Widgery, and there was a shocked silence as he conducted the weeping Lottie to the back door, with the command to return her uniform later that evening, or else it would be the very worst for her.

Rose could hardly believe it. Mrs. Petifor and Mrs. Amey sat down to their tea and cake, and Mr. Widgery went upstairs to answer His Lordship's bell. Everyone resumed their tasks, as if nothing had happened, and more important to Rose, no-one, but no-one, had asked Lottie where, or from whom, she had got the tart.

Lottie herself had said nothing. But would she continue to say nothing? Would she return the uniform without mentioning the fact that Rose had been party to her heinous crime? Would she not wish to drag Rose down with her?

"Here's the uniform, sir."

Lottie's little figure crept into the servants' hall and presented the bundle of clothes, together with the pair of black shoes and the little white hat.

Rose was not the only person to notice that there were bruises and cuts on Lottie's face, that her eyes were quite swollen from crying, and that she walked with difficulty as if she had been beaten across her back so hard that she could no longer straighten herself.

Mr. Widgery chose to speak in the silence that followed her departure.

"Let that be a lesson to the junior servants," he said, "let that be a lesson to you all that rules are rules, and rules are to be obeyed and not to be flouted. Thou Shalt Not Steal. Thou Shalt Not Covet Thy Neighbour's Goods. It is all contained in the Bible and at Southwold all we do is to abide by the Bible. I should say so."

Rose shivered, and thanked her stars that Lottie had said nothing. Her replacement was a girl who had been born in London. Rose regarded her with suspicion. She was older than Rose, and had had experience elsewhere. Her name was May.

May was as pretty as a picture and there wasn't one footman or groom, or one red-blooded male at Southwold, who didn't notice her as soon as she arrived. She swung up the drive as if she had worked there all her life, and what's more, as if Southwold was lucky to have her.

Perhaps by virtue of her different accent, and her

knowing ways, there wasn't anyone below stairs that could say they weren't impressed by May. She didn't giggle or chatter and she wasn't lazy or idle. On the contrary she was quick and efficient and she only spoke when spoken to. But what May didn't say, she thought. And what she thought, she showed in her eyes, and in her eyes Mrs. Petifor could read disrespect and Mrs. Amey could see impertinence and Mr. Widgery— challenge.

She had large, blue eyes with long black lashes, although her hair was blonde, and her cheeks were as soft and as downy as the peaches from the green-houses. A fact that filled Mrs. Petifor with spite.

Mrs. Petifor would have liked to have caught her out, Mrs. Amey would have liked to have scolded her, but what Mr. Widgery would like to do with her, he hadn't yet admitted to himself.

Rose fell in love with May the way younger girls often fall in love with older friends. She worshipped her at first from afar, and then as an intimate, an honoured confidante. May had only to sigh, and Rose would want to know why. May had only to do her hair in a different way, and Rose longed to have hers the same. May spoke with a London accent. Every night, however tired, Rose would practice her accent on the way home. May said 'really' in such a pretty way, and she said 'go on,' if Rose managed to make her laugh. And she said words like 'lawks' if she was surprised, and she was wonderful at doing everything. Rose felt that if she could do things the way May could, then she, Rose, would become a maid like Miss Hodges, and quicker than she could dream about.

It was obvious from the way that Mr. Widgery re-garded May that she would be due for promotion as soon as one of the housemaids got married. Mr. Wid-gery often looked at May. When she was bending down to put something away, or when he passed her on the stairs, he would give her one of his quick, dark looks, and in those quick, dark looks Rose felt that she could sense Mr. Widgery's admiration of May, and his determination to single her out for promotion as soon as he could.

"Rose, I think I dropped my handkerchief on the stairs. Would you be a dear?"

Rose ran up the stairs as fast as she could. It was on one of the upper landings where she and May had been making beds. May could make a bed look so neat, and so exact, that you couldn't have dreamt that anyone slept in it. She had a way of folding the top sheet and pressing down the edge so that it looked as if she had straightened it with a rule. And she could twitch a cover, or plump a pillow so that it looked a picture.

Rose was thinking over May's bed-making, and how best she could emulate her, and how much she wished she had blonde hair like May, when she heard Mr. Widgery's voice.

"Come here, you little slut," he was saying.

Rose froze. Poor May was in trouble, the way Lottie had been. Mr. Widgery sounded dreadful.

"Come here, you little slut," he said again, "I've been watching you, waggling yourself around the servant's hall, cavorting in front of the footmen. Women like you should be strung up, do you hear?"

"Yes, Mr. Widgery."

"I would take great pleasure in stringing a woman like you from a tree, did you know that?"

"No, Mr. Widgery."

There was a silence. Rose's heart beat faster. She heard Mr. Widgery make a funny noise. It sounded as if he was panting, and then he appeared to whisper 'please, please' several times. Rose wanted to laugh. What on earth was he doing? May appeared to be saying nothing. Perhaps she wanted to laugh too? She couldn't wait to ask her what had happened, but when she saw her half an hour later, something stopped her. There was a look on May's face that she hadn't seen before, as if she wanted to be sick.

"Here's your handkerchief, May," Rose whispered at the earliest opportunity.

May took it, and said nothing. Rose hoped that she hadn't hurt her feelings.

Later, May said "Men!" That was all she said, but for a second her lip curled in such a way that she looked quite hard, and the eyes that were normally so bright blue looked cloudy with disgust. "They're filthy creatures."

"Nothing's 'happened', has it, May?" Rose put her hand on her arm.

"No, nothing's 'happened' to me. I'm not going to go catching scarlet fever, if that's what you mean."

"You're so pretty May, you have to be careful, being as pretty as you are."

May shook the hand from her arm impatiently.

"One day I'm going to be someone, one day some dirty old butler won't be allowed to come sniffing round my petticoats, because if he does I'll kick him in the teeth."

Rose looked at May in awe. She wished she had May's spirit, May's dash, and May's daring. And even more she wished that she could look as pretty as May, and that her hair was blonde like May's, and that she had big blue eyes like May, in fact as Rose admitted to herself sometime later, she would dearly have loved to have been born May, and not Rose.

May's background was somewhat mysterious. She never spoke of it to anyone. She was London born, but she had arrived at Southwold from another country estate, sent on recommendation of a friend of the Countess'. Whether she liked to pretend she was mysterious, or whether she was ashamed of where she came from, Rose couldn't find out, but once or twice she had the impression that May's early life had not been easy, or as May said 'being brought up hard makes you hard.'

Rose wondered what Mr. Widgery had done to May, but she didn't ask her any more about it, and anyway she had to lay Hodges' tea.

Rose admired Miss Hodges, not just because she was a lady's maid, but because Miss Hodges was a person of firm opinions. Even Mr. Widgery was treated with some disdain by Miss Hodges. An ignorant male, a creature who couldn't tell taffeta from grosgrain.

The Earl was a person who never entered Miss Hodges' orb, and whenever he did, it had to be admitted, he did little to heighten Miss Hodges' respect for the male species. It was obvious that, like Mr. Widgery, the Earl was yet another poor creature unable to distinguish good from bad, and completely incapable of noticing even such trifling details about the Countess as a change of hairstyle, or even, it sometimes seemed to Miss Hodges, whether or not she was in a ball gown or an afternoon dress. The Earl was head of Southwold, lord of all he surveyed, but in Miss Hodges' opinion he was to be pitied.

"I think His Lordship is a little shortsighted," she murmured on occasions when like today, she had worked especially hard on the Countess' appearance.

"He can shoot straight," said Nanny loyally. She was on a short visit to Southwold, from Lady Marjorie's house in Eaton Place, and in a loyal mood, "and there's nothing wrong with either Hugo's or Marjorie's eyes."

"Yes, but that's different," Miss Hodges sighed, because Nanny's loyalty depressed her.

She departed to lay out the Countess' evening gown. A delightful confection, in her opinion, of satin swept to each side and pinned with black humming birds on each shoulder. After Nanny's remark, Miss Hodges hoped that His Lordship would not take a shot at them.

Rose was always disappointed by Miss Hodges' evening departure. She felt that by being near Miss Hodges, and by listening to her, something of Miss Hodges' elevated position at Southwold would rub off on her. And then she wanted to learn what Miss Hodges' secret was. What had made Miss Hodges what she was? How did you graduate to being a lady's maid? Or, indeed, did you graduate at all? Was it necessary to be something more than Rose herself was, the simple daughter of the Lodge Keeper? All these questions enthralled her so much that she didn't notice that Nanny had been staring at her for some time.

"Are you Lucy Buck's daughter? Come here, girl, I can't quite make you out in that light. Why, I'd swear you were Lucy Buck's daughter."

"Yes, I am, thank you, Miss."

Rose felt totally confused by this sudden interest from Nanny, and at that time realised that she didn't know whether or not Nanny was in fact a 'missus' or a 'miss.' Mrs. Amey being traditionally a 'Miss' who was always know by the courtesy title of 'Mrs'. To her relief Nanny, however, appeared not to be listening to Rose's mumblings.

"I thought my eyes couldn't deceive me with those looks. You're no farm labourer's daughter, you're Lucy Buck's child. I could have seen that any day of the week. So you've come to work at Southwold, have you?"

Rose nodded.

"Well, you'll have a hard time of it no doubt, as all the young girls do, but if you keep your head and mind your manners you'll last as long as your mother did. God Rest Her Soul, for she was surely one of the best that ever walked through the servants' hall and a great favourite of the old Countess, God Rest Her Soul, too."

Mrs. Amey looked uneasily at Nanny after her last remarks. All this 'God Resting' this and 'God Resting' that smacked too much of Popery and other nonsense as far as she was concerned, but Nanny was Nanny when all was said and done, and the Countess abided by anything she said, as far as the welfare of Hugo and Marjorie was concerned. To this very day Hugo could only be quieted by Nanny if he took it into his head to be off in one of his sulks, and that was a fact that everyone knew of.

"I remember when your mother came to this village," Nanny looked at Mrs. Amey, "and you remember when she came to this village, don't you, Jane?"

Mrs. Amey looked uncomfortable at Nanny addressing her by her Christian name in front of an under-housemaid, but she nodded quickly, because she respected Nanny, if only for the length of time she had been at Southwold.

"She came to this village on foot. She had run away from the orphanage, they said, and no-one would have helped her if it hadn't been for the old Countess. That morning, on one of her whims, she had decided to take a drive and stop off to buy some sweets for the village children.

"At least, she sent poor old Madame Vilanova in for the sweets, and herself sat outside in her carriage. And who should pass by but your mother, and as the old Countess said to me herself later, some people can judge a horse at twenty yards, and she, it appeared, could judge a maid at thirty. And heavens above, if she didn't that minute, there and then in the middle of the village, engage your mother to become her maid."

There was a silence as Rose imagined what she had just been told, and Nanny, knowing that she had the ears of her audience, supped her tea and then continued.

"Naturally, the Countess herself was horrified, but she was well accustomed to the old lady's fancies so she said nothing, thinking that before very long young Lucy Buck would give herself away and rile the old lady so she would be rid of her soon enough, no doubt. But no such thing happened.

"Eventually, Lucy was the only maid that the old lady would tolerate, besides poor old Madame. It seemed to me sometimes that she knew what the old lady's whims were going to be before the old lady knew them herself, and so in the end even the Countess grew to be grateful for her. In my opinion it was a sign of how fond of her she was that she consented to her marriage. And when Lucy died, why the old lady never quite got over it. 'Poor little Lucy' she would say, so often to Daisy, 'Poor little Lucy.' Still, that's the way things are. Women are born to suffer, so they say."

No-one in the room cared to disagree with the statement since they were all women, and because it was so obviously true. Women were born to suffer.

Rose looked at Nanny and Mrs. Amey. They hadn't suffered because they'd been sensible. They hadn't made the mistake of getting married. They were able to sit drinking their tea and eating their cake in a lovely warm room with a pretty tablecloth, because they had had the good sense to stay in service and not to get married.

Later, when she was able to talk to May, she said, "I'm never going to get married, are you, May?"

May shook her head.

"Marriage is for fools."

"I want to be in service all my life, May, I do. I want to be," Rose paused before allowing herself to reveal her ambition, "I want to be a lady's maid."

She hoped that May wouldn't laugh at what she had said because the idea of little Rose Buck, not yet fifteen, becoming a lady's maid, when all she had ever known was the country, was laughable. In fact, as soon as she had named her ambition, Rose saw just how laughable it might seem to other people, so she wasn't exactly surprised when May did laugh. At least, May's mouth laughed, but her eyes didn't. Her eyes, as always, were saying something else.

"You haven't much ambition have you, Rose? No, what you might call, *real* ambition, have you? You want to be a lady's maid? You really want to be someone like Miss Hodges, sitting all day sewing on buttons or waiting up for Her Ladyship to return from a party? Is that what you think life's about? Well, I don't know."

Rose blushed scarlet. She wished to goodness she hadn't said anything. May always succeeded in making her feel stupid.

"What do you think life's about, May?"

"I don't know, Rose," said May grimly, "but I'm sure what it's *not* about, at least not for me it isn't."

Claude, one of the footmen, passed them. May watched him.

"He's another, that one. Always giving himself airs and graces, when he's really just an old man pretending to be young."

After that they separated quickly. It wasn't good to be seen talking, even below stairs, or anywhere. Perhaps because of the Earl's love of seclusion, it was inevitable that everywhere there was the rule of silence, except when at table, and even then May and Rose could only speak after the vegetables. So conversation during the working day was something to be snatched, and held in whispers.

At table, the talk was confined to the older staff holding forth and the junior staff listening dutifully. This was not only because the younger servants felt self-conscious about talking in front of the others, but because Mr. Widgery's dark personality dominated the long table.

He would place himself and Mrs. Petifor at either end of the table, rather as if they were the Earl and Countess, but unlike the Earl, who was in the habit of propping up a book next to his place if his wife and he were dining alone, Mr. Widgery watched everyone who sat at his table with the eyes of a man who, while knowing that this was a time for staff to relax, nevertheless would make a note of any person who took it into his or her head to disagree with him, or even voice an opinion with which he was not in sympathy.

His staff knew this and it was an unspoken law that any new junior servant who had the temerity to pipe up at table was given a sharp kick on the ankle and a crisp warning later. And if they valued their job it was something that they did not do again.

The result of the imposition of so much discipline on even talk at table was that the younger members of the staff were very inclined to giggle at the slightest provocation.

"These are very tasty parsnips. Most tasty, do you not think so Mrs. Petifor? I should say so."

Mr. Widgery looked down the table at Mrs. Petifor.

"I like a parsnip almost as much as I like a marrow," agreed Mrs. Petifor, "but then I like a carrot more than any of them. Carrots are most felicitous."

Mr. Widgery did not betray the fact that 'felicitous' was a word that he had not, as yet, come across. He hadn't, of course, omitted to search Debrett's for 'abnegation', but he was sorry to say, without any reward. He made a mental note to seek both 'abnegation' and 'felicitous' in His Grace's dictionary when he had a moment alone in the library.

There was a pause in the conversation, everyone having been defeated by Mr. Widgery's effort. Parsnips and carrots were not the kind of subject that made the imagination race and certainly there were no minds racing in either one direction or another, only a healthy sound of eating.

Miss Hodges, like the rest of the company, found Mr. Widgery's topic of conversation not only boring but vulgar. She didn't think it at all proper to discuss food at table, in fact she had always been brought up not to.

"The Countess informs me that there are some young ladies from Apton coming across to dine when the young Viscount comes down next month."

This was another non sequitur, since none of the servants dining knew what they should say in reply to this. They all knew that the son and heir to Southwold was expected to be visiting next month, but they had no idea what they should say to the fact that some young ladies had been invited to dine with him.

Eventually Mrs. Amey said, "it was so nice to see Nanny, even for such a short visit."

"The young Viscount is all the rage in town, I believe."

Miss Hodges had ignored Mrs. Petifor's remark, because she did not think it quite nice to discuss other members of the staff, particularly when she could be discussing members of the Upper Class.

"I always think he looks a picture in his riding clothes," Mrs. Amey helped herself to some more parsnips. "He's a chip off the old block. The spit of his grandfather I should say. The absolute spit."

It was time for Mr. Widgery to butt in. He did not like to hear Mrs. Amey, however good her cooking might be, discussing in front of the younger servants, the fact that the Viscount was the 'spit' of his grandfather. Everyone knew that his grandfather had been a great lover of the ladies and that it was only the old Countess with her fiery temper and her wild Russian ways who had been able to keep him on the straight and narrow. Rumour had it that she had once threatened him with a gun because he had been somewhat taken by a young lady in the neighbourhood.

In his mind Mr. Widgery shivered. There was no sight more terrifying than a woman with a gun. Any man met at the door by a woman with a gun had his sympathy. He looked down the length of the table. There was some disturbance. What's more it looked to him as if one of the under-housemaids was giggling. He frowned at her. She caught his look, and tried to stop. Mr. Widgery made a mental note to watch her work. There was nothing he hated more than to see the younger staff smiling and laughing. Just as if they were at Southwold to enjoy themselves. He sat back and focused his attention on Mrs. Amey's discussion with Mrs. Petifor. They were still at it.

"In my opinion the young man should settle down as soon as possible. Gadding about never did any young man the slightest good and only serves to get him into bad habits."

The discussion had grown into almost open criticism of the son and heir to Southwold. Mr. Widgery saw that it really was time for him to interrupt.

"I always think—"

But no-one was fated to hear what Mr. Widgery thought because quite suddenly he leapt to his feet, and screamed.

Chapter 8

The fact that Mr. Widgery had a terror of spiders
was now known to everyone, and it was something
that Mr. Widgery realised that he would have to live
with. If his soul had never been the essence of love,
now it was seething with the opposite to that virtue.
For a butler to have to be revived in the steward's
room by two giggling footmen was not only shaming,
it was degrading.

It wasn't as if the matter could have rested at Southwold either, or that only his employers would have
got to hear of the incident. By now he knew the whole
village would be laughing at the story.

Day after day, he watched the laughter being suppressed behind the servants' eyes. Even the tradesmen,
it seemed to him, looked at him with their mockery
thinly disguised. It was enough to drive a man to
seek solace in the gin bottle, except that he was not
especially partial to alcohol. (This fact having commended him particularly to the Earl's attention, because there is nothing more irritating than to find that
your butler has been knocking off some of your best
claret.) Even after some days had elapsed since the
incident, Mr. Widgery imagined he could still hear
the footmen's giggles as he came round and the noise
gave him sleepless nights. He vowed he would get his
revenge, but he knew that it was impossible. Just as it
is impossible to imprison vast numbers of protesting

people, so it is impossible, even if you are a butler, to punish the whole staff.

However, if leniency towards his staff had never been one of his practices, now he was the epitome of the avenging angel, complete with sword to strike down the ungodly or those who paused for a minute while in the throes of their duties. He found dust where there was none, dirt where there had never been any, and fault with everyone.

Mrs. Petifor and Mrs. Amey, and naturally Miss Hodges, were not victims of his new policy, because it was difficult for him to find fault with *their* work, but nevertheless they were made to feel most uncomfortable, and since they knew that Mr. Widgery had his Lordship's ear, on account of his impeccable record, even they were afraid to voice any kind of protest at the sullen atmosphere that now pertained below stairs.

Rose's only respite in her long and arduous day was when she served them their tea, and although she could not enter into their conversations, nevertheless she heartily agreed with their sentiments.

"I think Mr. Widgery is a little exacting to expect the footmen to polish their buttons every day, do you not, Mrs. Petifor?" said Miss Hodges.

"He is a perfectionist, so he tells us. However I think that perfection can sometimes lead to perfidy."

"Very near," Miss Hodges nodded approvingly at Mrs. Petifor.

She respected Mrs. Petifor's use of words. Education made such a difference to people. It took intelligence to know how to apply polish.

"I think Mr. Widgery has the idea that someone—"

"Yes, yes," Miss Hodges agreed hastily, and frowned at the same time to try to warn Mrs. Petifor not to say anything too much in front of Rose.

"I don't imagine that anyone would do that. I mean, who would have *known* of his fear? We certainly did not."

Mrs. Petifor was impervious to frowns.

"I set out the puddings with my own hands, and I never saw a spider. In my opinion it must have crawled under the lid, or some such, while they were waiting in the pantry. That's my opinion."

Everyone had heard Mrs. Amey's opinion of the incident more than several times now.

"And then none of the footmen could have put it there, seeing as they were all busy elsewhere, and there's not one *girl* that I know of that would have the courage to pick up a spider. Girls faint and scream at spiders, everyone knows that, the same as they do at mice. It's unheard of for a woman to touch a spider."

There was a silence as everyone agreed silently with this thought.

"It's so *unusual* to see a man faint," Miss Hodges bit delicately into a biscuit, a satisfied expression spreading over her face at the memory.

"I've never seen anyone fall like that, or heard a scream to match it," Mrs. Amey enthused.

She had, of course, but they all loved to dwell on the subject of Mr. Widgery's spectacular faint. Nothing exciting had happened for a long time, at least not since a few months ago when someone had fallen into the village pond and drowned after rather too long a sojourn at the Southwold Arms.

"Rose, will you fetch some more biscuits, please?"

Rose knew she was being sent out of the room, so that they could talk some more about Mr. Widgery without her hearing. She didn't mind, because it seemed to her that she had heard enough of Mr. Widgery fainting to last her a lifetime. Even her father talked about it if he was still up when she got home. That was the trouble with the country. Nothing much happened. If you were even just an under-house-maid in town you would be bound to have a more exciting life.

However, the incident of Mr. Widgery's faint passed

out of the servants' gossip when it was superseded by
a new piece of information. That the young Viscount
was not *coming* down to the country, but being *sent*.
All the difference in the world, as everyone down to
the scullery maids knew. Apparently—this was according to May who had got it from Claude—apparently his being the rage of the town was one thing,
but he had got into debt besides, in spite of his generous allowance, and it was considered prudent that
he should have a sojourn in the country and, as the
Countess had been overheard to remark to one of her
more intimate friends, "There's nothing like giving the
boy *no* temptations, is there?"

In the Countess' view the country was devoid of all
diversions. If she could find very little to occupy her
when at Southwold, she was certain that it would be
quite impossible for Hugo to get up to mischief. She
considered, and her husband agreed, that being away
from town and temptation for a few months would
most probably settle Hugo down better than anything.

The prospect of having her son to amuse her at
dinner, instead of continually having to try to attract
her husband's attention by conversation, was pleasant
to the Countess. Hugo was amusing. He might be a
bit of a scamp, but at least he liked other things
beside books. Now Marjorie had children it was difficult for her to get down to Southwold as often as
she had, and the Countess found country life even
duller than before, if that were possible.

Of course, it was all her husband's fault. He didn't
take any interest in anything, not even in the rose
garden, and yet he expected her to fill in her time,
just as if he was willing to accompany her everywhere,
which of course he wasn't. She supposed that if she
had his every meal sent into the library on a tray,
she would quite probably never set eyes on him at
all. It wasn't as if she was yet in her dotage either.
The Countess touched her immaculate coiffure. Although her hair suffered from being frizzy, neverthe-

less Hodges always managed to make a good job of it. Making good jobs of things was something that Miss Hodges prided herself on, and the reason why the Countess put up with her silly ways.

If the Countess was looking forward to the young Viscount Ashby's visit, so were the staff of Southwold. The atmosphere below stairs lifted the nearer it got to the date of his arrival. Everyone liked to hear, or see, young people, and although the Earl and Countess weren't old, they weren't young either, and it was a long time since there had been a bit of gaiety, since His Lordship was somewhat set in his ways to say the least.

"Here, my girl! Get polishing at once."

Mr. Widgery had crept up behind Rose, as she stood in the room known as the Great Ante Room. She had been detailed to go there, clear out the grate, and start polishing the floor. Naturally having finished the grate, she had stood up and gazed round her, since it was the first time that she had ever been in this part of the house.

"Sorry, Mr. Widgery."

"Get going, girl, the Viscount arrives this evening and Her Ladyship wants every part of this place as shiny and as polished as the day it was laid. I should say."

"Yes, Mr. Widgery."

"Where's that other girl, you know the one I mean?"

Mr. Widgery made a gallant attempt to pretend that he didn't.

"May, sir? Why, she's next door, sir, finishing the grate there, and then she's going to join me here sir. We're going to do the floor."

Rose put down her kneeler and started to polish the floor. She pretended not to notice Mr. Widgery creeping next door to the Music Room, but she couldn't stop herself going to the door and listening.

"Why, Mr. Widgery, what *can* you be wanting?"

She heard May saying. "You'll have to be a much better boy before I allow any of that nonsense, won't you?" Again Mr. Widgery murmured 'please, please', as he had done before.

Rose's eyes widened. May hated Mr. Widgery. She hated him as much or more than the rest of the staff hated him. Yet here she was calling him a 'boy', and carrying on as if—as if she liked him. There was a sound of a slight scuffle, and May giggling.

Rose quickly returned to her kneeler. She didn't want them suddenly coming in, or hearing her outside the door.

A little later, May joined her.

"Scum," she said shortly, after she and Rose had been polishing for some time. "They never have anything else on their minds, men don't. You should see the scum that used to visit my mother. You wouldn't have bought an apple off them, let alone let them—" she paused, "but she, poor woman—she had me and me brothers, and how else could she live?"

"Does Mr. Widgery kiss you, May?" Rose felt embarrassed to ask May such a question, but her curiosity overcame her.

"No, he doesn't kiss me, Rose. He wants more than kissing, much more than kissing."

They polished for a little while more in silence. And then May said, "Some day I'm going to be in there with them, Rose, some day I am, you know."

Rose's eyes opened wide. She respected May's determination. She was sure that what May said she was going to do, she'd do.

"Perhaps you'll marry well, May?"

"Nothing less than a knight will do for me," May laughed. "No dirty old butlers, thank you very much. Still, I got my own back on him all right. You see, that's what you've got to be in this life, Rose, if you're going to survive. Fly and quick, and you've got to notice things. The way I noticed that dirty bastard's terrified of spiders."

"It was you!"

That morning Rose's respect for May grew to Olympian heights.

That evening the Viscount Ashby arrived.

His mother greeted him in the hall.

She had had Hodges lay out one of her most elegant confections. When she was happy she looked almost beautiful.

"Hugo!"

"Mama! You're looking wonderful."

The convention was so secure that neither of them, while they greeted each other with restrained enthusiasm, cared to mention, or forsaw a time when they would mention, the fact that Hugo was not at Southwold of his own volition. The family lawyer might wring his hands at the enormity of his debts, but his parents could be relied upon not to introduce the subject within his hearing.

The Countess was so delighted to see her son that she forgot to be displeased when she saw that he had brought someone else with him, without having had the forethought to tell her. And Hugo, knowing that his mother would be pleased to see him, had waved aside any thought of letting the Countess know that he intended to bring his friend, Charles Littleton, with him.

Charles, like himself, was in a spot of trouble. In fact, he was not just in one spot of trouble, but rather more than one. He had certainly been pushing his luck as far as his funds were concerned, but more than that, he had gone a little too far with a certain gentleman's delicious wife, and when it had been broken to him by Hugo that he had been more or less ordered to Southwold for an enforced holiday, Charles had deemed it wise to accompany his friend to pastures new, even though pastures of the kind that contained buttercups and daisies bored him to ribbons.

Hugo and Charles had been friends since they were both little brutes together at Eton. They had for some time run rival gangs at that establishment, but the rivalry had ceased once they found they had a com-

mon interest along with other young men of their
age group and position, that of horses and women,
and most properly, their interest in both sports was
strictly in that order.

Luckily, for her own peace of mind, the Countess
did not see standing in front of her two young men
who had been busy getting up to no good in the
metropolis, but rather she saw her dear Hugo, so tall
and handsome, and his friend Charles, who was such
a nice boy and always had such nice manners when
he was a little boy, both come to stay at Southwold
and divert her from the tedium of country life. Of
course, when her husband had been active in politics
she had been glad to get down to Southwold and loved
the peace of the great house as opposed to the busy
life of the politician's wife. But, since his premature
retirement from that field (and goodness knows, everyone knew that he could have been Prime Minister if
he had wanted) she had resented his addiction to
Southwold more and more. She thought he had taken
to the country and to his books and his cataloguing
in the kind of spirit that other people might not understand. It was almost as if he had been disgraced in
politics, instead of just not wanting to make the final
fence and pass the finishing post ahead of the rest.

Of course, she had never argued with him. It had
seemed to her that another man's wife might have.
Another man's wife might have even collapsed from
boredom, but she had refused to be as other men's
wives, mostly because she knew the Talbot-Careys
far too well. She knew that once one of them made
up their minds about something, there was very little
use in trying to dissuade them, very little use indeed.
Her father-in-law, a man of great charm, who had
put up with his Russian wife's tempers with remarkable fortitude, never could be moved on a point, once
he had made his decision. The old Countess had even
been known to hurl things at him, so put out would
she be at times by his stubborn attitude, but to no avail.
And, like his son, it was impossible for anyone to

bring up the subject ever again in his presence if he did not wish to discuss it. It wasn't that they would remark on it, or even become bad-tempered. They simply did not appear to hear what you said. It was maddening sometimes, particularly in relation to something you had quite set your heart on. But there you were, life was by no means easy.

"Hugo was very naughty not to have let you know," Charles Littleton smiled down at her, and the Countess noted how sparkling and white his teeth were, and how black and thick his hair was. It curled round the back of his neck with a seduction that was an art in itself.

"Yes, he is naughty," the Countess agreed, but it was quite evident that she was only too pleased to have the company of not one young man, but two.

"Here's Widgery," Hugo winked at Charles. He had already warned him what an old codger Widgery was, but you could always get round him. "Widgery, Mr. Littleton is staying. He hasn't brought his valet with him, but you'll fix him up, won't you?"

Widgery was sure that he would be able to fix Mr. Littleton up in the way that most people are sure that they will be able to swim once they've been pushed in. The fact that it meant re-arranging the table, making up a new bedroom, airing a bed, detailing Martin to valet for him, and generally shifting the emphasis of the next few weeks to having not just the young Viscount, but his friend, and no doubt soon enough some members of the opposite sex entertaining themselves round the house, was not merely irritating, but maddening to a man of such precision as himself. He didn't mind what he did so long as he knew what he was about. He liked to know what he was about because, in his opinion, if *he* didn't know what he was about then no-one at Southwold would, and it would only be a matter of hours before the whole place would be in chaos.

"May! Rose! Upstairs and make up the Blue Room for Mr. Littleton."

"Has he brought no manservant with him? How extremely lackadaisical."

Mrs. Petifor liked a bit of excitement. Something going wrong was always of interest to her, but she was disappointed that there was no manservant to expect in the servants' hall. Particularly since the guest was only an 'esquire'. It wasn't often that a person of her upbringing could prove to outsiders what it was to *be* a person of a certain upbringing, but on the rare occasion that there were guests and their servants at Southwold, she was presented with ample opportunity to do just this.

Mr. Widgery glanced at Mrs. Petifor briefly. Sometimes he felt that she added tone to his staff, but tonight he felt nothing but impatience towards her. 'Lackadaisical' was another of those words that he felt sure that she made up. He had once searched her room for a dictionary, convinced that if she didn't make up her vocabulary then she must be learning a new word every day in order to annoy and distress him. When he had found no dictionary he had again become convinced that she was making words up.

Mrs. Amey grumbled into her cooking pots. It was a good thing that the menu tonight was perfectly suited to accommodating another diner, but not thanks to anyone letting her know.

Rose followed May upstairs. Mrs. Petifor would be up in a minute to supervise them, but until she arrived they had time, while taking down some clean sheets and preparing to make up the Blue Room, to whisper together.

"Have you seen the young Viscount before, Rose?"

"Of course, May. Why, I've even danced with him."

For the first time since they had met, May looked at Rose with envy. She had never danced with anything you could call a man, let alone a gentleman, let alone a real Viscount.

"It was on the occasion of Lady Marjorie's wedding celebrations. It was wonderful, May. Everyone danced with everyone, and there were candles everywhere, and I danced with Viscount Ashby himself, and I wasn't more than twelve. It was wonderful, May."

"Still, you were probably too young to appreciate it, Rose. I should say twelve was far too young to appreciate a Viscount. Most definitely. It wasn't as if you were a woman then, Rose. Dancing when you're a woman is quite different. We danced at Christmas at my last place; they gave a servants' ball every year. You don't have servants' balls here, do you? This place is rather dull for young people—compared to where I was before with Mrs. Langston-Smith."

Rose couldn't help feeling irritated with this remark. It was all very well for May with her blonde looks and her wonderful eyes to keep on about her last place, but everyone knew that the Langston-Smiths had sent May to Southwold because they were very rich, but had no title, and if you had no title, you always wanted to be friendly with those who had. And the Langston-Smiths could be as grand and as rich as they liked, but they would never equal Southwold, because Southwold had what you couldn't buy. It had history.

"Well, May, I don't know about not being a woman, but dancing with a Viscount is not something that happens to everyone," Rose said this quite firmly, and May looked at her surprised.

"Perhaps so."

She was shrewd enough to know that if she wanted to keep her position of power over Rose, she would do well not to belittle her experience. And anyway, there was no doubt about the fact that what Rose said was true, dancing with a Viscount was—dancing with a Viscount—and it didn't matter what age you were when you did it.

May knew she was not, and never could be, jealous of Rose. Rose was thin and dark, and May was rounded and blonde. In short, May knew she was far prettier than Rose, but having heard this previously untold anecdote from her, she resolved that it was something that she had to match. There is nothing quite so galling to someone who is prettier than her friend than to know that she has had an experience of something that she, with her better, prettier looks, has not had.

"Don't you two stand about there," Mrs. Petifor ignored the fact that both girls were busying themselves about the room. She pulled back the bed cover to make sure that Mr. Littleton's sheets were as they should be. Smooth as a crisp piece of paper, with the 'S' for Southwold and the coronet embroidered on the top sheet, set firmly in the middle of the bed. She looked through into the dressing room. Martin had brought the young gentleman's effects upstairs and was laying out his evening clothes.

"May, you will heat a stone for Mr. Littleton's bed, and both of you will bring up some hot water."

There was nothing Mrs. Petifor liked better than supervising the arrangement of a guest's rooms. She made a note in her mind to arrange some flowers for the mantelpiece. Even gentlemen liked flowers in their rooms. And then there was the fire to be seen to. The rooms at Southwold were so large, they needed fires in both summer and winter. She must arrange for May to light Mr. Littleton's, and for Rose to attend to the Viscount's. There was so much to do.

The next morning the two girls hovered outside the young men's bedrooms. Although neither of them cared to admit it, they had never cleared a grate in a bedroom belonging to a single man before. They eyed the closed doors with some trepidation. It would be terrible to do anything that might attract attention to themselves, at least in the wrong way.

"Well, I'm off," said May defiantly, and she turned the handle of the door with a firmness she did not feel.

"See you later," Rose whispered, and she went further down the corridor to the Viscount's room. Seeing May disappearing gave her courage. If May had gone in, then she would too.

The room was lit only by the bedside light, and although it was summer, the curtains were still drawn because Hugo hated to see the light too soon, and yet he liked to be awakened early with a cup of tea and a biscuit, so that he could enjoy the very fact of lying in bed doing nothing in particular, except perhaps turn over in his mind the events of the evening before, if there had been any; or if there hadn't been anything in particular, then he liked to try to remember pieces of poetry that he had been made to memorise at Eton, or try translating pieces of one of the books on the bedside table into Latin. It had been a habit with him since school.

This morning, as Rose pushed open the door, he was busy thinking about his parents, and about Southwold, and the fact that when all was said and done, although life in the country could be very dull, it was better than nothing, and anyway it probably was just as well to be away from town at this moment. He was glad to see his mother was looking pretty, and his father had been really quite witty at dinner. He was amused that even Charles was a little in awe of him; even Charles, who appeared not to think very much of anyone except himself.

The door started to open very slowly. Hugo removed his gaze from the ceiling, and his eyes travelled lazily to the entrance of his bedroom. There was a great deal of floor space between him in his bed and the double doors, one of which was now opening, but even so he could see just how slowly it was opening, as if a very small animal was about to appear. He wanted to laugh, and if Charles had been with him he would have, but laughing on your own was a rather self-conscious experience, so he slid a little further into the bed, and remained silent.

For how long the door proceeded to open inch by inch, he couldn't have said, but by the time it was open, and the person, or door pusher, was half way into the room, his self-control had quite broken down, and he was laughing out loud.

Rose stood inside the door, and blushed to the roots of her hair. For a girl to find herself in the room of a young gentleman alone was an experience in itself, but to find the young Viscount lying in his bed roaring with laughter was simply terrible. For one awful minute she thought her petticoat was showing, or that her hair had fallen down.

"That was so funny," gasped Hugo, "I thought you were a mouse."

Rose was too terrified to reply to this remark. She switched her eyes from the ground to the fireplace and hurried over to it. It was all that she could think of doing. To reply, or make an answer to someone who thought you were a mouse, was not something that she knew how to do. She knelt down at the fireplace with her heart beating.

Hugo stopped laughing, and lay back on his pillows. Ever since he could remember this was one of the sights that he had always woken up to at Southwold. The maid kneeling down to light the fire in his bedroom. The little glimpse of black stocking as she bent to her work, and her white cap and black dress outlined against the red wallpaper. It was a sight so familiar that he had rarely ever thought about it, but today he noticed the procedure, as if he had never seen it before. If absence from Southwold had made him look with new eyes at its beauties, now he looked at its comforts with the same surprise. It was very agreeable.

Rose stood up, and turned to go. She hadn't made a sound, hardly a sound, as she had cleared out the grate and lit the fire. She thought that the young Viscount must have been laughing at a book he was reading, because she was now quite sure that neither her petticoat was showing, nor her hair was hanging down, so there could not be any other explanation.

Hugo watched her from his bed, as a marksman watches his bird, before he takes aim. He had been having a bet with himself as to whether or not he could remember the name of the maid. He hadn't been able to catch sight of her face, before she had knelt down by the fireside, and now she was turning to go he looked at her quickly, to see if he had been right. He had thought the waist too trim to be Daisy, and the hair too dark to be Rosalind, and now he saw that he was right in the first instance, but wrong in the idea that it was Margaret. It was someone younger than Margaret, and also prettier, he was surprised to see.

"What's your name?" he asked, and then he said, "I've never seen you before."

Rose's pale face went pink again. She didn't think it would be right to say that he had seen her before, and even danced with her, so she said nothing, and then after a minute because she realised that he had asked her a question, she suddenly said, in little more than a whisper, "Rose."

"What was that you said?" Hugo leant forward from his pillows to try to catch what she had said, "what was that you said?"

"Rose, mi'lord."

"Ah, Rose, I thought I hadn't seen you before."

This constant reference to not having seen her before was more than Rose could stand.

"You have, mi'lord, once at Lady Marjorie's celebrations for her wedding, you danced with me."

Hugo stared at her in surprise. It was amazing what servants insisted on remembering. They would know what you wore on such and such an occasion, and who came to stay last year, and how old your mother was, and how many years your nanny had been in service, all sorts of things that you yourself never gave a thought to, and yet they had no brains to speak of. Or at least if they did it would have to be a different kind of brain. The kind of brain that remembers things, but then can do nothing with what it remembers.

"I danced with you, did I?"

Rose looked down at the carpet. She knew by the

Viscount's tone that she had stepped out of line. Her knees felt like water. Supposing he told Mr. Widgery that she had been answering him back, and that she had made conversation when she shouldn't? She would undoubtedly be dismissed, like Lottie had been. Only, thank goodness, her father wasn't like Big Jim. He would be sad to see her home, and not get her wages, but he wouldn't thrash her.

"I danced with a lot of—with a great deal of people at my sister's wedding celebrations," he stopped himself from saying, as he had begun to, 'a lot of servants'. He didn't know why but he thought it might be slightly distasteful to call a servant a servant to her face, particularly when the servant was as pretty as the one standing in front of him.

Rose was so relieved that he had answered her, instead of ringing the bell for Mr. Widgery, that she hastily bobbed a curtsy, and started to hurry out of the room.

The way she did so seemed so comical to Hugo, and again so like a mouse, that he started to laugh again.

Rose didn't stop, she kept on going, and quickly shut the door behind her. She didn't care what happened, or how much he laughed at her, just so long as she could get away quickly, and hope that he wouldn't complain that she had been rude. She hurried down the corridor, and as she did so, she was met by May, who was looking if not exactly triumphant, then very pleased with herself.

Hugo lay back against the pillows. Any minute now Martin would come in, and he would have to start dressing; still, there was the pleasant prospect of breakfast in the dining room. He liked to eat a good breakfast. Tomorrow he would go riding before breakfast, then he would enjoy it even more. He might even be able to drag Charles along with him. There was a nice half Arab in the stable called Firefly. He'd give a fair amount of money to see Charles on Firefly, that is if he had time to see him before Firefly flung him off.

"Charles," Hugo glanced sideways at his friend, "I can see you have been enjoying yourself."

They had breakfasted with the Countess in the Dining Room, helping themselves to the dishes laid out on the heavy mahogany sideboard. His mother had changed most of the eighteenth century furniture in the dining room, and replaced it with something more fashionable. Hugo had liked the older furniture better, but she had had her way and put it around the house —some in the Music Room, some upstairs in the Long Gallery, and other pieces in the Great Ante Room.

"What are you boys going to amuse yourselves at today?" the Countess had looked with pleasure at the two young men sitting on either side of her, and eating their breakfast with evident enjoyment. She herself ate hardly anything, but it was always wonderful to see the young enjoying themselves.

"We thought we might go riding, Mama."

It was then that Hugo had noticed that Charles had a light in his eye that had not been there since before he had become involved with that poor little man's wife. The light in Charles' eye reflected mischief, and more often than not, mayhem. Usually Hugo enjoyed seeing it there, but he couldn't help feeling nervous at this particular moment in his life. He wasn't a funk, at least he thought he wasn't, but he knew that if he got into any more trouble his parents could well become irritated with him. At this particular moment they were humouring him, taking him away from temptation, but not really punishing him. However, if he pushed his luck too hard, things might change.

"Charles, I have a good mount for you, something you'll really enjoy."

"Really, Hugo?"

The light was still there.

Hugo hoped he imagined it. After all, there was nothing to do at Southwold, except ride or shoot, or hunt, according to the season, none of which sports Charles particularly favoured. Charles' favourite sport was quite different.

Chapter 9

Rose and May were able, if they were lucky, to arrange to have their time off together and it had become something of a habit for Rose to take May down to the Lodge. When she saw May with her family it seemed to her that just for a few hours May's eyes would soften and her whole manner changed when she played with Tim and Tatty in the garden, or talked to Mary in the kitchen.

The situation between Rose and her stepmother had improved, not only because Rose was now up working at the big house all day, but also because Mary had shown such patience and sweetness towards Rose's grandmother now she was bedridden. Secretly Rose wondered how Mary could be quite so patient, running up and down the narrow wooden stairs all day long in answer to the old lady shouting for her. And once or twice she even imagined that her grandmother had become bedridden on purpose, just so that she could make Mary run up and downstairs. Just so that she could cling to what little power she had left, even if it was only the power of an invalid.

The young Viscount had been at Southwold for some weeks before they were able to have any time off, on account of the fact that Mrs. Petifor had been 'incapacitated' as she liked to put it—although the rest of the staff were quite happy to think of her as being ill. Anne always took Mrs. Petifor's place if she was unwell and she had been unable to give them any free time on account of the fact that she was short-handed, even if it was only by one.

Everything had to be done twice as quickly to satisfy Anne, since she was inclined to be over-eager as acting housekeeper. She expected fires to be lit, beds to be made, and floors polished twice as fast, and twice as well, as even Mrs. Petifor's exacting standards.

Rose and May's routine had become well established since the advent of the young Viscount and his friend, Mr. Littleton. Their mornings started off with cleaning out the grates and lighting the fires in the young gentlemen's rooms, and even though Anne was so exacting and punctilious about everything, she did not dare to penetrate either of the young men's bedrooms in the early morning to see if they were doing their work properly. This meant that for a short twenty minutes every day there was some light relief going on in both the Viscount's room and the Blue Bedroom next door.

"Good morning, Mouse," Hugo looked over the top of his book at Rose, and Rose as usual blushed and tried not to laugh.

It was some time since the Viscount had explained to her that she reminded him of a mouse, the way she crept in and out of the room in the mornings.

"Good morning, mi'lord."

"Are you coming to scrabble at my grate again, Mouse?"

"Yes, mi'lord."

"Well, don't scrabble too loudly, Mouse. I am reading and I don't like mice scrabbling too loudly when I'm reading."

"No, mi'lord, I'll try not to, mi'lord."

There was silence as Hugo went on reading, and Rose set to clean out the grate. Then after a few minutes Hugo said, "do you like cleaning out grates, Mouse?"

"Yes, mi'lord."

Hugo looked at Rose's back view, puzzled. Servants were amazing, constantly amazing. How could they possibly like cleaning out grates? Particularly a girl. How could a girl like cleaning out grates and getting her hands dirty. They hated getting anything dirty. Harriet Cadogan was about the only girl he'd ever known who didn't mind getting dirty. He'd seen her wade through mud up to her waist out hunting, just to get her crop or some such thing, and then she'd fling herself up again and carry on just as if she was as fresh as the hour she'd started out. But then Harriet was a madcap, everyone knew that.

"Don't you mind getting your hands dirty, Mouse?"

"No, I don't, mi'lord, not really."

"Wouldn't you like a day when you didn't get your hands dirty?"

"We have time off, mi'lord."

"Do you?"

"Yes, we do, mi'lord."

Rose stood up and bobbed a curtsy, and was gone before Hugo could puzzle out what she had said. Why should time off have anything to do with her hands? After a minute he realised that she had indicated that there was a time when she didn't have to dirty her hands, and because of this she was quite happy. He sighed at the book he was holding. It all went to show just how extraordinary servants were. They were made of stuff that was quite different. Utterly different. And perhaps it was just as well.

"Hugo?"

"Yes, Charles?"

Hugo went on reading.

"Hugo, put your book down at once before I fling it on the fire."

"Charles, you can fling it on the fire, but I do assure you it won't hurt me as much as when Firefly flung you."

"Touché."

For the first time Charles appeared not to mind being reminded of his first disastrous ride at Southwold.

"Hugo, please stop reading, I wish to speak of something of import to you."

"You've been up to something for the last few weeks Charles, and now you're about to tell me about it."

Charles grinned. He was quite accustomed to Hugo's ways with him. Hugo liked to pretend that he was too lazy, and too interested in higher things, to be as heavily engaged with the opposite sex as Charles himself, but Charles knew that Hugo, like most of his own sex, needed but a hint and he could be as easily tempted as a maid.

Downstairs Rose looked at May.

"He's asked us *both* to go walking with him?" She was so excited that she could only whisper.

"That's right," May nodded briskly, "and he's bringing his friend. And we're going to have a picnic."

"May, do we dare?"

"Dare? What's daring about going on a picnic?"

Rose looked at her brushing up her pretty blonde hair on top of her head. They both knew exactly how daring it was to go on a picnic and left to herself, Rose felt that she might have refused. She wavered. May was older. If May thought it was all right perhaps it was. She suddenly thought of something.

"What friend, May?"

"Why the young Viscount, his little lordship himself, that's who."

Rose thought she felt about to faint.

"May, we shouldn't go. If they find out."

"If who finds out? They're going to be careful, don't worry. They're buying all the stuff and meeting us at the Folly."

"But May, supposing someone sees us, supposing someone got to hear. It would be the end."

Rose had lived too long on the edge of a village not to be aware of spies everywhere.

"Listen, no-one's going to see us, it's our half day off. We'll be very careful, now get dressed and stop worrying. Well I never, you're an awful scaredy cat Rose, really you are."

Rose looked at May doubtfully. She hadn't felt so frightened for a long time, not since poor Lottie went.

"May! What shall I wear?"

May looked at her triumphantly. She knew that now there would be no more argument.

"Don't worry, I'll lend you something."

Hugo knew that it was very probable that Charles' plan to picnic with the maids at the Folly was more than, must be more than, a plan to picnic. Charles did not like picnics, or pastoral get-togethers, and it seemed very unlikely that he had just woken up one morning and become filled with a desire to inspect the Folly at close quarters.

Hugo felt that he should deflect Charles in his keen desire to picnic, particularly since the other members of the party promised also to be members of his parents' large staff, but he couldn't quite think how he could put Charles off. He'd been brought up to respect members of the lower orders, not to 'consort' with them, although at the same time of being instructed against 'consorting' he had only a hazy idea of exactly what it embraced. His ideas were now less hazy, but he was basically somewhat lethargic and by the time he realised that Charles might be up to no good at all it was far too late to put him off. The picnic was already packed, and Charles was sniffing the wind like a hound on a frosty morning.

"I say, Charles, you're not up to anything, are you?"

Charles looked at him, and his black eyes sparkled.

"Why, Hugo," he said, "what should I be up to? We're just going to have a picnic in the woods with a couple of innocent young maids."

"Charles, maids have a habit of becoming less innocent when you're around."

"True," Charles sighed, and a twig snapped under his boot as he looked reflectively ahead of them at the woods and the sunny summer morning. "My grandfather, you know, was not allowed any female staff at all towards the end of his life. My grandmother simply would not permit it. He didn't seem to mind if they were ugly either, he just couldn't keep his hands off them. The fact that they were just maids was enough for him."

They made their way through the woods slowly, because the baskets of food and drink that Mrs. Amey had made up for them were heavy. Hugo had only ordered picnics for two, because he knew there would be gossip if he had doubled that number. He felt compromised by the fact that he had got to know Rose, albeit out of an innocent motive, as Charles had been getting to know whatever her name was, the other one. It was perhaps because of this that he felt a trifle uneasy about the whole expedition, although, now they were embroiled in it, he couldn't help feeling amused by the idea. It wasn't often that you had the opportunity to picnic with a couple of innocent country girls and, it seemed to him, it would be a wonderful opportunity to get to know the workings of the lower class female mind.

The Folly had been built by his great-great-grandfather, a man of some foresight, who having done the Grand Tour returned to Southwold with fresh ideas on landscaping and gardening. Ideas that were to prove quite novel at the time, but were now accepted as classic. He had built Grecian temples beside the lake that he had moved hills to create and he had planted trees that he never saw as more than saplings, and now they were mighty edifices to his glorious imagination.

Hugo envied the man his ancestor must have been when he stood inside the Folly with its marble columns and gazed out over the lake. He knew that he could not become such a man as he had been, he knew that he lacked his imaginative powers, he knew that his mind was the classic mind, the mind that appreciates precision and understands it, that can admire imagination, but never produce anything imaginative. Because

of his precise, exacting mind he knew his own weaknesses the way that he knew his Latin declensions.

"They're not going to come," Charles started to
laugh. It was one of his qualities that he had a good
sense of humour, but like most men it extended to
everything except his horsemanship.

Their voices echoed strangely in the Grecian temple,
but it was cool inside, so they sat in its shade and
looked out over the lake, neither of them feeling very
disappointed at the sudden collapse of their plans. They
were young men who knew by now that a disappointment today could always be made up by some new
diversion tomorrow and anyway they had been brought
up to contemplate and appreciate beauty, so they sat
for some half an hour discussing the merits of English
gardens as compared to Italian and French. They
came to the conclusion that of all countries England
was the country that could produce perhaps the best.

"Versailles is too precise. Brilliant but too precise."

"Yes, but then that is the problem with French in-
teriors, they too can be brilliant, yet they cannot produce a sense of gentleness and homeliness the way even
the grandest English interior can somehow convey
those qualities."

They were enjoying their conversation the way two
well-matched chess players enjoy their game, each
knowing that neither was really any more brilliant
than the other and so the ultimate victory could only
be academic and would not involve any disgrace.

"Hugo, my dear fellow, I do believe I can spy two
fat little pigeons making their way towards our Folly."

Charles gazed down the slope to the right of them,
and Hugo saw that he was right. The two fat little
pigeons, as he had described them, were coming towards them, both now out of their maids' uniforms and
looking more like butterflies than pigeons.

"Forgive me interrupting your—what Proudlock
used to call—ruminations, Hugo, but our guests sont
arrivées, quite, quite unexpectedly."

Charles got to his feet.

Rose looked up towards the Folly. She felt like running away. She had felt like running away ever since she had set out, decked out in May's second best, May's first best very properly sporting itself on May. She knew that they were doing wrong but she couldn't quite work out why she thought they were doing wrong. There were no rules to suggest that maids might not picnic with gentlemen who invited them on their days off, but even if there weren't any rules, Rose still felt that it was wrong.

She also felt almost cross with May for bringing them along the path that led straight up to the Folly instead of through the woods, which although a longer route was nevertheless one which brought them less into view than the pathway. May seemed quite unaware of the possible consequences of being seen by one of the gardeners, or another member of the staff out for a walk. When Rose had argued with her, she had simply tossed her head and said, "I don't mean to get myself hot and flustered scrambling through woods. You go that way, Rose. I'll meet you there."

Of course she knew that Rose wouldn't dare go that way because Rose was afraid of meeting the young gentlemen on her own and anyway it took all Rose's courage just to trot along behind her.

"What are you doing, May?" Rose whispered.

May had licked her finger and was running it over her eyebrows, she also straightened her bonnet and dress.

"Just cooling myself. A lady should never meet a gentleman in a fluster, I read that in a magazine."

Rose looked at May. She was only a couple of years younger than her but she always felt that May was in fact about ten years older. Shrewdly, she wondered if it was the difference between being brought up in the country and the town. So many of May's ways must be town ways, and her eyes were definitely town eyes. They had a look in them that not even Daisy, a quite notorious flirt, could be said to have.

"Why ladies," it looked to both girls as if Mr. Littleton was almost bowing to them, just as it looked to Hugo as if Charles was bending down in order to stop himself laughing. "We are so honoured that you care to come to our Folly to lunch with us."

Rose stood directly behind May, hoping that she couldn't be seen. When May bobbed a curtsy she did likewise. She kept her eyes on a piece of stone floor a little way ahead of her and hoped that no-one would notice that she was blushing.

Hugo noticed.

"My friend and I cannot be too honoured by your deigning to visit us."

Even Hugo felt like laughing now. Charles was going it a bit; any minute now they would both be in convulsions. What with the two maids standing there in their simple little rustic frocks and bonnets, and Hugo pretending they were Duchesses at a debutante ball.

"Good morning, mi'lords."

May was clever. She knew that by upgrading Mr. Littleton she would flatter him.

"Come, come now, no 'mi'lords' here in this temple dedicated to the Goddess of Nature. Here we are but lads and lasses, as in times gone by, no titles, no lords or ladies, just people."

This was too much for Hugo who walked away from his friend, and gazed intently, if unseeingly, at the words inscribed at the back of the temple. The coolness of the Latin restored his peace of mind. He did not want to give the game away by laughing, but it was damned difficult. Charles was such a ham. He always did overdo everything.

"Would you like to sit down, May?"

Rose was startled by hearing Mr. Littleton call May by her first name. She didn't know why but it sounded strange, particularly when May had her best dress on and they weren't in uniform. Some things were all right in uniform, but not the same out of uniform.

Charles saw Rose's eyes flying to his face and realised both from her frightened look and from the way May drew herself up that he had taken his fantasy too quickly for them. It would have to go slower; the working class mind was always slower. They couldn't catch on to something, or fly to another subject in the way his own class did. But, he was often very sorry to see, this did not stop them from having what he could only describe not too originally as a native shrewdness. Native shrewdness had often got in his way in the past and he saw that if he wasn't too careful it would easily get in his way this afternoon.

"What a beautiful morning it has been, hasn't it? It reminds one of some lines from Keats' 'Ode to a Nightingale', do you not think?"

The two girls looked at him doubtfully.

"No, perhaps not, perhaps you're right. More Shelley perhaps?"

"I've never read a great deal of poetry," said May proudly, and she managed to make poetry sound as if it was something slightly improper.

Charles realised that his task was going to be even harder than he had at first thought, but this realisation only fanned his enthusiasm.

There was a silence. A bee hummed. The two girls watched it from their cold stone bench. Rose was glad of both the cool of the temple and the cold stone bench. She had no idea why she had agreed to accompany May but now she had she was glad that at least she had time to cool down. May was right, ladies should never meet gentlemen in a fluster, whatever that was. The bee had settled on a dandelion, it was creeping slowly towards the centre of the flower, its striped body round and furry and bristling with purpose.

"Hugo?"

Hugo turned and managed to look into Charles' dancing eyes.

"Hugo, do you not think we should offer the ladies some refreshment? Why, Hugo, they have come all this way and they must be thirsty."

"Yes, indeed. Ladies, would you not like some refreshment?"

Rose looked at May. May did not hesitate.

"We should be very partial to some refreshment, I'm sure." She said this with dignity.

Rose was content to nod her agreement. Then she wondered what she had consented to when she saw that the young men were opening the hampers and taking out bottles of champagne and glasses.

"I'm terribly afraid it might not be as chilled as you would like it."

The echo from the cork exploding from the bottle made Rose jump and May started to laugh.

"I do like a bottle of champagne," she squealed. Then remembering herself, she added, "it's awfully refreshing on a hot day, don't you think?"

Rose held the glass under her nose and the bubbles tickled it. She took a sip. It wasn't very sweet but it didn't taste too bad, better than some things that gentlemen liked to drink, like ale and whisky, stuff that no lady or girl would like, that was for sure.

"To two lovely ladies," Charles lifted his glass.

"Yes indeed," Hugo was finding it easier to enter into the fantasy now that he had a glass of something. "To two lovely ladies and the great honour they have done us by visiting us here."

Hearing the young Viscount making a speech like that startled Rose. She could not tell whether she was becoming affected by the champagne or not, but she thought it was like a fairy tale, seeing the young Viscount toasting her, Rose Buck's, health. It was just like a fairy tale, or a dream, only dreams usually ended up with you waking up to Grandmother coughing.

"Delicious, I'm sure," May had drunk her first glass down in one. She was so thirsty and it was most refreshing.

Charles moved slowly towards the hamper that contained the wine. He did not want to seem too eager to refill her glass.

"Did you know this temple was built by Hugo's great-great-grandfather?" he asked casually as he poured May another glass. "His name was—what was your grandfather's name, Hugo?"

Both girls looked towards Hugo and Charles took the opportunity to top up Rose's glass while their attention was distracted.

"My great-great-grandfather's name was Hugo, like mine, and he built this a little over a hundred years ago. So it's very old."

"Yes, it must be," May nodded wisely, "it's got an old smell."

"Do you think so?" Hugo had great difficulty in controlling his features, "I hadn't noticed that it had any particular smell, I must say."

"I always think old things smell different, don't you, Rose?"

Rose nodded and, perhaps because she had finished what she thought to be only her first glass of champagne, she added, "my grandmother smells old."

This was too much for Hugo. He burst into fits of laughter.

The two girls stared at him, and then May too started to laugh.

"Goodness Rose, you are a laugh, really you are."

Charles watched her. She had very pretty teeth. Unusual.

"Well, ladies, do you not think we should spread out our picnic? You must be quite famished, after your walk," Charles' face was the epitome of concern.

"I am a trifle hungry," May admitted mopping up her tears of laughter. "More than a trifle, now I come to think of it."

"Shall we picnic inside here, in the cool? Wouldn't it be more agreeable?"

"Yes, of course, it would be much more nice," May agreed, "shall I do the honours?"

"If you would."

May noted with approval that his manners were impeccable. No boldness, no checking her now they were in company. It was right that it should be so. She was no slut to be treated any old how.

"I'll help you, May," Rose knelt down beside her on the rug that Hugo had spread upon the floor.

They unwrapped the most delicious food that they had ever seen. Perhaps their appetites were sharpened by the walk, all the excitement and the champagne, but it seemed to them that Mrs. Amey had done herself proud with the delicacies she had prepared, just for a picnic. Rose remembered the picnics that she and Tim would have at harvest time. Picnics! A hunk of bread and perhaps a piece of bacon, a bottle of water, whatever you could swop or beg off your neighbour. Still, they'd enjoyed them, even though they were nothing like this. No feathery light pastries wrapped around pieces of game cooked in wine. No creamy custards spread over strawberry tarts, no glasses of sparkling wine. She lifted her glass to her mouth again. She loved the bubbles.

There was less to talk about, once they had finished the picnic and Rose had tidied the plates away, and they were left amply satisfied with only the wine to finish up. Less to talk about, because once the girls had finished exclaiming over the provisions, they couldn't think of any subjects that might interest gentlemen and the gentlemen were, it appeared, far too replete to wish to think up new topics of conversation.

They all gazed out on to the view of the lake and noted in their separate ways the heat haze that shimmered above the water. The way that the blue sky didn't appear to have a cloud in it and the fact that the trees were so much in leaf that their outlines were like the outlines of trees in a painting.

"I love doing nothing," May looked round for someone to agree with her. Rose who was sitting with her back against the bench nodded.

"Especially on my day off," she agreed and then thought that she had said something rather foolish because if this was not doing 'something' on her day off, well, then nothing was. She blushed.

Hugo looked at her, and suddenly realised that she was beautiful. She wasn't fashionably beautiful. She didn't have a rounded body and prominent breasts like the other girl, but she was beautiful like a doe. Her dress was too big and obviously borrowed, but where she had pulled it in to try and make it fit her, you could see that she was delicately made and her very slimness only emphasised her large dark eyes and her long thin fingers, that she held so properly in her lap. She was like a child at a party, sent in her elder sister's frock. Now that she no longer wore her uniform he realised that she was probably very young and that if she had been upper class she would most likely still be in the school room,

"Shall we go for a walk?"

Charles appeared to be asking no-one in particular.

"A walk in the woods and gather wild flowers. Shall we go and admire nature, all of us?"

"I don't see why not," May got to her feet and creditably managed not to sway once she was up.

Rose also got to her feet and then, because she felt a little giddy, she stood quite still, hoping to feel less so very soon.

"Will you take my arm, Ma'am?" Charles held out his arm, albeit a very formal one, for May. She took it and smiled. He was treating her just as she had always known she should be treated, like the lady she knew herself to be deep down, when someone would let her.

"Thank you very much."

They walked solemnly out into the sunshine, arm in arm. Hugo and Rose walked behind the other two in silence. Charles continued to make the kind of conversation that would apply to everyone and therefore it didn't seem very necessary to join in too much.

"I always remember these woods in the spring from when I was a boy, full of bluebells and primroses. We used to pick them and give them to our mothers, didn't we, Hugo? And then of course in the winter, with the snow, they are wonderful, aren't they? Magical."

Hugo glanced sideways at Rose walking beside him. She looked even more like a doe in the woodland setting.

"I'll tell you what—" Charles looked back at him,

"why don't we go this way and you go that way, and we'll see who can be first back at the Folly. How about that?"

"Yes, let's," May skipped ahead. Her eyes had quite lost their hard look and were sparkling, but not quite as brightly as Charles' were.

"You don't care to be left alone with me, do you?" Hugo looked at his doe, but her eyes were so large they now appeared to take up her whole face, and even her body appeared diminished in contrast to their size.

"I don't mind."

"I think you're frightened, but there's no need to be. I won't harm you, you know."

He was about to say that he wasn't like Charles, when he stopped himself. It was ridiculous to say such a thing because of course he wasn't like Charles. He held out his arm and eventually, because he stood very still, his doe came up to it and put her hand through it.

They walked in silence. The rest of the woods were silent too. As if the birds were watching them, having suspended their song to see what they were doing. The doe picked her way through the bracken and the grass delicately, as if she was afraid that she would suddenly come across a hunter.

"Would you like to rest a minute?"

"All right; I don't mind."

They sat down in the long grass, Hugo having first spread out his jacket for her to sit on. She looked at it. The stitching on it was so fine, and his initials and crest were embroidered on the lining. She felt him watching her and looked up.

"I was wrong you know, you're not a mouse at all, you're a doe."

She smiled a little at that.

He smiled back at her, and put out his hand. When he looked down at hers he was surprised by its nakedness. It had no rings, no gold or silver, only pink nails neatly trimmed and long fingers that were so unsuitable, it seemed to him, for cleaning out grates and polishing floors. He was normally slightly repulsed by people outside of his class but he felt no such repulsion towards his doe, only something by turns protective and destructive. He wanted to keep her as she was and yet he wanted to destroy her, so that no-one else could touch her, so that she wouldn't grow up and she wouldn't stop being soft, young and frightened.

"Wouldn't it be wonderful," he said, "if things could always be like this? Nobody else, just always summer and just—us."

When he said 'us' it gave him a shock. He didn't think of himself on a level with her, even at this moment when she was sitting doe-like on his jacket, looking up at him. The 'us' gave him a shock and at the same time it made him want to laugh. He was getting more like Charles every minute. Fleetingly he wondered how Charles was getting on and then he turned his attention back to the doe.

"Don't you think that would be wonderful?"

She looked doubtful about that.

"Don't you?"

"Wouldn't you get bored?" she asked shyly.

He wanted to add 'with you and all this', but he thought that might be going too far. And when he looked into her eyes he was certain it would be going too far.

She was laughing at him. It was like a cold shower splashing around his ears.

"What are you laughing at?"

"You. At least, not really. It's just that you don't believe what you're saying. I mean you like holding my hand a little, but you wouldn't like to stay here all the time holding it. You know you wouldn't."

"Yes, I would," he said lamely and discovered what his friend Charles already knew, that it was a mistake to underestimate even a maid.

"You can't even lie in bed in the morning without reading, you know you can't."

Surprise turned to astonishment. Hugo wanted to

order her off his coat and then go home. She was nothing but impertinent.

"You have no business observing what I do in the morning," he said coldly.

"No, mi'lord."

"And don't call me 'mi'lord', it spoils everything."

"I'm sorry."

"In fact, I think you've spoilt everything already and I wish you wouldn't. We were getting on quite well."

He meant 'I was getting on quite well', because he couldn't help thinking of what Charles was up to and how *he* was getting on. He couldn't help hoping that he wasn't faring better and yet suspecting that he most likely was. He hadn't really wanted Charles to get him into the situation in which he found himself, but now he was in it honour begged him to satisfy his pride. And besides she was rapidly appealing to him more and more.

He had dropped her hand. Now he took hold of it again.

"Don't you feel romantic? Can't you feel the romance of these woods? How much they hum with the miracle of life?"

He couldn't remember where he had got that from but he felt sure he must have read it in some novel belonging to his sister.

"No," said Rose doubtfully, "I can't, I'm afraid."

This time he flung her hand down.

"You are so rude," he cried, getting to his feet and walking away from her. And at that moment he looked to Rose for all the world like Tim when he was in one of his sulks and not at all like Hugo Talbot-Carey, the Viscount Ashby.

Sometimes it is difficult to trace a moment of weakness, because it happens so quickly and very often in such a subtle form that afterwards it is impossible to find out when it could have been. Hugo's petulant backview was Rose's moment of weakness. She did not know it, but it was at that moment that she misjudged

him, thinking suddenly that he was no more than Tim
—just a boy.

Hugo had not counted on this. He hadn't realised
that his weaknesses could be his assets, as Charles
would have done. He was inexperienced enough to
know that where sophistication so often fails, the boy-
ish sulks, the appeals to the maternal and the protective will always suddenly conquer. He no longer appeared to Rose as someone rather frightening, someone
she knew could harm her, but only as a boy, like Tim
was a boy, someone she could coax to eat up his dinner, or tell off for bringing mud into the house.

She put her hand up to rub his cheek and as she did
so Hugo caught her to him. He was so cross he could
have hit her. Yet he didn't. She pulled away from him
and ran. He ran after her. Now she really was a doe.
Leaping and laughing through the bracken; darting
ahead of him so quickly that at one point he was sure
he would lose her. And he panicked at the thought.
He could not let her go now. Not for anything.

Eventually when he caught her and felt her cheek
against his, it was as soft as it had looked for the past
two hours, and her mouth was the same. He knew
what he wanted to do and he couldn't see that anything
would stop him. Even the fear and then terror that he
saw in her eyes only excited him more. Just as when
he was hunting or shooting, the very beauty of what
ran in front of him only made him more keen to kill
it, so that it would stop exciting him with its beauty
and at the same time, so that he could prove to himself, over and over, that he was not affected by its
death.

Now he understood the light that came into Charles'
eyes when he saw a new prey. He had not, before this
moment, understood why a man should cajole and
coax and eventually win what he could have for only
a few sovereigns at any time. Now he understood, and
it was a devastating discovery. He knew that the longer she struggled against him the more rewarding his
ultimate victory would be. He was convinced that he

had to have her, right up until the moment that she was his for the asking and then suddenly, just as her laughter had angered him, her terror contorted him, and he knew that he would have to let her go.

He watched her running off. Not leaping now, but stumbling, catching her borrowed dress on the briars, running and running, as if she was still unconvinced that she was free.

He got up and walked back to the Folly, wondering why he had stopped at the ultimate victory? Charles would never have stopped. No man he could think of would have stopped. He kicked one of the columns of the temple and then pressed his head against its cool marble. It was so difficult.

Chapter 10

Rose ran and ran. Home to the Lodge. She never stopped to consider what she looked like and how torn May's dress had become.

"Rose!"

Tim looked at her in horror. Rose put her hand over Tim's mouth.

"Is it safe? Can I get upstairs without them seeing?"

Tim nodded. This was an old routine of theirs.

"It's safe all right, Rose, but what's happened to you? What's happened to your dress? Has someone tried to hurt you, Rose?"

Tim put his hand on her arm, and it was more than Rose could stand.

"Yes, they have, Tim," she sobbed, "they tried to hurt me very much, and it was all my fault. I didn't realise. It was terrible, Tim, terrible."

Tim looked at her gravely.

"I've got Big Jim's training whip, shall I go out and whip them for you, Rose?"

"No, Tim, don't worry. I'll be all right. Any minute now I'll be all right."

Later that night Rose crept downstairs with May's dress in a bundle under her arm. She put it on the fire and watched it burn. Nothing like that was ever, ever going to happen to her again.

Chapter 11

The ripple that had been caused by Mr. Widgery's spectacular faint was now totally eclipsed by the scandal that sprang up from the Viscount's friend Mr. Littleton running off with one of the under-housemaids. For obvious reasons it was a scandal that caused Mr. Widgery some satisfaction. It not only replaced the subject of his faint, but it allowed him to re-join the hallowed circle of Mrs. Petifor, Mrs. Amey and Miss Hodges at tea.

For the past months, aware that they were highly amused by his demonstration of weakness, he had avoided this ritual, in the knowledge that they would merely talk about something else until he was called away and then promptly continue to talk about him. Now he was able to join in their tongue clicking and their endless scandalising. It gave him great satisfaction. No-one likes to be on the outside of anything, least of all the sacred circle of the local gossips.

"I was always, with deference to Her Ladyship, I was always in some doubt as to why Mrs. Langston-Smith had been so eager to pass on someone whom she had given it as her opinion was so terribly efficient. Why would not Mrs. Langston-Smith have wanted to keep her herself, I asked myself?"

Mr. Widgery was warming to his subject so much that he almost forgot himself and dunked his shortbread in his tea.

"I'm sure you said as much to me, Mr. Widgery," Mrs. Amey nodded.

"I never liked the look in her eye. No, never. She had a way of looking at a person that contained impertinence in it, I didn't like her look at all. I should say so."

Briefly Mr. Widgery remembered the look in May's eyes and equally briefly he remembered how shapely she had looked, even in her uniform. The memory caused an inner tremor. Mr. Widgery might, unlike some others, be totally trustworthy as far as the wine cellars were concerned, but every man has his weakness.

"Staff are better acquired from the estate than they ever are from other sources, junior staff, that is," he added quickly in deference to the fact that none of those present had been acquired from the estate.

"You're right Mr. Widgery, Rose is one of the best under-housemaids we have ever had and Anne has always been most efficient. You don't get the loyalty, the devotion from other girls, the way you do when their families belong here." It was a novelty for Miss Hodges to agree with Mr. Widgery.

There was a pause as everyone trod delicately around the fact that the devotion and loyalty that was given by those whose families came from the estate, was more than due to the fact that their fathers and mothers would give short shrift to those who were dismissed. And short shrift from estate workers was a prospect that no-one relished the thought of.

"It is terrible the way girls give away their virtue nowadays, quite wantonly. It means nothing to them it seems, nothing at all," Mrs. Petifor sniffed. Even with her father's fall in fortunes she was glad to say that *she* had never been tempted, not for one minute. And even if she had been a little tempted by a certain young officer in the cavalry, then it had only been for a minute and then, she was glad to say, good sense had prevailed and she had taken up a post, following upon a course in domestic management. She shuddered to think of what would have happened to her had good sense *not* prevailed. She would certainly not have been sitting in the steward's room helping herself to short-bread and madeira cake, goodness me no, things would have been very different.

She re-joined the conversation. Mrs. Amey was giving a graphic description of the fate of girls like May.

"And of course once they are abandoned then there is nothing for them but to take to the streets, and we all know what that means."

They all nodded. And again they were silent. Not one of them had lived such a sheltered existence that they hadn't seen what happened to women who were forced to earn their living from the streets. Miss Hodges, who was more tender hearted, could not help hoping that the inevitable down-hill tilt in fortunes that happened to most women of easy virtue would not reproduce itself with May. She had liked May. Pretty face. Knowing men it was more than likely that her looks had not escaped Mr. Widgery's attentions either. Miss Hodges sniffed. She really had no time for the opposite sex at all. They were so devious. Women gossiped perhaps, but men were devious.

"Informing the Countess of May's disappearance was one of the more unpleasant tasks that I have performed in my career. I should say so."

Mr. Widgery had indeed found the prospect of in-forming the Countess unpleasant. He had felt angry, very angry, when he had slipped up the stairs to find that wretched little piece and discovered she had gone. Promises, that's all she had ever made to him. And never once had she fulfilled her promises, the little slut. She'd had him begging for her favours and then once it looked as if she would finally give in to him, once he'd seen an end to his frustrations, she'd gone. And not empty handed either. He'd even given her his mother's watch. The slut.

"Your Ladyship, I have the unpleasant task of telling you that it appears that one of the under-house-maids has disappeared."

The Countess' foot tapped.

"Which under-housemaid, Widgery? Really. I hate to be bothered by these problems. In most households the subject of under-housemaids is not one that you discuss, really it is not. I should never have known about under-housemaids when our last man was here."

This reference to the previous butler made Mr. Widgery wince, even though he knew he had been dismissed on account of his addiction to port.

"I should never have brought the matter to Your Ladyship's attention, I do assure you, if it had not occurred to me that a situation of some embarrassment might have occurred, and it is my anxiety to avoid Your Ladyship any embarrassment which forces me to bring up this distasteful subject, mi'lady."

Mr. Widgery stopped. The Countess' singular lack of patience usually prevented him from making speeches of the length that he had just delivered, but he knew that he had her attention today and he knew that he would have her every ear when he had finished.

"It had been noted late last night that the under-housemaid had disappeared—" He forebore to say 'I noted', because it would have been improper to a degree for a butler to have noticed anything about any of the maids' rooms since they were strictly for the maids and no-one else. "This had been noted, but it wasn't until Anne, delegating for the said housemaid, went to take Mr. Littleton his tea that it was noted that Mr. Littleton's bed had not been slept in and that Mr. Littleton had taken his luggage to whatever destination he was heading for. Your Ladyship no doubt noticed that Mr. Littleton did not come down for breakfast this morning?"

Her Ladyship had indeed noted that Mr. Littleton had not been down for breakfast that morning, but it hadn't seemed to her in any way unusual since young men were apt to get up early and go riding in the summer, and Hugo and Charles' absence had been put down by her as nothing more than being involved in the kind of things that healthy young men involve themselves in.

"Where's Lord Ashby, Widgery?"

The Countess snapped out this question because her concern for her son was as deep as any mother's and she had no desire for Hugo to have been found messing about with housemaids. If it turned out that he had been guilty of this, his father would get to hear of it and then things would go from bad to worse. His father was liable to regard alliances with housemaids as something that should be not only frowned upon, but that would even lead to him having his allowance stopped altogether.

Widgery was glad to see that he was not the only person at Southwold to be affected by the disappearance of the under-housemaid.

"His Lordship is just coming in from riding, mi'lady. Shall I inform His Lordship that Your Ladyship would like to see him?"

"Yes, do so at once."

The relief that the Countess felt that it was not, after all, Hugo who had been guilty of defaulting with one of the maids was swiftly replaced by annoyance that she had been so led astray by Charles as to think that he was not capable of such a trick. Charles Littleton had always been such a charming little boy, now it appeared he was a too charming big boy. However the memory of his white teeth and dark curling hair made it not unsurprising that he had acted as he had. His grandfather and his father had both been devils. Absolute devils.

Hugo had just finished reading Charles' note when Widgery knocked at the door.

"Hugo—I'm afraid to say that making May while the sun shines proved irresistible—Charles."

Hugo stared at Charles' handwriting. Typical Charles. He had always had to go too far with everything. Now there would be the devil to pay, the very devil. His mother wouldn't care a fiddle about the maid but she would certainly not take kindly to a friend of his having gone off with one of the staff, and thereby causing a scandal in the servants' hall.

There was another knock at the door.

"Yes?"

Hugo screwed up the note and threw it away as Widgery entered.

"Yes, Widgery?"

"Her Ladyship desired me to send for you, Your Lordship. She is in the Music Room."

"Thank you, Widgery."

No-one is too sophisticated to have completely outgrown parental fear. It is too well established from the early days of childhood to be shifted easily. Hugo felt the tremors of a boy who knows that while he is not guilty in every way, he is still in some ways culpable. He had gone riding early, as early as he could, in order to avoid seeing the maid. To think that he could have even been tempted by her puzzled him now, now that he was afraid of what she might have said. He knew that it was not unusual for butlers to hold court martials below stairs. And knowing Widgery, he would have got every detail from her if he had even remotely suspected anything.

"Did you know anything of this ridiculous business, Hugo?"

"No, Mama."

"Is Charles Littleton aware of the trouble he has created by his action? Does he know what a scandal this will have caused in the servants' hall?"

The idea of Charles worrying about causing a scandal in the servants' hall was ludicrous, but Hugo was too much of a gentleman, and a loyal friend, to inform his mother of this. Charles was a devil. He did what he did and if you couldn't accept this about him then there was very little use in talking about him. He tried to distract his mother's attention from this particular line of conversation.

"Had the maid been with you long, Mama?"

"Hugo, do not, I beg of you, be childish. How long

the maid has been with us is nothing to do with anything, nothing at all. Maids come and go and that is no concern of mine, only of Widgery and Mrs. Petifor but when they start coming and going with your friends it is no longer a matter for just the butler and the housekeeper, it becomes a subject of my concern, I'm sorry to say. Most sorry to say. Charles is most irresponsible, most irresponsible. I shall have no compunction in writing to his parents and informing them of his action."

"His parents are abroad, Mama."

"Then I shall write to them abroad. We can't have young men going around the countryside and disappearing with maids. I hope you had no part in this, Hugo?"

"No, Mama."

Hugo hoped devoutly that the wretched little maid would say nothing. One word and there would be the devil to pay. The memory of her disappearing through the woods filled him with fear. He hadn't meant to harm her in any way. It had taken him by surprise, this desire for something so innocent.

The Countess looked at her son. She knew that he was very probably lying. It would be unusual for a young man not to know of another young man's intentions, particularly if they were to do with the opposite sex. Still, whether or not Hugo knew of it did not matter greatly, so long as his father did not also get to know of it. If his father found out, things would be very different and he might take it into his head to send Hugo abroad, the way he had been threatening to do when he heard of his debts. She did not want Hugo to be sent abroad. She would miss him.

"We will not refer to this matter again Hugo, if your father asks you about Charles, you must tell him that he was called back to town—urgently."

"Very well, Mama."

Hugo hurried away from the Music Room. He knew he could not get to see the maid until the following morning without causing suspicions to be aroused.

Tomorrow morning seemed a long way off when he knew what she could have already said about him.

In the end it did arrive. He had been awake for some time when, as usual, the door was pushed open very slowly and Rose came in, carrying her cleaning things.

"Good morning, Mouse."

Hugo had decided to play it casual.

"Good morning, mi'lord," Rose bobbed a curtsy and hurried over to the fireplace.

"Is it a fine morning, Mouse?"

"Yes, mi'lord."

Rose knelt down and got out her cleaning materials. Her backview remained as uncommunicative as her monosyllables. Hugo wondered how the devil he was meant to bring up the subject of the picnic and its repercussions. His casual approach did not appear to be very effective. He tried another.

"Will you come here, please?"

"Sorry, mi'lord?"

"Will you come here, please?"

She approached his bedside reluctantly.

Seeing her standing there in the light of his bedside lamp disconcerted Hugo more than her backview. Now she was back in her black dress and little neat white hat she appealed to him even more, her eyes looked, if anything, larger and rounder and he noticed she was trembling. Effortlessly he remembered now exactly why he had acted as he had. She was almost irresistible to him. Almost, because, unlike Charles Hugo prided himself that he had some common sense and did not consider that the gratification of his desires came before absolutely everything.

"Have you spoken to anyone of the picnic?"

"No, mi'lord." Her voice was hardly above a whisper.

"You will not do so, will you?"

"No, mi'lord."

"Good, that's all."

"Thank you, mi'lord."

She hurried back to the fireplace again and Hugo

was suddenly hard put not to laugh. She looked as much like a mouse as on the first day he had seen her.

He didn't know why he should have believed her promise, but he did. Then, as he watched her cleaning out the grate, he knew exactly why he believed her. She was a servant and he wasn't. If she was found out it would be worse for her than it would be for him. He was very glad he had been born a Talbot-Carey and not a servant; it might be a little difficult at times, but it was always worse being something else.

He picked up his book and became so engrossed in it that he didn't even notice when she left the room.

If Rose could have, she would have leant against the doors of Hugo's room and breathed a sigh of relief, but she was too frightened to allow herself the luxury of doing such a thing. Too frightened and too relieved. Instead she hurried off down the corridor. Her heart was still beating when she arrived in the closet to put away her cleaning materials. She hadn't slept for two days; not since the picnic. She was so frightened that someone would have found out that she had been with May. Not that anyone else knew that it had been the picnic that had started everything off. But Rose knew that if anyone ever did find out she would be dismissed on the spot and even her father's position would be in jeopardy.

Her fear of dismissal and disgracing her family had been stronger than her revulsion at the memory of what had nearly happened to her. Now that she knew she was safe and that the Viscount was as anxious as she was not to say anything about the matter her revulsion flooded back to her. May had been right, men *were* always out to harm you. But if that was so, why had May gone off with Mr. Littleton? It didn't make sense. He would only hurt her, the way Rose had nearly been hurt. The memory of her mother's words came back to her: 'God help us for having been born women, Rose, God help us.'

"Rose! What on earth are you doing in here day dreaming? That's not at all like you," Mrs. Petifor had pulled open the closet door. She looked at Rose. "Are you all right Rose? Not feeling ill I hope?"

"No, Mrs. Petifor, thank you, I feel perfectly well."

"Good, good, well get on with your work child, we can't afford to day dream in this life, can we?"

"No, Mrs. Petifor."

Mrs. Petifor watched her hurrying off down the corridor and hoped that the lines under her eyes were not symptomatic of something more serious. Rose was a good girl. She couldn't do with losing two under-housemaids in one week.

It would be more than lackadaisical, it would be careless.

As had been expected, the Earl noticed the absence of Charles Littleton that night at dinner. He enquired from his son as to the whereabouts of his friend.

"He was called away urgently," said Hugo.

The Countess looked down the table at her husband. He appeared to be taking this news without much interest. And Hugo, she was glad to see, had had the good sense not to embroider some story. He had not even looked up from helping himself to the soup.

"Everything is urgent when you're young and nothing is when you're old, that is life's tragedy," observed the Earl.

"Marjorie's coming down soon, Hugo, and bringing the children. Richard is to follow later. She tells me in her last letter that James is quite the star of Eaton Place, everyone stops Nanny when she pushes him out in his perambulator."

The Earl was amused by his wife's sudden switch in conversation. He liked to notice women's ploys because they always prided themselves on being so subtle.

It didn't really matter to him in the least if his son's friend went off with some chambermaid. So long as it wasn't Hugo making an ass of himself, then he saw very little cause to be troubled. Nevertheless he liked to know what was going on in his own house; and he was grateful to Widgery for keeping him informed.

Chapter 12

Rose missed May and she often wondered what she was doing. She remembered how often May had said that she was going to make sure that *she* would do better than others. She remembered how much she had hated Mr. Widgery; and she wondered why she had chosen to run off with Mr. Littleton.

All these things puzzled her, because she had looked up to May so much and because she had thought of May as having sense and not being the kind of girl to get herself into trouble. But she knew too that May had brains and, when she had finished puzzling over her, she came to the conclusion that she would not have done anything foolish and very soon no doubt they would all get to hear of May getting married and becoming 'Mrs. Littleton'; and she would come down to stay at Southwold and lord it over all of them.

It happened. Rose knew it happened because she had read books where things like that happened and only the other day she had read one out to Mary which ended like that. Mary couldn't read and Rose had taken to reading her stories on her day off, knowing how much her stepmother enjoyed it. If she had had the time she would have liked to have taught her her letters, but she never seemed to have enough time for such things on her day off, what with Tim and Tatty to play with and going down the village to see Margaret, and young John growing up so much now you could hold conversations with him.

The incident of the picnic faded from her mind the way that most incidents, however distasteful, do fade from your mind when you are not yet sixteen. A result of it had been that she had thrown herself back once more into the life of the Lodge, and realised how much it meant to her, even though she shared very little of it now. She was no longer its mistress as she had been before her father's marriage; she was its grateful elder daughter. However late she crept back to it after work, she could still hug its warm kitchen and its bare wooden stairs, and wrap it around her like an old but friendly blanket.

The realisation of what had nearly happened to her made her cling to the security of her roots and she no longer despised her background as she had done earlier, wishing that it was better, or that she had been born differently. Rather she over-appreciated it, and if her family became once more dependent on her, if only for her loving ways, she became dependent on them in a way she had not been before.

It was for this reason that Mrs. Petifor's words came as such a shock to her.

"Rose, I'm glad to say that you have been deeply honoured. I have recommended to the Countess that you should accompany Lady Marjorie back to town after her visit and that you should take up residence in Lady Marjorie's house at Eaton Place. Now what have you to say about that, Rose?"

For a full minute Rose had very little to say about it. Naturally, just the way Mrs. Petifor had put it made her feel grateful. She was definitely grateful, there was no doubt about that. And then of course she was proud. It was wonderful to have been chosen to work for Lady Marjorie, who was so beautiful, and everyone below-stairs admired her so much. But then she realised that it would mean leaving Southwold and she wanted to pass the honour up.

"Well, Rose, have you nothing to say about this? You realise what an honour this is? I hope you do."

"Yes, of course, Mrs. Petifor. I'm most honoured. Thank you very much," Rose bobbed a curtsy.

"I should think so too, child. You are still very young I know, but to be chosen to go to London means, as I am sure you realise, that the Countess and I consider that your head will not be turned like some we know." Rose knew that she was referring to May, "and that you can be trusted to carry out your duties and stick to the straight and narrow in the same way as you have done here. Now run along girl, Mr. Widgery is about to brief the staff about Lady Marjorie's visit."

Rose listened to Mr. Widgery's instructions to his staff in bewilderment. Nothing meant very much to her in relation to what Mrs. Petifor had just said.

She was to go to London! Just like that. She was going to work for Lady Marjorie. It didn't seem possible that in a matter of a few minutes her whole future could be changed. It took only Mrs. Petifor and a few words from the Countess, and next month she would be on the coach to London. As usual there was no-one awake when she crept into the Lodge that night. She wished that someone had been up so that she could tell them what had been decided. She wanted to be reassured. She knew it was an honour, but it was an honour that brought a lump to her throat every time she thought about it.

"Rose, that is an honour," Mary's mouth fell open.

"Your wages will be increased, won't they?"

Her father's mind flew in the direction that most men's do, when they have knowledge that their children are about to have good fortune.

"Yes, I'm to get a shilling more."

"I thought that's how it would be," her father nodded happily at Mary. If Rose's wage went up, her monthly contribution to the family expenses would also go up, he was happy to say.

"We shall miss you, Rose," said Mary, "but it's wonderful for you, isn't it?"

Rose nodded. She didn't feel it was wonderful at all.

Tim looked at her from across the kitchen.

"Tatty will miss you," he said, and Rose knew he was speaking for both of them.

"Of course it's not until next month," she explained to Mary, trying to take the relief out of her voice. "Not until next month," she said again and wondered for the twentieth time what 'London' would be like, and what it would be like to go to sleep in a strange room, and how it would feel never to see her family, even on her day off. It would take so much money to buy a ticket and come home to Southwold. She doubted whether she would ever have that much.

Of course there would be visits. She knew there would be visits because Lady Marjorie would come down to Southwold and of course she could write to Tim, and now his lessons were coming along so well, he could write to her. And most likely one day he would come up to London and learn to be someone's coachman. Most likely.

"I think I'll just take a walk down the village to see Margaret." She got up and picked up her shawl. "I won't be long."

Her father watched her go.

"I knew Rose would go far, Mary," he said proudly. "The way she used to manage here was something wonderful."

Rose walked down the main street.

It was the time of evening in summer when an English village would appear to be one of the most pleasant places that any man could think of. When the light has softened into evening and the occasional lamp has been lit in an upper window. Brick and thatch look as mellow as the worn cobbles of the inn yard. A dog sits in the main street, every now and then getting up to inspect a passer-by, and then returning lazily to his place, aware that at this time no strange scents pass him.

The homeliness of Southwold had never struck Rose so forcibly as it did now. She wanted to stay where she had been born, in and around the village where her

mother had come as a stranger. She could hear the
voices of her father's friends in the inn, laughing and
talking. And ahead of her she could see Margaret's
cottage. The door was open, and she could hear Margaret scolding one of the children, and the baby, one
of the many babies, crying. She turned back. Margaret's kindness would only make her sadder. She
headed instead for the churchyard.

Someone stepped out of the twilight into her path.

"Why, Albert! Lawks!" She had never stopped using
May's expressions even now she was gone, "I didn't
see you!"

She stopped.

"I could have fainted from fright, really I could.
Albert, you shouldn't do that, really you shouldn't.
What are you doing here anyway?"

Albert swung from foot to foot.

"I was reading, Rose. It's always so quiet here, I
come here to have a read and think. Father doesn't
like to see me thinking and it gets under his skin to
see anyone reading. He's that type of person, the type
of person that can't stand to see someone reading."

"I'll have to sit down after that, I've never had such
a fright," Rose sat down on one of the older grave-
stones. It didn't seem quite proper to sit down on a
newer one. She patted the stone. "Sit down, Albert."

. She looked at him sitting beside her. Poor Albert,
he was taller and skinnier than ever, if that were possible. The last time she had seen him he'd been at
Lady Marjorie's—no at her father's wedding. Heavens,
her mind was so muddled tonight, she didn't know
whether she was coming or going.

"How's Mrs. Dickinson?" she asked after a few
minutes, during which time Albert, who was never at
his best when conversation was demanded of him,
breathed deeply.

"She's in very good health," replied Albert.

Rose stared at him.

"You don't normally talk like that Albert."

"No, I don't Rose, I'm practising. I've been reading

more and more books since we last met, and that's how folk talk in books."

"Not all books, Albert," Rose reproved him. "Otherwise they would all read the same."

"Yes, you're right, Rose, not all books, but most of the ones I've been reading lately seem to have folk talking like that."

"Yes, well, perhaps they've all been by the same person," said Rose kindly.

"No they haven't, Rose."

There seemed very little point in pursuing this line of conversation, so Rose changed the subject.

"Have you seen Eddie lately, Albert?"

"Yes, Rose."

Albert was aware that every girl in the village had an eye to Eddie. Eddie was what Albert would have liked to have been.

"He's going to join the Yeomanry."

"That's nothing, I'm going to London."

For the first time Rose realised that she was going to seem quite someone to everyone at Southwold. It wasn't everyone that went to London, in fact very few of the village had ever been further than the neighbouring town.

"I'm going to work for Lady Marjorie Bellamy at Eaton Place."

"Are you, Rose?"

"Yes, and I'm going to be her first under-housemaid."

Rose had no idea what under-housemaid she was going to be, first, second, or ninth, but she felt instinctively that if she was going to talk about her new position it had better sound not just important, but very important. Since Albert made no reply to the information she had just given him she added inconsequentially, "anyway Eddie's always saying he's going to join the Yeomanry, and he never has done yet."

Eddie had been taking an interest in Daisy lately, much to the scandal of the village, who considered

that a young man taking out an older girl, and everyone knew that Daisy was no chicken, wasn't right.
Rose thought much as the rest of the village.

"I think he will though, Rose, Eddie's determined
to leave Southwold some time. He's not interested in
farm work, he says he never had been."

"He's not interested in anything, that Eddie. Never
was."

"I'm not interested in farm work either," Albert
looked at Rose, fully expecting her to be scandalised.

"No, I know, Albert, but then you're a book lover.
Mrs. Dickinson said that about you. She's going to
train you to be a good teacher too, Albert, so I
wouldn't worry about farm work, not if I was you."

"My father—"

"Your father, don't think about him, silly old goat.
One day he'll be an old man, and he won't be able to
thrash you any more, just remember that, Albert. When
we get older, parents become our children, Mrs.
Dickinson said that."

Rose said this to encourage Albert. Poor Albert,
who was so thin and so nervous, and yet he could add
up quicker and knew more words than anyone else in
the village. She saw her words brought a look of encouragement to his face. She wished he'd stop wanting
to be like Eddie. Eddie was as broad and handsome
as Albert was the reverse, but there was something
gentle about Albert that no-one except Mrs. Dickinson
seemed to appreciate. He might not be the ladies' man
that Eddie was, and there was no denying, Rose
thought ruefully, that Eddie was uncommonly attractive and very much a man, but nevertheless Albert was
not as silly as everyone liked to paint him.

"I expect I'll see you before I go to London, Albert,"
she extended her hand to him in the way that she had
noted that gentry did, "but if I don't, I hope you will
call at Eaton Place sometime."

Albert looked so crestfallen by this idea and so hurt
by her suddenly grand manner that she quickly stopped
pretending to be grand and said, "you will come and

see me if you ever come to London, won't you, Albert?"

He pumped her hand up and down, "of course I will, Rose. I'll—we'll miss you, everyone will miss you. You're a nice girl, Rose."

Rose felt herself blushing.

"Well, I might see you again before I go, but it depends—on my days off. Father likes me home."

"Goodbye, Rose."

"Goodbye, Albert."

She walked off down the village. She could see the smoke curling up from the Lodge and she could almost smell the stew that Mary was cooking before she reached the door. One more day off and then she would be somewhere else.

She still couldn't believe it.

Like the days of a holiday, the weeks leading up to departure appear to move quicker than at any other time. The extra burden on the staff from having Lady Marjorie, Nanny, and the two children staying at the house might have had something to do with the fact that it appeared to Rose as if the days were only minutes. On the other hand it might also have been very much to do with her reluctance to leave Southwold, and also Mrs. Petifor's determined efforts to make her into an even more efficient product of Southwold, than she already was.

"I hope you won't think that Lady Marjorie's dusters can be skimped in this way, Rose?"

"No, Mrs. Petifor."

"I hope you won't think that Eaton Place has floors whose corners are better for being unpolished?"

"No, Mrs. Petifor."

"In London, Rose, people like their staff to keep their uniforms as neat and as tidy as a new pin. I know you can't help the fact that you are slight, but slightness is not an excuse for untidiness, please do up your apron tighter."

"Yes, Mrs. Petifor."

In Rose's imagination Eaton Place grew to the proportions of a palace, twice the size of Southwold. She saw herself polishing floors that would be a mile or two wide and at night in her dreams she continually washed and wrung out her dusters and mops, over and over again. She knew that if she got dismissed from Eaton Place all would be lost. To be returned to Southwold would mean that she would never ever again be able to hold up her head in the village.

"Now, Rose, I know you are aware of the great honour that Lady Marjorie and the Countess have done to you in allowing you to go to London and broaden your career, not to mention your horizons. Are you going to do your best to justify this honour? Are you going to prove yourself worthy, Rose?"

"Yes, Mrs. Petifor, I hope so, Mrs. Petifor."

"So do I, Rose, so do I. I beg you remember the training you have received here at Southwold. Bear in mind that everyone will be watching you. You will be representing Southwold at Eaton Place, your standards will be taken to be Southwold standards and if you do not uphold those standards to the best of your ability your weaknesses will be put down to Southwold's weaknesses, and we can't have that, can we, Rose?"

Rose had very little idea of what Mrs. Petifor was saying. All she was aware of was that Mrs. Petifor was taking up the last few precious hours she had to spend with her family, before her departure the following morning.

"Can we, Rose?" Mrs. Petifor looked at her searchingly and repeated her question.

"No, Mrs. Petifor."

"Your mother worked here, and now *you* have had your training here, and I know you will always remember what Southwold has done, and is doing for your family. As my own personal gift to you Rose, because I know you have tried hard, I am giving you this picture. You will see that it is an illustration from the Bible. I suggest you put it in your Bible and take its story to your heart. Ruth was a good woman, Rose, and I hope you will grow up into a good woman, too."

"Yes, Mrs. Petifor, thank you, Mrs. Petifor."

Rose took the picture, and later that afternoon, she put it carefully inside her Bible and packed it with her good dress and bonnet that she'd bought for her father's wedding, and her three pairs of black uniform stockings, two vests, two nightdresses, two caps (white), one pair of extra shoes, two aprons and three or four other items of under-garments.

Supper was a sad affair since she did not feel like talking and nor did anyone else it seemed. Mary had cooked something especially good, and her fruit tarts and scalded cream were as good as anything they ate at the big house, but still they did little to cheer anyone or make the evening convivial.

Tim and young John stared at her as if they were neither of them ever going to see her again and Father didn't even look in her direction.

"I expect I'll be down for Christmas," Rose remarked to nobody in particular.

"Lottie's never come back, Rose," Tim tried to look as matter of fact about this as he could, and failed dismally. "She went off to service and never came back."

"That was because Lottie was dismissed, Tim, that's different, she had to go into service with other people. I shall be in service with Lady Marjorie, and when she comes back to Southwold she'll bring me too, the way she brings Nanny. Nanny told me that herself at tea yesterday."

Nanny had been kind at tea. She'd said that any daughter of Lucy Buck's would be welcome at Eaton Place and that had given Rose confidence. At least she'd know Nanny when she got to London, if only from serving her tea and madeira cake.

"Your grandmother wants you to go up to her, Rose," Mary had brought Grandmother's tray down.

Rose looked at the old woman lying in the bed. She'd never liked her grandmother and now she was old and in bed she found it even harder to like her. Grandmother hadn't liked Mother, and she'd been glad when she died. And now poor Mary had given her no more grandchildren she bit into her all day long, banging on the floor with her stick just as soon as Mary got downstairs, or calling to her continually if she was in the garden.

"Is that you, Rose?"

"Yes, Grandmother."

She could still feel the clout that her grandmother had given her round the ears.

"So you're going to London, child?"

Rose twitched with impatience. Everyone was 'child' to her grandmother, except Mrs. Burrows or one of the old ladies in the village, even Mary was 'child'.

"Yes, Grandmother, I'm going to London."

"Going to learn new fangled ways, and I'll be lying in the graveyard e'en now before you're back, no doubt."

Rose said nothing. She could see very little difference between lying in the graveyard and lying in bed all day. Except it would be more difficult for Grandmother to bang on the floor with her stick from the graveyard, although knowing her, she'd soon find a way, no doubt.

"You're a good girl, Rose, a good girl, even though I say it for myself. Folk would go a long way before they found a better daughter than you've been to your father, I'll say that for you, child."

This was surprising. Rose looked distrustingly at the old lady and waited for the sting to come after.

"I want you to have this. I won't need it any more."

Rose looked at her in astonishment.

"But Grandmother, that's your shawl."

"Of course it's my shawl," said Grandmother testily, "I may be going blind but I can tell a shawl from a dish mop. I want you to have it. It's a town shawl, Rose, a shawl for London. It came from London and it should be worn in London. You'll be the belle of the place Rose in that shawl, so you'll be. You'll let them town folk know that Bucks are Bucks, and not folk to be looked down upon. Put it round you, I like to see

you, then I can remember when you're gone and hold
it in my mind."

Rose turned to and fro in front of her grandmother.
They both grinned at each other.
It was a beautiful shawl.

Chapter 13

The coach swayed from side to side and Rose stared
very hard at Nanny's bonnet, to take her mind off the
picture of her family standing by the gate and waving
to her over and over again. Tim, and young John
standing in front, and Father and Mary behind. They
had kissed her, and she had kissed them, even Tim,
who hated being kissed. And they had all pretended
that they didn't want to cry. All, that is, except young
John, who had wet the collar of her cloak with his
howls and had to be given a piece of barley sugar to
suck.

She had been allowed to say goodbye to her family,
by kind permission from Lady Marjorie. And then the
coach bearing Nanny and the children had rolled to a
halt in front of the Lodge and Rose had climbed in and
sat down, without looking back, until they turned out
of the gate, and then she had waved from the window,
the lump in her throat growing sorer by the minute.
She knew she must not cry and that she must control
herself, not just in front of Nanny, but in front of Lady
Marjorie's young children, James and Elizabeth.

They stared at her, the two children. And she in her
turn stared at Nanny's bonnet, and it was for this reason perhaps that no-one said very much for the first
couple of miles. Eventually Nanny said, "James, put
your legs out straight. I do not want you sitting on
your feet and dirtying the seat of your trousers."

James stuck one immaculate foot out in front of

him, and then as Nanny stared at him, he reluctantly
stuck out the other one. Elizabeth sucked her thumb.

"There we are," Nanny twitched Elizabeth's frock
beneath her cloak. "That's a fine wee frock Her Ladyship gave you, Miss Elizabeth, isn't it?"

Elizabeth nodded.

"You can take your thumb out of your mouth, Miss
Elizabeth. Thumbs don't improve our appearances, do
they, Rose?"

"No ma'am, they don't."

"Come on now, Rose, call me Nanny Southwold
the way everyone does. Nanny Southwold I've been
since Lady Marjorie was a child, and I've no reason
to see my changing it now."

"Thank you ma'am," Rose's eyes dropped from the
bow on Nanny's bonnet to Nanny's face which was
regarding her with some amusement.

"I expect you're feeling sad, and a little lonely.
You've never left home before have you, Rose? I remember when I left to come to Southwold. As far as
the villagers went they might as well have been speaking French, for all I could understand."

Nanny laughed a little at the memory, and stared
out of the window.

"Yes, they might as well have been speaking French,
really they might."

Rose wondered vaguely if Londoners spoke very
differently too. Certainly May's accent had been different, as different as Nanny's was from Mrs. Petifor's,
but she could still understand what she said. She hoped
to goodness she would understand what everyone in
London said. She twisted her handkerchief between her
fingers. How terrible it would be if they didn't understand her. Perhaps they would make fun of her, a
countrygirl who didn't speak the same as them? If only
they didn't, everything would be all right.

"You mustn't worry too much, girl. Life in London's
not very different from life anywhere else, I'm happy
to say. People are people you know, it's only the way

they go on that makes them different, together with where and how they're born," she added after a pause.

Rose couldn't understand this. She could see that people were people all right, but she'd been unable to follow the rest of Nanny's thinking. She sighed. There was no doubt at all but that life in London was going to prove complicated if it turned out that everyone here reasoned as Nanny did.

Nanny continued to talk.

Rose continued to listen.

It was dark when they arrived at Eaton Place. Rose alighted ahead of Nanny and helped to lift the children down. They were both half asleep and she therefore held Miss Elizabeth against her, to prevent her from falling over, while the coachman rang the bell and helped Nanny to alight from the coach, a little stiffly, but with all her speech powers still intact.

"Carefully now, Master James, there's no point in waking yourself up when you're about to have to go to sleep again. Now, Rose, make sure that Miss Elizabeth doesn't slip on the steps, she's a terrible one for slipping over, not having yet learnt how to walk very long. Now Miss Elizabeth, don't start crying, that won't help, will it, Hudson? No, of course not. Let Hudson carry you, Miss Elizabeth. Yes, yes Master James, you can give the horses some sugar, if you'll just come straight in afterwards. Goodness gracious, Hudson, it seems as if we've been away a year and not a month.

Rose stood awkwardly in the hall. In the bustle of everyone concerning themselves with the children she had been ignored, she was glad to say, and now she was still being ignored, and yet she knew that it was not proper that she should stand in the hall where gentry came in and out. Taking her own advice she slipped through what was obviously the staff door, and descended the stairs to the basement.

The kitchen and staff room were deserted, but determined to do the right thing, she put her suitcase neatly down by a chair, and herself sat down on it and waited.

It was possibly the fact that she had not slept very well, owing to it being her last night at home, or perhaps because she had been on a long journey and travelling in trains and coaches was tiring when you weren't used to it, but she could barely prevent herself from falling asleep. She kept straightening her back. The clock ticking helped to keep her awake, but it was a tough fight to stop her eyes from closing.

"Goodness gracious, what are you doing here?"

The butler whom Nanny Southwold had called 'Hudson' turned quickly when he saw her.

"You should be in your bed, girl."

"Yes, sir."

"Yes, *Mr. Hudson.* Do you not know where your bed is? No, of course you don't. Well, follow me, girl, and mind you're quiet about it. The rest of the staff are asleep, and have been so for the past hour."

"Yes, Mr. Hudson."

Rose followed him up the stairs, until eventually he stopped outside what was obviously an attic bedroom.

"This is your room. You're sharing with another under-housemaid by the name of Agnes. Now I'll wish you goodnight, and see you in the morning for your instructions," he whispered.

Rose pushed open the door, and peered through the room. Her suitcase felt so heavy now it was all she could do to lift it into the room. She set it down as quietly as she could. There was a lamp still burning on the empty side of the bed, and on the other side she could see there was a young girl fast asleep. She undressed, as quietly as possible, and crawled into bed beside her. Happily, she was too tired to remember how lonely she felt. She blew out the lamp and fell asleep almost immediately.

She awoke not just to a strange room, but to a strange face staring into hers.

"You must be the new one, then?" said the face that was still half asleep as well. "We was expecting you earlier last night, but you didn't come. What happened to you?"

"We were delayed."

"What?"

"We were delayed," Rose raised her voice a little.

The little person bending so inquisitively over her straightened up.

"You were delayed, was you? Well, well, we mustn't be delayed now you know, or Mrs. Bridges will have our guts for garters." Her accent was practically the same as May's.

The two girls started to dress.

"Mrs. Bridges is our cook, and if we're late she lets us have it. Beatrice is our house-parlourmaid, and James is the coachman. Then there's the two footmen, cheeky devils both, and you and I, and Patty the scully, and Nanny, and of course, Miss Roberts, Lady Marjorie's maid. By the way, what's your name?"

"Rose."

"Well, Rose, I'm Aggie, and if you stick close to me you'll be alright. Come on. Hats straight, shoes polished, aprons tied and off we go."

She gave Rose a cheeky grin, and Rose followed her downstairs.

"Good morning, girls," Mr. Hudson took out his watch and inspected it. "On time by half a minute, I'm glad to say. We try to keep naval time here, Rose. Naval time, one minute before time. This is Mrs. Bridges."

"You're the new one, eh?" Mrs. Bridges looked up from her tea, "well work hard and keep your nose clean, and things will be all right for you."

Mr. Hudson sniffed. He didn't really like Mrs. Bridges using that expression. It was a bad example to the junior staff, but unfortunately a cook of Mrs. Bridges' calibre was not easy to come by, so he had to be prepared to take the rough with the smooth. Lady Marjorie had been some time finding Mrs. Bridges.

They had been through a succession of women with cooking that would have given even the Prince of Wales indigestion, before she found the right one. Mr. Hudson was well aware that a young wife does not like to see her husband pushing his plate away from him after a hard day at the House.

Mr. Hudson called "Beatrice!" and a young girl with blonde hair presented herself. "Rose will be in your charge from now on, Beatrice. Since she has received her training at Southwold I feel sure that she will need very little supervision. It will be more a question of her acquainting herself with the geography of the house and getting used to a different routine, and the later hours we keep in town. Now get on with it, girls."

During those first few weeks Rose felt that Mrs. Petifor's words followed her everywhere around Eaton Place. She was convinced she was being watched closely. She imagined the other girls and the other staff were all watching her to see if she was going to let Southwold down. She worried so much about this that she hardly ever spoke unless spoken to, and also because she was too busy trying to pick up a London accent. She felt she could not open her mouth until she had learnt to talk as everyone else besides Mr. Hudson and Nanny seemed to.

Every night she listened carefully to Agnes as she chattered away after the long day. Agnes said 'lawks' the same as May, although not quite so often. She also said 'blimey' which Rose thought might not be very nice, and she said several other things which Rose also guessed couldn't be anything very nice either.

She found the work almost light after Southwold, and was astonished that everything was so much smaller. The floors, the furniture, everything. She had imagined London to be larger and grander, and instead it was smaller and more cramped. After the first month she wrote a letter to her family. It took her a considerable time. Agnes watched her with some envy.

"What are you writing, then? I mean, what can you think of to write about? You haven't been 'ere very long, have you? I mean what can you write about when you haven't been 'ere very long?"

Rose said nothing. Her writing materials had cost her so much of her money, she was determined to use them carefully and that her first letter home would be the model of all that Mrs. Dickinson had taught her.

She wrote—

"Dear Father, and Grandmother, and Tim, and Young John. I am very well. I hope you are very well. I arrived safely. Please send my love to Tatty, and to everyone, and to Margaret, and to Albert, love Rose."

She didn't know why she had suddenly included Albert.

Agnes peered at the letter when Rose had finished.

"That looks really quite good, Rose. You must be a good writer. Could you teach me?"

Rose nodded.

Agnes stared.

"Sometimes I get the feeling you're blooming well dumb, or do you think you're a cut above us lot, Miss Snotty from Southwold?"

Rose blushed. Like everyone who hopes they're being unobtrusive, she had been convinced that no-one had noticed that she hardly spoke. To her consternation Agnes started to cry.

"I suppose you think you're too high and mighty for the likes of us cockney girls? I suppose you don't even like sharing a bed with me, and being in the same room. Well, it's not my fault I'm like what I am."

Rose felt so ashamed she hardly knew how to comfort Agnes. She tried to explain how she felt, and failed. Agnes went on crying.

"Please, Aggie, Beatrice will come in and you'll get me into trouble," Rose begged.

"I don't care, you hurt my blooming feelings with your snooty ways."

"I won't any more I promise, please Aggie, please stop."

The little face looked up at her.

"All right, I'll stop if you promises to talk to me."

"I promise."

"Cross yer 'art?"

"Cross me heart Agnes, really."

"Hurrah!"

Agnes flung her arms around Rose's neck.

"I've been wanting a friend of me own ever since I came 'ere, and the last girl went and got into trouble before I had time to know 'er. Now I've got you, and now you'll be my friend, won't you, Rose?"

"I'd love to be your friend, Aggie, really I would."

"If we have our days off together I'll show you some sights, Rose. Bet you've never been on a tram."

The following day Mr. Hudson noted with satisfaction that the new girl from Southwold was looking less peeky. He didn't like his staff looking peeky, any more than any other man. He liked a fit and healthy staff, God fearing and healthy.

"Rose?"

"Yes, Mr. Hudson?"

"You have settled in now, haven't you, Rose?"

He made this a statement of fact, since he didn't like to encourage the idea that it was not possible for anyone not to have settled in at Eaton Place.

"Yes, Mr. Hudson."

"Good, good. Well, let's get on with the day, then."

"Agnes?"

"Yes, Hudson?"

"Run and take this to Miss Roberts on the first floor."

"Yes, Mr. Hudson."

Mr. Hudson watched her running nimbly upstairs. She was a cheeky young thing was Agnes, but full of spirits. It wouldn't be surprising to him if she didn't turn out very well in the end, providing she kept her nose clean, that is. He really must remember not to use that expression of Mrs. Bridges.

Mr. Hudson looked at his watch. Soon Lady Marjorie would be ringing for him.

After that time seemed to slip by.

Rose came to be able to accept her life at Eaton Place. She missed the country and her family a little less day by day, and although she found it difficult to sleep, and strange to wake up and not hear the sounds of the country, Aggie's ability to fall asleep almost as soon as she had climbed into bed, and her cheery way of waking up as if she had only been asleep for a second, was as infectious as her grandiose plans for spending a day off together and going to see some sights, and maybe even having a cake in a tea shop.

"Sometimes, when Lady Marjorie's away for a house party, Mr. Hudson has been known to give some of the staff a day off together. So there's more of us on when she comes back. Least I think that's what he does it for," Aggie added doubtfully.

Rose knew that it was most probably a figment of Aggie's colourful imagination in just the same way as she had told Rose that she was sure that Mr. Hudson had a soft spot for Mrs. Bridges, and that Nanny had a soft spot for Mr. Hudson.

Aggie was not happy unless she was inventing stories, and the stories she invented were as romantic as her very favourite story, which was about her and Rose walking along the street, and two gentlemen seeing them and falling for them, and whisking them away to a castle in the country, which was 'shrouded in mist.'

Rose sighed. She didn't like to tell Aggie about what really happened with gentlemen in the country, so she said, "Everything's always 'shrouded in mist' in your stories, Aggie."

"I know, Rose, because that's the future you see. The future is always shrouded in mist, so that's why there's a lot of it in my stories. There's an awful lot of future, everything's future really, isn't it? I mean, your *life's* more future than anything; when you're young that is. And then it's more past than anything."

"I think we'd better go to sleep now, Aggie."

Rose was getting in a muddle over Aggie's philosophy.

"Yes, Rose."

Rose listened to Aggie sleeping. It would be wonderful to be able to spend her next day off with someone else. On her last, it had been all she could do to summon up the courage to go into a shop and buy herself some writing materials and then she had hurried back to Eaton Place, and only too thankfully joined Nanny and Mrs. Bridges in having a cup of tea. Aggie was a cockney, and she would be able to show Rose the sights of London, there was no doubt about that.

" 'Ere, Rose, guess what? You're right, it's blooming well happened, we're going to get the day off together, and Mr. Hudson just said as much! I 'eard him tell Mrs. Bridges. Isn't it marvellous?"

Aggie skipped up and down excitedly in front of Rose.

"Aggie, really! You'll get us into trouble."

"We're going to have the day off, the day off," Aggie continued to skip, and Mr. Hudson heard her.

"Agnes! Come here at once."

"Yes, Mr. Hudson."

Looking into Aggie's perky little face, even Mr. Hudson found it difficult to tell her off the way he knew he should do. He was not a man who possessed a huge sense of humour, but nevertheless he couldn't help wanting to laugh when he saw how crestfallen Aggie looked. She looked like a sorrowful sparrow who'd just had its crumb snatched away.

"Agnes, you are not to make displays of this kind."

"No, Mr. Hudson."

"Upstairs quick, girl, Beatrice needs a hand in the dining room."

"Yes, Mr. Hudson."

Mr. Hudson looked at Rose who was still dutifully laying the staff table.

"I can't have disorder, Rose."

"No, Mr. Hudson."

"You must not let Aggie's—Agnes'—high spirits run away with her, Rose. She's very young and inexperienced, she doesn't yet know what is what."

"Little devil," said Mrs. Bridges affectionately as she put down some caper sauce on the table.

"Quite," said Mr. Hudson, his Scots puritanism struggling with the affection he too felt for Aggie, "but little devils grow into big ones, Mrs. Bridges, as I'm sure you realise yourself."

"I do, Mr. Hudson, but no-one could imagine Aggie having any harm to her, she's too,—too, well, I'm hanged if I know how to put it."

"And hanged she'll be if I have any more displays from her," said Mr. Hudson grimly, but no-one believed him. You could as well be cross with Aggie as with a puppy or a kitten. Even Lady Marjorie held her in affection.

"Do you know, Richard, Robert says Aggie remembers everybody's birthdays? Isn't that strange? She can't write, but she buys them a card out of her savings. She can't have anything left for her days off."

Richard Bellamy looked across at his young wife. She was looking particularly beautiful tonight. He hadn't heard a word she had just said, but he realised that he should put in a word about whatever she had just mentioned, so he said 'really?' which seemed to satisfy her, and then he returned to contemplating how beautiful she was. He couldn't quite make up his mind as to whether he preferred her in that stunning blue, or the grey and white she had worn for Anna's ball the other night. It was a problem he was happy to toy with for the rest of the evening.

"Richard, you haven't heard a word I've just said."

Lady Marjorie, like all women, was quite happy not

to be listened to when she saw that particular look on
her husband's face.

"Where shall we go first, Aggie?"

Although Rose was in the habit of feeling superior
to Aggie, on account of what she considered to be
her greater experience of life—she now felt very much
her junior. Aggie seemed to know every street and
every paving stone in London, and whereas Rose felt
quite lost as soon as she left Eaton Place, Aggie headed
in one direction or another with the sureness of someone who knows the city she's been born in like the
back of her hand.

"I'll take you up the 'dilly first, Rose, and then
we'll go down Regent Street, and then—listen, you
'aven't seen nothing to what I'm going to show yer
today."

Aggie executed another of her famous skips.

"You may have been brought up within a stone's
throw of Lady Marjorie's stately 'ome, Rose, but I'm
a blooming cockney. Born within the sound of Bow
Bells that means. And I'll show you things, I really
will."

Perhaps because Rose had an inbuilt reverence for
what she had once called the 'gentry', now as she wandered about London in Aggie's wake, she liked the
sight of the fashionable ladies and gentlemen more than
anything. She liked to see the high stepping horses,
and the coaches and pairs, and the liveries of the
coachmen.

At one point they stopped outside a restaurant, and
Rose saw a lady of such magnificence that she gasped.

"She looks more beautiful than a peacock, Aggie,"
she whispered as the lady stepped by her, followed
by the rest of the party.

"With her looks, it won't be long before the Prince
of Blooming Wales takes a shine to her," said Aggie
knowledgeably.

Rose said nothing. She was secretly impressed by
Aggie's suddenly sophisticated turn of conversation.

She thought of May as she so often did, and wondered if she too at this moment was stepping into some wonderful sophisticated restaurant, all perfumed and powdered, with a party of grand people following her? May had been sure to get on. With May's looks all she could have done was go up in the world, Rose was sure of that.

They wandered on.

"Where's your family, Aggie?"

Aggie shrugged her shoulders.

"Over there," she said waving her hand in the opposite direction, in a somewhat vague manner. "They're over there, Rose. All tucked up with some gin bottles no doubt, and me mother bent over her buttonholes at a halfpenny a time. I was lucky. One of them do-gooding ladies took me in and that's how come I got into service, but the rest of them's gone down hill as fast as the gin slips down their throats. Still, they're happy, I suppose. They've never been ones to grumble much, my lot haven't, and as for me mother she says I was the youngest and the least wanted, but I was born with a blooming silver spoon in me mouth, and when I look at where I am today, Rose, I reckon she was blooming right," Aggie grinned. "Listen, Rose, I'm going to have a cake the size of me hat when we get to that tea shop, and a cup of tea twice the size of me hat, and then I reckon that'll be me lot for the next few hundred years, because I won't have a penny of me wages left."

Rose looked at a carriage dashing past them, and the two girls instinctively stepped away to avoid the mud splashing the hems of their skirts. Aggie squealed with delight.

"Rose!"

Rose looked up from shaking the mud from her hem. It was not Aggie who'd just addressed her. Aggie was already skipping ahead again.

"Rose!"

Rose looked around.

"May!"

She stared at May with delight, and then with horror.

"May!" she said again, "you look terrible."

As soon as she'd said that she was sorry.

"Have you been ill, May?"

The blonde hair was still there, but it was no longer glossy, and May's once proudly pink cheeks were sallow in comparison to how Rose remembered them at Southwold, and her figure once so curved and buxom was now as thin as it had been rounded.

"Yes, I've been ill, Rose—I've been ill."

May looked at Rose hopelessly.

"Yes, I've been ill all right."

"I was just thinking about you, May, and wondering how you were getting on. Did your ears burn?"

May hardly smiled at this old joke.

"No, my ears didn't burn, Rose."

"You were always saying your ears were burning at Southwold, do you remember, May?"

"Yes, I remember. Well, I must be getting along Rose, nice to see you."

Rose realised that because Aggie had turned and come back to join them May was put off staying and talking to her. She ran after her.

"May, since we haven't seen each other for such a long time, shouldn't we stay and have a chat? We have so much to talk about, May, haven't we?"

"No, we haven't, Rose."

"Please come, May, please. We're going to have a cup of tea and a cake in a tea shop. We can pay for you to have a cup of tea and a cake too, can't we, Aggie?"

"Course we can, Rose," said Aggie stoutly, "I got Mrs. Bridges her card last month, so I shan't be needing no more of me wages."

May had no idea of who Mrs. Bridges was or why her card was of any importance, but she was hungry, and the sight of Rose after all this time, weakened her resolve.

"All right then, but I can't be long, mustn't keep my trade waiting."

This remark had more effect on Aggie than it did on Rose, who was too busy thinking about May's ill appearance, and wondering what she'd had wrong with her.

The tea shop Aggie led them to was down a side street and Aggie greeted the owner, a buxom lady as plump and as cheerful-looking as her jam tarts, as though she was an old friend.

"She's very nice, Aggie, this is a very nice place," Rose looked round approvingly even though she had never been in a tea shop before, and had no yardstick to judge it by. "I like tasteful furnishings," she added.

"She's a kind of aunt of mine, by marriage once removed. She done well for herself," said Aggie, meaning the manageress, "she'll give us a good price, Rose, so don't worry. She's good at wangling things to suit her old friends, is Margaret."

"I know a Margaret," said Rose, "she lives in the village. She's not a relation or anything though, Aggie."

Having exhausted this particular topic both girls now tactfully turned their attention to May.

Rose was dying to ask May how Mr. Littleton was, but she'd noticed that May was not wearing a wedding ring, and so she decided not to. Instead she wondered what trade she was in remembering her previous reference to this subject.

"What trade do most girls like me end up in, Rose?" May stared at Rose cynically, and Rose who hadn't thought very much about what kind of trade girls like May ended up in, blushed to the roots of her hair. She would have liked to have exclaimed with horror, but she didn't.

The idea of poor May having to earn her living on the streets was terrible to her.

"What happened to Mr. Littleton, May? Did he not want to marry you?"

May laughed humourlessly.

"You've got some funny ideas, Rose, what on earth made you think he wanted to marry me?"

"Well, nothing really, May, it was just that you

having run away with him, I imagined, we all imagined, well that is, I just thought you might have done well for yourself, May, that's all."

"I've done well for myself, Rose, really well. I've ended up as a prostitute, that's how well I've done for myself."

The word 'prostitute' seemed to hang in the air, and for some time none of the girls addressed each other, only Aggie said 'ooh' unaffectedly delighted by the size of the slices of cake when they were brought to their table.

"A good cup of tea'll do you good," Aggie nodded encouragingly towards May, as if a cup of tea was going to cure May's troubles. "Mrs. Bridges makes a good cup of tea," she added for no reason.

Rose frowned at Aggie. She felt it was tactless to mention Mrs. Bridges in front of May, as a rich relation would forbear to mention their wealth in front of a poorer one. The memory of how May had laughed at her when she confessed that she'd wanted to become a lady's maid came back to her. If she had had anything but kindness in her nature Rose would have felt smug at the memory, but as it was, all she felt was sadness. May had once been so beautiful, it didn't seem possible that she should come to this pass, and that she should be sitting at the tea table opposite her looking so ill, and almost old.

"I'm luckier than some though, at least I haven't had any babies. At least that bastard didn't leave me with a bun in the oven."

This statement didn't seem to have much effect on Aggie.

"You are lucky," she agreed cheerfully, "some people in your line have one little bugger after another."

"Aggie!"

Rose felt so upset by May that she turned on Aggie as if it were her fault May had to become a prostitute.

"You shouldn't talk like that, really, it's not nice."

"Why isn't it *nice*, Rose?" May sneered, "Still being the little lady all the time, I see? Your friend's right,

Rose, most girls in my trade do have one little 'bugger' after another."

"Yes, they do, don't they?" Aggie nodded sagely, "at least May's been spared that, Rose. It makes it much worse you know, me mother always used to say that, on account of the fact that if the babies are girls —well it goes hard for them, it does."

"I wish there was some way I could help you, May," Rose cut across Aggie's wisdom. "I hate to see you looking so—unwell."

"Don't you worry, Rose, I'll be all right. Girls like me survive you know, somehow. We don't have to starve you know, we get by."

But by the way she ate her cake, and drank her tea, and by the thinness of her figure Rose knew that she was most likely lying.

There seemed very little to say after that. If Rose had wondered what had happened to May, and hoped that she would turn out like the lady they had seen stepping into the restaurant earlier, she now knew how wrong she'd been. She thought unhappily how she would much rather that her fantasies about May had come true. May had been so determined to do better than the rest of them, and by the way she'd been, and her lovely looks, Rose had been as convinced as May herself that she would get on. "No dirty old butlers sniffing around my petticoats," she had said. Now there were men, perhaps worse than Mr. Widgery, sniffing around her petticoats.

"Well, I must be off now," May got up, " 'bye Rose, nice to see you, but I can't stop. 'An hour away is an hour to pay' as they said in the trade. 'Bye."

"Goodbye, May."

Both girls watched her go out of the door and into the street, both of them imagined themselves to be her, and at the same time wondering what it would be like to be her.

"She didn't finish the icing on her cake," Aggie reached forward to May's plate.

"She never did like icing," said Rose.

Chapter 14

Mr. Hudson looked at his watch.

Aggie had once calculated that Mr. Hudson looked at his watch about twenty times a day. "It's a wonder he 'asn't worn the face out with his looking at it," she'd said, and there'd been one of those silences during which everyone looked at one another, afraid to be the first to laugh, and then, unable to resist Aggie's funny face and her innocent look, they'd all burst into fits of laughter.

"That Aggie, honestly she'll be the death of me with her ways," said Mrs. Bridges later to Nanny.

"Ach, she's a bright wee thing," said Nanny, "and there's no getting away from that. She may be a mite too forward at times, but her heart's in the right place, Mrs. Bridges."

"You're right, Nanny, and that's the main thing in my opinion," Mrs. Bridges nodded vigorously, and drank her second cup of tea with gusto. Lady Marjorie had a dinner party that night and Mrs. Bridges had been on her feet cooking all day and all the previous day, and she felt like a second if not a third cup of tea, even before she got through the first.

The reason for Mr. Hudson consulting his watch was that Mr. Bellamy had not returned from the House, and late though it was, Mr. Hudson was required to wait up for his return.

Knowing the exact time when a person is waiting for someone, is of a peculiar comfort, if not of prime interest, to the person in question. The reason for Mr. Hudson's interest, however, was not just that of a man employed in passing the time, but because Aggie, much-beloved of the staff at Eaton Place, was ill. She had been removed to hospital only two hours earlier, and Mr. Hudson was waiting for Rose to return and give him news of her.

It seemed that Aggie had gone to bed as usual, having not previously complained of anything, but then all of a sudden she had clutched her stomach and complained of pains, and Rose being the sensible girl she was had called Mr. Hudson, who had called the doctor, and within a very short space of time Aggie was being carried up the basement steps and conducted by carriage to the hospital.

The fact that one of his staff was ill would have always been a source of concern to Mr. Hudson, but the fact that it was little Aggie, made it worse. He was quite frank in admitting this to himself. In fact, he thought it only proper that he should admit this to himself, and now he thought of it he wasn't in the least ashamed of his concern, although to other people it might seem a trifle too interested. Mr. Hudson was well aware that as his position was that of a butler, it behoved him to be restrained in all things, but tonight his restraint was less conspicuous.

He walked up and down. He hoped that Rose would return with news soon.

Naturally, Lady Marjorie had had to be informed, and it was she who had expressly desired that her doctor should be called.

"Aggie's such a favourite," she'd said to Mr. Hudson, and Hudson at that moment had been even more glad that he'd had the good fortune to find employment with Lady Marjorie at Eaton Place. Few of her kind ever bothered, and even fewer would have expressed anything but a passing interest in the fact that an under-housemaid was ill.

"Have James come round to the door with the carriage, just in case the doctor thinks she should be removed to hospital," she'd told Hudson.

"Very well, mi'lady."

Mr. Bellamy returned.

"Her Ladyship required me to inform you that she has sent the carriage to hospital, on account of the fact that one of the housemaids has been taken ill, sir," Hudson removed Mr. Bellamy's coat, and took his hat, cane, and gloves from him.

Richard tried not to smile.

Marjorie was so impulsive. It really wasn't quite suitable to send carriages careering all over London with sick housemaids in them, but then it was so very like her, that he couldn't help smiling. He hoped that she would never stop being impulsive. She was his beautiful, impulsive Marjorie. So beautiful that tonight as he sat in the House he had been unable to think of anything except her radiance. Theirs was no fashionable marriage, he was happy to say. No blind eyes turned once the heir had been born. He couldn't have taken that, not for a minute. Any more than he could take the thought that she would ever stop being as beautiful and impulsive as she was at the moment.

"Have you had news of the poor girl yet, Hudson?" he turned as he went up the stairs.

"No, not yet, sir. With your permission I shall wait up for Rose to return with news of her condition."

"Yes, of course, of course."

Richard turned, and went up the stairs, slowly, because he didn't wish to seem too eager to go to bed.

Mr. Hudson consulted his watch again. It was now two and a half hours since Rose had departed with Aggie. He couldn't help feeling more anxious than he would have liked to admit. If Aggie was only ill of a fever, Rose would surely have returned with the prognosis by now. He descended the stairs to the staff room, and resumed his pacing, but this time below stairs. It gave him a peculiar comfort to pace up and down and listen to the large clock ticking, even though it might appear to be unnecessary to someone else. Mr. Hudson was very conscious of how he must seem, and he was sure that to others of his calling he might appear to be exercising undue concern over a trifle, but at that particular moment all he could think of was poor little Aggie being carried up the steps, her face so white and drawn.

"Rose!"

Mr. Hudson opened the basement door, and let Rose in. She was drenched with the rain that was pouring down outside, and just at first he was too concerned with bustling her into the house to notice that she looked as if she had been crying.

"Rose, how is Aggie?" Mr. Hudson looked so grave that Rose knew that he knew the answer before he had even taken her cloak.

"She's dead, Mr. Hudson. She died about an hour ago."

Rose looked at him for a second, and then seeing him cross himself, she did the same.

"God have mercy on her, Rose, the poor little girl."

"It was her appendix, Mr. Hudson. The doctor said she'd probably had pains before, but never noticed them. You know what Aggie was like, Mr. Hudson, always bobbing up and down, and hopping and skipping, and worrying about whose birthday it was next, and I don't know what. Why, she wouldn't have noticed if her right arm had been hanging off, would she, Mr. Hudson?"

Mr. Hudson shook his head.

"No, she wouldn't. The poor little girl."

"She might have known I was there, I don't know. They say people can sense these things you know, Mr. Hudson. And that we don't know how much they know, same as babies, if you know what I mean. I sat with her and held her arm, long after they'd closed her eyes," Rose turned away. She did not like Mr. Hudson to see how affected she had become.

Mr. Hudson cleared his throat.

"You did well, Rose, very well. If I may say so, the

whole way you have acted has been with a maturity far beyond your years."

Rose could not make a reply. The memory of Aggie skipping ahead of her on their day off, her perky little hat set determinedly forward—"Used to belong to me grandma, Rose. She gorn and left it to me, made me mother hopping mad, I can tell yer"—flooded over her. Dear little Aggie.

"I will get in touch with the hospital in the morning and make the necessary arrangements," Mr. Hudson appeared to be talking to himself.

"Yes, Mr. Hudson."

"Goodnight, Rose."

"Goodnight, Mr. Hudson."

They both walked silently up to their separate rooms.

Neither slept, and when morning came and Rose dressed silently on her own without Aggie's usual 'hats straight, shoes polished, aprons tied, and off we go' her desolation was unbearable.

Mrs. Bridges was making a manful attempt to cook breakfast, and scold Patty in her usual way, but no-one failed to notice that her eyes were red, and every now and then when she thought no-one was looking she quickly wiped her eyes on her apron.

Normally meals at Eaton Place were a cheerful affair—unlike at Southwold—although the ritual of the older servants being served first and younger servants not eating until the vegetables was observed. Nevertheless Mr. Hudson's personality strict though it was, was considerably pleasanter than Mr. Widgery's, and then Aggie could always be relied upon to make some-one, if not everyone, laugh.

"There was something about her," Mrs. Bridges looked forlornly over the top of her cup of tea at Miss Roberts.

"Lady Marjorie is very upset," Miss Roberts shook her head sadly.

Lady Marjorie was upset. The first sadness in marriage is always taken hard. Everything at Eaton Place

had been so lovely. Their marriage, the birth of their
children, not a ripple had disturbed the prolonged
honeymoon, but now the young household mourned
Aggie's death, as if she had been a favourite little dog.
Normally housemaids were housemaids, but Aggie was
different. Just as the barking of a dog is missed, and
his lead and collar hanging sadly in the hall remind
the owner of its passing, so every little ritual at Eaton
Place seemed to miss Aggie's cheerful presence.

"I can hardly face my food now, I don't know why."
Mrs. Bridges had a habit of voicing what everyone
else was intent on being too polite to mention.

"Every time I pick up my knife and fork I seem to
hear Aggie saying something. It's putting me off my
food, I can tell you. Do you remember when she told
us that story about her uncle and the dog that leapt on
to the table and pinched the leg of mutton? And how
he and the owner chased it the length of Whitechapel
with a butterfly net and a mop? Lord, I can see her
face now, telling us about that."

"Even that silly wee canary in the nursery seemed
to like Aggie," Nanny got up, "and now you'd think
it missed her, you would really. James asked for her
this morning, but of course we said she'd gone on
holiday. Children don't understand about these things."

The general feeling following this remark was that
children were not the only ones that did not understand about these things.

Rose hated the freedom of her room unshared. Although she was working twice as hard until a new
under-housemaid could be found she found it impossible to sleep. Aggie's regular breathing, and her ability
to fall asleep on command, had had a soothing effect
on her. But now she was gone, not even reading her
Bible and attempting to memorise sections of it, managed to make her fall asleep. She would lie awake hour
after hour staring at the ceiling and remembering things
that made her sad.

"Rose! What are you doing here?"

"Mr. Hudson! Sorry, Mr. Hudson. I came down for a drink of water. I don't seem able to sleep these last weeks, and I came down for a drink of water."

"Rose, you know full well that is for—for—bidden to come down to the kitchen after you have gone to your room. Please do not let me catch you doing so ever again, do—do you understand—me?"

Mr. Hudson had one hand on the table, and he gestured awkwardly with the other. Having delivered his speech he then sat down very suddenly. He was drunk.

"I'm very sorry, Mr. Hudson."

Mr. Hudson appeared not to have heard.

Rose prepared to depart without her glass of water. The bell rang from upstairs. She looked at Mr. Hudson, he appeared not to have heard it. It rang again.

"Rose, where's Hudson?"

"I'm sorry, Mr. Bellamy sir, but Mr. Hudson is not feeling well."

"Not feeling well? What's the matter with him? He was perfectly 'well' at dinner."

"Yes, Mr. Bellamy, but he's not well now. I think it could be a sick headache. My mother suffered most dreadfully from sick headaches. I offered to wait up for him, until you retired, and he hoped you would excuse him, sir."

Richard Bellamy looked at Rose. He was quite sure that she was lying. If Hudson had not been feeling well, then he would most certainly have detailed Beatrice, and not Rose, to wait up in his place. He frowned.

"I wanted the decanter re-filled, but I imagine that is beyond your capabilities since Hudson has the key to the cellar."

"I expect I could find what you want, sir," Rose tried not to look too eager.

Richard Bellamy looked searchingly at her again. And then because he was tired he shrugged his shoulders. If there was trouble below-stairs, he would no doubt find out about it in the morning, and if there wasn't and Hudson had suddenly developed a tendency for sick headaches, well then that too he would find out about in the morning.

"Hudson, I understand you were suffering from a severe headache last night."

"Yes, sir?"

"Rose informed me, Hudson, that like her mother, you suffer from headaches, is that so?"

Hudson struggled with his conscience.

"I have been known to have headaches, sir, unfortunately, but they are very rare."

"I understand that last night you were suffering from just such a one?"

"I am still feeling the effects this morning, sir," said Hudson with complete truth.

"I hope these headaches do not become too frequent, Hudson."

"No, sir, I believe that judging from the last few years, sir, that these headaches are becoming increasingly rare as I have just said, and with good luck, they should soon cease to make themselves felt at all. Like Rose's mother, sir, my own father suffered from—"

"Yes, yes, thank you, Hudson. That will be all."

"Thank you, sir."

Hudson withdrew.

"Rose?"

"Yes, Mr. Hudson."

"I believe you informed Mr. Bellamy that I suffered from sick headaches, and that I was suffering from just such a one last night?"

"Yes, Mr. Hudson."

Mr. Hudson looked at Rose.

"We have both been suffering, have we not, Rose?"

"Yes, Mr. Hudson."

"We have all been feeling sad, and I'm afraid that because of this I gave into a former weakness." Mr. Hudson concentrated on the piece of silver he was polishing. It was not easy to say what he knew he had to. "Thank you for saying what you did, Rose."

"That's all right, Mr. Hudson. As Aggie would say —'anything for a friend'."

They both smiled.

Rose tried to close her Bible, but Eddie's medal stuck awkwardly out of its pages, as if that being the one memory that she had not re-lived, it was determined to bring itself to her notice.

Poor Eddie!

She remembered how excited she had been when he had called in his brand new uniform. As excited as when her father had brought Tatty home on her birthday. Eddie looking so broad and so handsome, that in her opinion he could have passed for an officer.

The day they'd spent in London had been like a dream, or a story that you read in a journal. Eddie'd had money to burn, and burn it he had. He'd even bought her a hat. A hat that she still wore on Sundays together with Grandmother's shawl, and she made sure that she kept them spotless and as smart as the day they'd been given to her.

Naturally they'd fallen in love. As so many other girls and boys were falling in love at that moment. The boys were off to fight for England in South Africa, and they were as brave as young men always were when they were off to fight a war. They were going to win, of course, they were going to come back heroes, of course.

"I'll send you my medal, Rose," Eddie'd cried as she waved to him at the station, and he had, only he'd failed to come back with it.

236

Rose sighed. *Men were awful fools, but it was no use telling them. Tomorrow was the first Wednesday in the month. Albert always wrote on the first Wednesday of the month. She wondered if he would remember it was her birthday. She hoped so.*

EDWARDIAN LIFE AND LEISURE

BY THE SAME AUTHOR

Worm in the Bud
The Table-Rappers
Victorian Sheet Music Covers
Victorian Popular Music

EDWARDIAN
LIFE AND LEISURE

Ronald Pearsall

ST. MARTIN'S PRESS : NEW YORK

All rights reserved. For information, write:
St. Martin's Press, Inc, 175 Fifth Ave, New York, NY 10010
Printed in Great Britain
Library of Congress Catalog Card Number 73-92162
First published in the United States of America in 1974

CONTENTS

LIST OF ILLUSTRATIONS

POMP AND CIRCUMSTANCE

Death of a Great Queen

AT 6.45 on the evening of 22 January a bulletin was issued by three doctors from Osborne House, one of the homes of Queen Victoria: 'Her Majesty the Queen breathed her last at 6.30 pm surrounded by her children and her grandchildren.'

So opened 1901, and predictably the nation mourned their dead monarch. Lady Battersea, a member of a famous Jewish family, wrote: 'The emptiness of the great city without the feeling of the Queen's living presence in her Empire, and the sensation of universal change haunted me more than any other sensations.' Memorial services proliferated throughout the Empire, and in Europe. Biarritz, one of the fun-loving resorts patronised by the nobility of the time, was ten days late, and among those who attended its memorial service was Mary Gladstone, the daughter of William Gladstone, the now dead Grand Old Man of British politics. She was characteristically brisk about the whole thing: 'Our Mem. Service at 12, crowded, all in deep black. H. read the lesson, by far the most impressive bit of the service, except perhaps the beautiful singing of "Then shall the righteous. . . ." '[1]

Most of Queen Victoria's subjects had never known a time

when she had not been reigning over them. Lytton Strachey looked back with sentimental hindsight in 1921. 'It appeared,' he wrote, 'as if some monstrous reversal of the course of nature was about to take place.'[2] Queen Victoria had become embodied in the national consciousness as the eternal mother figure, even to the ageing once-disreputable poet Swinburne, who declared:

> No braver soul drew bright and queenly breath
> Since England wept upon Elizabeth.

Lady St Helier was one of the many thousands who watched the despatch of the queen's body from Osborne to Windsor via Portsmouth, 'amid all the glories of an unparalleled winter sunset . . . the deeper chords in the heart of a people seem to be reached, and to respond in all their volume to the profounder feelings which play upon them.'[3] The body was escorted by 'Her' fleet—though she was no longer queen; this confusion, this numbness, was felt most strongly by the court. For twenty-four hours after her death everything continued in the name of the queen; and it was twenty-four hours before homage was paid to the new king, homage which was customarily paid immediately upon the monarch's death. Edward was being snubbed again, for the last time and from beyond the grave.

The newspapers vied with each other in tribute. The magazine *The King*, in its column 'Topics of Today', declared that 'One's first feeling is undoubtedly a dazed sense that the impossible has happened'. The *Illustrated London News* had problems: 'Think what it means that we can never again sing the National Anthem in its present wording. The point is rather delicate . . .'

Upon news of her death, the great bell of St Paul's tolled to the 'grief-stricken citizens of London'. There was a wave of warm feeling towards the kaiser, Victoria's nephew, when the public heard that, amidst the chaos and uncertainty surrounding the corpse, he had behaved with manly dignity, unceremoniously ejecting the undertakers from the room and himself placing the body of his aunt in the coffin. The public temporarily ignored the savage tasteless cartoons that were currently running in German newspapers, depicting the queen as a fat woman at a fair being prodded by Kruger (the leader of the Boers, then involved in a protracted war with Britain).

Nevertheless, it appears to us from photographs of the time that the predominant reaction of the crowds who thronged the gates of Buckingham Palace during the last hours of the queen, idly reading the bulletins posted on the metal barriers, was one of curiosity. They were more interested in the cameramen who photographed them; they stand there in top hats, flat caps, and bowlers, inscrutable, hands in pockets, puffing at cigarettes.

The more staid newspapers had had obituaries of the queen ready to print for years, but the 'Yellow Press' was beginning to make its impact, and at Cowes 500 reporters and photographers clamoured for the one extra titbit that would make their journey worthwhile. In spotted bow-ties, with the ubiquitous cigarette poking from the corner of the mouth, the journalists were under no obligation to behave solemnly. There were no shots to be had of the dead queen, so they had to make do with photographs of the various warships riding at respectful anchor or of the kaiser's two detectives, walking, uncomprehended and incomprehensible, in the streets of East Cowes.

After the initial shock, many people found that they were inconvenienced by the queen's death. Theatres and restaurants (including Romano's) were closed, court mourning would persist for a year, and mourning was to be worn by British Army officers for six weeks. But, declared the city columns of the newspapers, 'the year of mourning for the Queen which has been officially ordained can hardly fail to bring enormous profit to Jay's, Limited, and to firms engaged in similar sombre trades'. [ie the provision of mourning wear].

The Stock Exchange closed for a day in tribute. This did not make much difference, for things were slack anyway as it was a time of recession. The moneyed people were holding back their wealth for prices to reach rock bottom. The railway companies had £30 million waiting to be spent when steel dropped below £7 a ton. When the Stock Exchange reopened, little business was done; there was small profit to be made from calamity.

But some profited. Within a few days of the queen's death Cassell's brought out *The Life and Times of Queen Victoria* in weekly parts. Sir Theodore Martin, who had written the life of the Prince Consort, between 1874 and 1880, was confidently expected to be commissioned to write the official biography of the queen (though he was eighty-five and could scarcely be expected to finish it). In the event he was not. Then who would get the prestige-laden job of editing Victoria's letters? The choice eventually fell on A. C. Benson, an Eton schoolmaster.

The air of gloom was interrupted by the proclamation of King Edward VII, read out by town clerks throughout the country. The ceremony at Bradford, accompanied by military and brass bands, encouraged an audience of 30,000; while at Brighton 40,000 turned up. But the festivities were short-lived and the motley was doffed for the mask of tragedy:

> On the face of the world in its wideness
> Is there sorrow and grief to-day,
> For the woman of God has departed—
> The Queen that was with us alway.
>
> (words by D. L. A. Jephson;
> music by A. H. Behrend)

Or was it? For the eulogising and breast-thumping are in contradiction to the comments of observers who stood aside and watched. 'This morning I saw what I could, over the heads of a vast crowd, of the funeral procession of the queen. The people were not, on the whole, deeply moved, whatever journalists may say, but rather serene and cheerful.' So wrote the novelist Arnold Bennett in his diary, one of the acutest commentators on the social scene. Max Beerbohm was even more outspoken: 'I have never seen such an air of universal jollity. It is a city of ghouls.'[4]

Many watched the funeral procession with secret cynicism. Among the royal mourners was the reprobate king of Belgium, who although nearly seventy had retained the services of a prostitute for his trip to England. There was a jockeying for position between King Edward and Kaiser Wilhelm; Edward had never forgiven the kaiser for his dismemberment of Denmark or the annexation of Hanover. It was believed by many that the king, who had no wish to be outshone in the procession, had conferred on the kaiser the rank of field-marshal in the British Army so as to make him appear ridiculous in full ceremonial dress. Edward liked dressing up and looked well in uniform—despite being called 'the little fat man in red' by the *Pall Mall Gazette*.

In the crowd was A. G. C. Liddell, lawyer and man-about-town. He thought the military tone of the funeral absurd, and the khaki of the guns and gun-carriage carrying the coffin ridiculous. 'The pall was not good,' he wrote in his diary. 'It was white, with the royal arms embroidered on it, but of a small and poor design.' The horses drawing the gun-carriage were ill-trained and had to be replaced. The sensitive saw

BROTHERS IN TRIBULATION.
John Bull : '' Don't you wish we could start the New Century in peace, Sammy ? ''
— *Denver Sunday Post.*

The reign of King Edward VII began in an atmosphere of crisis. This American cartoon shows that this was not confined to Britain

hidden significances: 'There were several strange stories afloat connected with this event which are worth recalling. In a material age we regard them as coincidences—but were they? White birds came and rested on her coffin, and at night a new star appeared in the sky.'[5]

Things returned to normal with almost indecent haste. The theatres and restaurants speedily reopened. To those who had taken the queen's death most to heart it was disgraceful that people were actually enjoying themselves, or getting married. In the weekly illustrated papers, pictures of the wedding of Queen Wilhelmina of Holland faced photographs of elaborate wreaths in memory of Victoria. The Duke of Westminster married the daughter of Mrs Cornwallis West, a professional beauty and a close friend of Edward VII when he was Prince of Wales.

Abroad, the queen's death had solved no problems. Boer commandos were still a thorn in the side of the British Army in South Africa. Another 30,000 mounted men were to be sent to Lord Kitchener, to be swallowed up in the vast wastes, along with their officers who regarded the war, said Kitchener, as being like polo 'with intervals for afternoon tea'. On the continent, Britain was not loved. Austria had not even paid lip-service to the late queen, and a meeting of what passed for the Austrian parliament was broken up by members shouting pro-Boer slogans. The nations of Europe waited for a realignment of power; it was well known that the new king was pro-French and anti-German. Realistic Europeans wondered whether alliances with Britain were militarily advantageous after the army's poor showing in South Africa.

What sort of Britain was it in January 1901?

It was a commercially static Britain. She had been surpassed in coal and iron production by the United States, and in steel by the United States and Germany, though she was still the principal exporter of manufactured goods. The last year of the nineteenth century had seen a boom with £635 million in exports, but the last year of Victoria had been less impressive, and a sinister clue to the future was seen in the decline in

To go from west to east London was to encounter 'a new and different race of people, short of stature, and of wretched and beer sodden appearance'

demand for cotton goods. The import of cheap food, especially grain, had helped the urban proletariat at the expense of the farm workers, who in their thousands were leaving the rural areas for the towns. Between 1870 and 1914 acreage under corn went down by 30 per cent, though the overall decline in agriculture was to some extent alleviated by the increase in dairy farming. The introduction of the first petrol-driven tractor in 1902 also reduced the demand for farm workers.

The standstill at home contrasted sharply with the world picture. Between 1884 and 1900 Britain had acquired 3,750,000 square miles of territory, plus 50 million new subjects, demanding to be policed by a massive army that the home country could ill afford. National expenditure on the fighting forces went up from one-third to a half of the total budget. The most hazardous feature of the casual building up of an ill-understood and reluctant Empire was the amount of money invested in far-off places, leaving little capital free for the replacement of obsolete industrial equipment at home, or for the energising of industries whose output had been superseded, or was in the process of being superseded, by other countries.

Industry had had it too easy. Since the 1870s lethargy and self-complacency had reigned. The sons of manufacturers were 'content to follow mechanically the lead given by their fathers. They worked shorter hours, and they exerted themselves less to obtain new practical ideas than their fathers had done, and thus a part of England's leadership was destroyed rapidly'.[6]

For three decades the standard of living had been creeping up; after 1900 it began to decline. The pound sterling of 1895 was worth 18s 5d in 1900 and 16s 3d in 1912. Although between 1893 and 1908 nominal wages went up by 12 per cent, this disguised the real fall in living standards—for the poor, of course. In the same period, profits went up by $29\frac{1}{2}$ per cent. The equation is simple: the rich became richer and the poor became poorer. Edward VII, who worshipped money as much as he did pleasure, was not the man to alter this. He implanted the idea of the respectability of pleasure not only with his peers but with those who could not afford it. In 1901 one-third of the population tried to live as only one-seventeenth could afford to. Of 7 million households, only 400,000 had incomes of more than £400 a year. A third of the population lived in penury. And very few cared.

To go from west to east London was to encounter, wrote Jack London, 'a new and different race of people, short of stature, and of wretched and beer sodden appearance'. The public houses were open from 6 am to 11 pm, and the average working-class family spent 6s a week on drink, a third of its income. A quarter of the people who died in London in 1901 were buried at the expense of the parish.

The respectable were terrified by this submerged class, and of the power it could wield with the advent of socialism, a dirty word since the 1880s. Kenneth Grahame put this terror into symbolic form in *Wind in the Willows:* '[the proletariat] had little evil wedge shaped faces . . . all fixing on him glances of malice and hatred: all hard-eyes and evil and sharp'.

This was in sharp contrast to his heroes, Rat, Toad, and Mole, which were, according to the *Saturday Review of Literature*, 'very human in their behaviour and remind us of undergraduates of sporting proclivities'. Among those who had escaped from the working classes yet did their best to ignore them, was Edgar Wallace: 'As you probably know I hate the British working man; I have no sympathy with him; whether he lives or dies, feeds or starves, is not of the slightest interest to me'.[7]

Few had the courage to put the matter into such uncompromising terms, but many millions shared this sentiment. Apprehension at the way the world was going was combined with dread at the thought of a country where the working classes were in control—a dread brought almost to fever pitch when in 1903 a Labour candidate won Woolwich with a majority of more than 3,000. Fortunately for those who worried most, the bulk of the working class still supported the Liberals.

The poor, it was reckoned, had only themselves to blame, and *The Times* leader of 1 September 1902 voiced the feelings of

Suffragettes tried to change the allegiances of the poor, with scant success

The evening courts of Edward VII provided an opportunity for rich women to demonstrate their sense of occasion

the lower middle classes who felt themselves most menaced by the working classes: 'Their wages would suffice to keep them strong and healthy, but they are thriftless; they drink or bet, or they are ignorant or careless in housekeeping.'

The systematic pursuit of pleasure began as soon as the king was securely on the throne. He named Buckingham Palace 'the Sepulchre' and removed immediately the faded relics of his mother's reign. The task of modernising and smartening up was a difficult one as Queen Alexandra had as little taste—charming as she was—as his mother, and one lot of clutter was replaced with another lot. He detested Osborne House, and as soon as possible gave it to the nation for use as a naval college.

He dropped the venerable institution of the afternoon drawing-rooms, and substituted evening courts. He never tired of pageantry and high living, and at the state opening of Parliament he instructed all peers to use their coaches to the House of Lords. He had a child's delight in dressing up, and expected his court to share his enthusiasm. Woe betide the nobleman who wore an order upside-down, as the Duke of Devonshire did on one occasion.

Following his mother's retirement from a full social life, Edward had given a lead, in morals and attitude, to the aristocracy, and the 'top ten thousand' soon realised that things would go on as before—only more so. There would be no dabbling in the arts or intellectualism, as had been the case during Prince Albert's day. As regards religion, the king's approach was strictly perfunctory; his instructions to Lang, the new Archbishop of York were simple and brisk: 'Keep the parties in the church together and prevent the clergy wearing moustaches'.

It is interesting to speculate upon what would have happened had the king not ascended the throne in 1901, or had been mortally struck down by the illness that in the event merely postponed his coronation. What would have happened had Queen Victoria lived to be ninety-one instead of eighty-one? As it was, life styles did not change abruptly with the accession of King Edward. The repressions and inhibitions, the hypocrisy and double standards of the middle classes had all been less in evidence since the 1880s, despite a number of stern rearguard actions by the *ancien régime*—as in the prosecution and imprisonment of Oscar Wilde for homosexual practices, the hounding of birth control propagandists, and persistent attacks upon the 'licentiousness' of the music hall.

The rumblings of discontent among the working classes, which resulted, in Edward VII's reign, in Labour representation in Parliament and a wave of strikes and industrial disputes, had been felt since the 1870s, when a large number of strikes amazed those to whom the working classes had been dim fugitive figures locked in their East End fastnesses. Cracks had been appearing in the class structure for several decades; if anything, Edward VII succeeded in keeping this structure more or less intact for another ten years.

Whatever his faults, Edward was a strong king. He believed in personal intervention in matters of state, and was responsible for the Entente Cordiale, as well as being instrumental in engineering a rapport with Russia. His worship of wealth had side effects that he could not have foreseen; one of these was the assimilation of rich Jews into society, where they were said to be the only humanising influences. Another was the integration with society of the 'shopocracy'. Typical of society's attitude towards these interlopers was the incident related by T. H. S. Escott in his *London Society in the New Reign* (1904):

> . . . Sir Blundell Maple was doing the honours of his Tottenham Court Road establishment to a stately dowager shopping there in her son's company. 'I think,' naively observed the dealer, 'I had the pleasure of seeing your Ladyship at the Opera last night.' Turning round to her companion, the lady of quality indignantly asked, in an intentionally audible aside, 'What does this man mean?' 'That he will lend you his box whenever you want it, and if I were you I should borrow it like a shot,' came the son's reply.

A lot was expected of the new reign. It was hoped that the liberating forces of the Naughty Nineties would sweep across the board. Edward VII, however, was not only strong, but selfish. Osbert Sitwell summed it up:

'*The feast, it was recognised, went to the greediest*', wrote Osbert Sitwell

. . . the Rich Man's Banquet, which was to last for a decade, had now begun: the feast, it was recognised, went to the greediest . . . the Edwardians squandered their accumulated riches at the shrine of the strange new goddess Comfort; they spent them on the gilding of pathetic but vulgar dreams from South Africa and the Ghetto, on the installation of bathrooms, electric light, and radiators.[9]

Osbert Sitwell was writing as a member of the landed gentry who resented the intrusion of outsiders into the sacred purlieus of his class. His sentiments were shared by the novelist George Meredith, who wrote of 'folly perpetually sliding into new shapes in a society possessed of wealth and leisure, with many whims, many strange ailments, and strange fancies'. The true aristocracy had a love/hate relationship with the king. He was one of them, as Victoria had never been, in his tastes, his hunting proclivities, his amours, and his life style; but, because of his passion for money and his admiration for those who had it, he had let in the dreaded vulgarians of the middle classes. No longer did the rich middle class slyly emulate their betters; they bought themselves in.

The gentry were cut right out of the picture. They had no place in 'the crowd of smart and moneyed Medes, Persians,

Elamites, and Mesopotamians, New York dandies, Chicago belles, and Hebrew money-brokers . . . [one of the gentry] would find himself in an *entourage* rather less intelligible to him than that thronging the presence-chamber of the grand Lama'.[10]

How one viewed England at this period, therefore, depended on whether one was in the gallery, the stalls or the boxes. In a symposium on Edwardian England published in 1933, its principal features were tabulated as the waning of authority, the fading influence of the middle classes, a lessening of reverence and of hypocrisy, with taboos beginning to lose their hold. The chaperon vanished 'like a ghost at sunrise', prudery was diminished and parental attitudes were more flexible. In social life there was less starch, boredom and pretence. The writers of 1933 were looking back in nostalgia; it is clear that in Edwardian times there were still chaperons, that parental attitudes could be as inflexible as ever (vide the novels of Galsworthy), and that taboos were still in operation, as witness the furore that greeted the writings of Freud and Havelock Ellis.

One feature of the age was the feeling of unease and apprehension. War was never far over the horizon, and many recognised that when it came it would be a new kind of war. Nor, after a few brief flirtations with the kaiser, was there any question that Germany would be the enemy (though some would have preferred to fight the United States, which, like Germany, was stealing all Britain's trade).

This apprehension paralysed the driving force that had propelled the Victorian colossus—Progress and the belief in Progress. In business and industry there was lethargy and indolence, reinforced by cynicism. The underlying philosophy was one of drifting; small wonder that the motto of a typical figure of the time, Asquith, was 'Wait and see'. Small wonder, also, that many of the young men of the age, later to die in World War I, escaped from the brooding nihilism into a life of pleasure.

The years 1901–14 have been called the age of extravagance. It was, to the historian G. M. Young, 'the flash Edwardian epilogue'. When on the eve of the war Sir Edward Grey, the foreign secretary, commented that the lights were going out all over Europe, few could claim that this was unexpected, or—in more cases than might be imagined—altogether unwelcome.

King and Queen

Edward VII had been waiting in the wings longer than any other monarch in English history. He was fifty-nine when he was proclaimed king. Baldness and a long nose had been inherited from the Coburg side of the family, his stoutness and lack of height from his mother. He had heavy-lidded protruding eyes, and his pouting mouth was hidden by neatly clipped beard. His voice was deep and guttural, and he rolled his r's.

The custom of denigrating or patronising past monarchs has produced the image of a kind of stuffed turkey floundering in a world compounded of exuberance, ostentation and vulgarity, of a little fat man who could always get a cheer from the working classes, but who was too passé for the true aristocracy, and surrounded by nouveau-riche sycophants. His personality was in fact more complex. His loyalty towards his friends was remarkable, while his affection for his wife and her influence over him had a telling effect.

He was the first cosmopolitan king. An accomplished linguist, he spoke German and French as fluently as he spoke English, and also had a good working knowledge of Italian and Spanish. On his frequent trips abroad he was much better able to gauge the mood of Europe than most of his ministers, who deplored the king's eyeball-to-eyeball diplomacy, preferring more traditional codes of conduct. They distrusted his judgement, which they knew to be based on intuition and feeling rather than thought. They were taking their cue from Queen Victoria, who once wrote to him: 'The country, and all of us, would like to see you a little more stationary'.

This view was shared by many of the king's subjects. 'I think the king goes about a damned sight too much,' declared Edgar Wallace, 'and I wish to heaven he would give up processing; one gets very tired of fossicking around after the old cove . . .

after I had got through writing about "lovely consorts", and "kingly presences" and "kindly smiles" I got fed up.'[1] Typical of the import invested in the monarch's visits to Russia, Germany and France was the photograph of the king with Sir Henry Campbell-Bannerman, with the caption 'Is it peace or war?' In fact the king was pondering whether halibut was better baked or boiled.

Edward was ignored by the intellectuals, who deplored his flippancy towards matters which, they considered, he could not understand. The king once said to the scientist Lord Rayleigh, 'Inventing something, I suppose?' commenting to a companion, 'He's always at it.' This was construed as a calculated insult to a clever man, not as a way of putting the scientist at his ease. However, there was less chance of misinterpreting his observation, after a performance of *Arms and the Man*, that Bernard Shaw was 'a damned crank'. Even the most hidebound intellectual, however, must have agreed with the king's reference to 'the trash which the Poet Laureate writes'. The works of Alfred Austin had few admirers.

Some have seen Edward's reign as a mixture of operetta and French farce. It was no accident that *The Merry Widow* was staged in 1907. It reflected all the external signs of the age, in a never-never land in which it was always high summer—gaiety, extravagance and sentimentality. To some observers, Edward's affairs may have indeed appeared farcical, while certain events were reminiscent of a Gilbert and Sullivan opera. At the coronation, for instance, the Archbishop of Canterbury 'blundered sadly, adjuring the king to give his special protection to "widowers", and then with painful conscientiousness substituting "widows"; the efforts to prompt him only seemed to muddle matters further, and he had to be left to stumble through as best he could'. Worse was to come. At the close of his oration the accompanying bishops 'pulled different ways in their efforts to raise him to his feet, and but for the timely assistance of the King, he would have been dragged off his feet by the Bishop of Winchester'.[2]

Matters were not to end there. When it was time to employ

the holy oil, 'the Dean of Westminster narrowly escaped emptying the contents of the chalice upon the Queen', and after the ceremony everyone tried to break through the file of Grenadier Guards drawn up to stop people leaving before the royal procession. The Duchess of Devonshire pressed on, missed her footing, and rolled over on her back at the feet of Sir Michael Hicks Beach, her coronet flying off and striking the stalls with a loud crash.

Such mishaps, it was felt, could not have happened in relation to the dead queen (though in fact Victoria's coronation had its own chain of misadventures). Foreboding looks were cast at the royal favourites incarcerated in the special part of Westminster Abbey known as the 'King's Loose Box'. Here was the raw material of bedroom farce; would the king continue to run after pretty women, or begin to be faithful to his wife?

It was a question admitting of only one answer. The presence

King Edward demanded the presence of pretty women, who were always in evidence at court

*Mrs George Keppel, the last and most
lasting of the king's alliances*

of pretty women acted upon him with the certainty and rapidity
of a blood infusion. Nor was he reluctant to admit it. He had his
apologists, among them Princess Alice, Countess of Athlone:
'Aunt Alix (Queen Alexandra) was renowned for her beauty, very
lovely, with a gracious presence and a disposition which endeared
her to the public who worshipped her. But being stone deaf and
not mentally very bright, she was not much of a companion for
an intelligent man like Uncle Bertie.'[3]

Queen Alexandra was well aware of her husband's infidelities.
She could hardly fail to be, when one of his favourite horses
was named Ecila (Alice back to front)—Alice being the name of
Mrs Keppel, the last and most lasting of the king's alliances. The
queen was a woman of tact and discretion, and something more.
Her one liaison, when she was Princess of Wales, was with the
Honourable Oliver Montagu, and conducted on a lofty plane,
though when he died in 1893 she was desolate.

Before her marriage to Edward in 1863 there had been more
than a breath of scandal about her. On 15 January 1862 Countess
Bluecher wrote to diplomat Augustus Paget:

> Bad as human nature is, it is impossible to believe that, out of interested
> motives, persons of a position in the world can invent histories to injure the
> reputation of an amiable and unoffending girl! Yet such must be the case in
> the present instance and I am full of indignation and disgust at it. I cannot say
> I believed the report which had been spread, and had it only been from one

quarter I should never have troubled my head about it, but from vriousa
quarters the same thing having come to me and others, all probably emanating
from the same source, it became most important to *approfondir*.

Paget's wife took up the story:

I have not yet seen the Princess alone, so I have not found out who spread
those wicked stories, but I strongly suspect, from a word she said, and for
which the Prince reprimanded her, that it was the Princess of Dessau. If it all
goes straight the marriage will be next spring, and I am determined it shall go
straight. [4]

Lady Walburga Paget was one of those determined mid-
Victorian matrons who exerted considerable influence behind
the scenes.

Six children were born of Alexandra's marriage, the last in
1871. By degrees she centred her life on Sandringham and her
children, and gave the impression of a docile happy wife
unconcerned with what happened outside her immediate circle.
Edward's love life encompassed Mrs Greville, the American-born
Duchess of Marlborough, Lady Londonderry, Mrs Arthur
Sassoon, Mrs Willie James, Lady Troubridge, Lady Lonsdale, and
Mrs Cornwallis West. And, of course, the wife of the Honourable
George Keppel. There was no question that as Prince of Wales
he had slept with others less respectable. When Lillie Langtry
had a child, Edward had flipped a coin as to whether or not he
was the father (this affair ended in 1881). Then there was
Sarah Bernhardt, cold-shouldered by the aristocracy, who had
had an illegitimate son when still in her teens.

In the society that centred around Edward it was understood
that there were delicate alliances that should be treated with
discretion. Bedrooms were allocated accordingly. There were
some even more sensitive liaisons which could more conveniently
be consummated in private rooms. Rule's, in Maiden Lane, was
a favourite rendezvous of Edward's, also Kettner's, where the
King Edward Room was said to have a secret passage to the
Palace Theatre opposite for the benefit of actresses and others on
whom the royal gaze had alighted. Kettner's supplied maids to

help undress women who had had the misfortune to leave their own at home.

There were times when even private rooms were too public. Edward's private secretary, Lord Knollys, asked Lord Rosebery for the use of his London house so that the king and his younger brother Alfred could entertain actress friends—a request that met with a refusal. The king was more successful in persuading Sir Ernest Cassel, the financier, to lend his rented villa in Biarritz to accommodate him and Mrs Keppel, together with her children, to whom he was known as 'Kingy'.

The forebearance of Queen Alexandra must be admired. As early as 1870, when she had been married seven years, she had had to watch her husband's affairs paraded in public when he was involved in the Mordaunt divorce case. Shortly after the birth of her first child, Lady Mordaunt told her husband, 'Charlie, you are not the father of that child'. Among the candidates for paternity, Lady Mordaunt admitted, was the Prince of Wales. In due course Edward was served with a subpoena, though he was protected from answering any 'improper questions', the phrase used by Queen Victoria when she was acquainted with her son's predicament.

Edward had written twelve mildly compromising letters, and was cross-examined for seven minutes, an occurrence that was 'painful and lowering' to his mother, while the Prince of Wales had the rare experience of being booed in the street. Though the case was less dangerous to the stability of the monarchy than it might have been, it was perhaps fortunate that Lord Mordaunt lost his divorce suit, on account of his wife's insanity.

There was little that Alexandra could do; to divorce her husband was unthinkable, as unrealistic as returning in humiliation to her native Denmark. She came to terms with her husband's infidelities, the tension was relaxed, and it is not surprising that he humoured her in some of her whims.

Easy-going and amiable as she was in the humdrum business of everyday life, in one respect Alexandra was uncompromising and stern. This was her deep abiding hatred of Germany. Her father was on the throne of Denmark when the Germans invaded and

Alexandra had been resentful that Britain had not done more for her country. Admittedly the British Government had tried to put Alexandra's brother on the throne of Greece, but this had been so mismanaged that the party most concerned had only read of his possible elevation when he opened a newspaper in which his sardine sandwiches had been wrapped. In the event, he only got the Ionian Islands.

Had she had her way Alexandra would have got Victoria to wage war on Germany for what she considered the rape of her country. 'This horrible war will be a stain for ever on Prussian history,' she wrote, 'I think it is very wrong of our Government not to interfere.' After the birth of the first child, the royal couple visited Denmark. Alexandra insisted that the Prussian flag be hauled down from the mast, asserting that she would not move a step until this was done. When the Prince of Wales met his brother-in-law, the Danish Crown Prince, there were more ructions: 'It was not pleasant to see him and his ADC always in Prussian uniform, flaunting before your eyes a most objectionable ribbon which he received for his deeds of valour (? ? ?) against the unhappy Danes'.

The Prussians were stigmatised by Alexandra as 'the Robbers', Prussia as 'the Robber State', and she did not hesitate to declare these sentiments in open telegrams. Victoria was displeased by this attitude. She refused to allow her daughter Princess Helena to marry the Crown Prince of Denmark, though there was no objection to her marrying into the Prussian aristocracy. 'This alliance, of course, cannot be popular to Bertie's wife and family', the queen wrote, 'but that cannot be helped and is of no consequence'.

Not surprisingly the Danish royal family were indignant. King Christian wrote: 'They show us not the slightest consideration and wound our most sacred feelings. That is typically English. They think of nothing but their own advantage, and never consult their heart.' To the Danes there was some satisfaction in the marriage of Alexandra's sister, Thyra, to the Hanoverian Pretender, in 1879, which dismayed the Prussian statesman Bismarck. What did Alexandra want? 'Bismarck's head,' retorted the Princess of Wales briskly.

In the context of the growing hostility towards Germany, Alexandra's hatred fanned the flames. The proposal by Joseph Chamberlain of a race union between Britain, America and Germany seemed an act tantamount to high treason. Occasionally this hatred boiled over, to the surprise of guests. On one occasion when Alexandra, then queen, was brought out on the subject of the kaiser there was 'an explosion of rancour'. He 'has a mania for domineering over everybody and occupying himself with what is no concern of his'. Any entente between Germany and Britain was therefore hampered by the queen's hostility and the king's personal dislike of the kaiser, combined with his partiality for France and all that was French.

Unlike his ministers, the king did not believe in appeasement, but was ready to bury the hatchet if the kaiser would; Wilhelm's exemplary behaviour at the time of Queen Victoria's death had somewhat diluted their mutual distrust. The prime minister, Lord Salisbury, was too old and ineffectual to contribute anything to a rapport. The spokesman for the government seemed to be Joseph Chamberlain, the colonial secretary, who had said at Leicester in November 1899: 'The natural alliance is between ourselves and the German Empire . . . both interest and racial sentiment unite the two peoples. . . .'

This tolerance of the kaiser and all he stood for lasted only a few months. Chamberlain realised that he had stepped out of line, and when the German newspapers attacked the British for their atrocities towards the Boers and their use of concentration camps, he rounded on the Germans, and asserted that the British Army had never been so barbarous as the German Army—or the French or the Russians, thereby creating three possible enemies instead of one.

The first inkling of the coming line-up of powers was sensed by the press. Alfred Harmsworth of the *Daily Mail*, with its circulation of 836,700, and Leo Manxe of the *National Review* did some effective sabre rattling. In 1902 the *National Review* declared that it was necessary to 'combat German anglophobia by working all round for the isolation of Germany'. The tabloid papers were baiting Germany with what that country feared most

Leaving nothing to chance : or preparing for a battue in the Imperial Forest of Hochderkaiser.

The attitude of the press towards the Germans is evident from this 1909 cartoon

—encirclement. In doing so they added a further nail to any prospects of permanent peace.

Throughout the Edwardian period the great powers behaved as though they were playing musical chairs. Statesmen were manipulated by events. It seemed to be a matter of chance who would strike the first blow, and where. After Japan had soundly trounced Russia in a relatively obscure war on the other side of the world, even the languid Arthur Balfour thought that Russia might be worth having a crack at, eventually coming through with the Machiavellian conclusion that 'the most formidable aspect of an Anglo-Russian war is admittedly the difficulty of hitting Russia herself'.[5] The sinking by the Russian Baltic Fleet of a number of British trawlers on the Dogger Bank under the impression that they were Japanese warships was neither here nor there in the context of these comic opera confrontations.

It was quite evident to true blue Englishmen that foreigners could not be trusted. They would have liked to have stopped the clock in the last year of Victoria's reign when Britain had no friends and no irritating alliances, and when there was, in fact, a

After 1907 the king became increasingly depressed and the camera caught him more and more off-guard

comfortable and effete alliance—the Franco-Russian alliance of 1894—unmistakably directed against England.

It was only to be expected that during this game of musical chairs someone would want to shoot the pianist, and amid the confusion the presence of the unflappable king was invaluable. The uneasy atmosphere communicated itself to men of letters and aesthetes who normally did not concern themselves with international matters. Max Beerbohm was more interested in the effect of the Russo-Japanese War on his personal affairs, as is clear from a letter he wrote to his close friend Reginald Turner in March 1904: 'Soon we may be dragged into this beastly war, and then there will be no chance of a sale for any book for a long time to come'.

The king's great asset was his innate honesty. His friend Lord Redesdale put it well:

No diamond could be more purely clear and honest than King Edward, and it was that pellucid truthfulness which made him so powerful in his relations with foreign sovereigns and statesmen; they knew that when they were dealing with him they had to do with a King as honest as Nathanael, a man in whom there was no guile. [6]

After 1907 the king grew increasingly depressed; from 1905 the winter had played more and more havoc with his health, and not even the escape to Biarritz with Alice Keppel could remedy the effects of high living and old age.

It was at Sandringham that the greatest impression of stability was given. Edward had bought Sandringham House from Mr Spencer Cowper in 1861, and it was rebuilt in the High Victorian style between 1869 and 1871. This massive building standing in 7,000 acres was the king's favourite home, where he could relax despite the clutter of bric-à-brac and mementoes of a bygone age. The saloon, with its oak walls and beamed ceiling, was crammed with objects, including two bronze cannon named 'Eugénie' and 'Louis Napoleon', screens, a piano, groups of palms and stands of flowers, while the walls were covered with sketches and paintings. There were curios from India, Japan, Egypt and Turkey; the hoof of King Edward's racehorse, Eclipse; weapons retrieved from the battlefields of the Franco-Prussian War; and under glass cases, set precariously on little tables, a multitude of gold and silver caskets.

Only in the king's preserves was there any semblance of restraint; the bowling-alley 'after the best United States models' was strictly functional, and sketches by the humorous artist John Leech enlivened the walls of the billiard-room. Elsewhere amateurish paintings by the royal daughters hung side by side with stilted full-length glorifications of the king in uniform; life-size white swans were matched with sentimental genre pictures, such as 'Girls Bathing'. In the ante-rooms, there were tiger-skins and tusks and other trophies of the chase in abundance. The queen's boudoir was 'marvellously full of every trivial detail'.

Prince Christopher of Greece observed sardonically:

At Sandringham, royal stability was preserved, a buttress against reality

The Queen's positive genius for collecting trifles of every description and hoarding them long after their origin had been forgotten; books, photos, china, letters, old programmes, odds and ends of ribbons and laces were heaped together indiscriminately anywhere and everywhere, for she never could throw any of them away. Beautiful miniatures and Georgian snuff-boxes occupied a table with Earl's Court china pigs and bog-wood charms from Ireland; she kept the fishing-fly given her by a gillie in Scotland as carefully as she kept a brooch from one of the Indian maharajahs.[7]

In the grounds was a miniature zoo with tigers, elephants, kangaroos and bears; in the kennels were up to a hundred dogs, including the queen's favourite basset hounds.

In such an environment it was easy to forget the troubles and anxieties that lay outside. Sandringham was a buttress against reality—the prospects of war and the social turbulence being whipped up by left-wing agitators. How different were the lives of city workers from those of the labourers on the estate! Every 'village' had its picturesque clubhouse, with billiard and reading rooms, and the men were prevented from squandering their earnings on beer for the simple reason that no pubs were allowed to be built. To Queen Alexandra it was an Arcadia. Bazaars gave the impression that the villages on the estate were *real* villages; at one bazaar a 'fair vendor' was asked by the king for a cup of tea. 'Now the cup of tea is five guineas', said the woman coyly. The king sipped it. 'Will you please give me a clean cup?' he asked. Even the dwellers of this world within a world could be disconcerted.

Marlborough House had had a special place in the affections of Edward and Alexandra, but when Victoria died and they were obliged to move to Buckingham Palace, the house was taken over by the new Prince of Wales, later George V. On Edward's death in 1910, it became the home of Queen Alexandra. During Edward's tenure, guests at Marlborough House were met by a gillie in national costume and two scarlet-coated powdered footmen. Pages wore dark blue coats and black trousers, and for special occasions black velvet breeches, silk stockings, and gold garters. Like Sandringham, Marlborough House was cluttered with objects from Asia and the Orient.

The royal residences were symbols of the old order, and Edward's determination to revive the ceremonial circumstances of the monarchy, that had been in decline since the death of his father, was reflected by the grandeur of his life style. In their hearts the king's circle knew that it could not last, and in early May 1910 the end came. Bronchitis took him off. 'When the black news came a deadly pall fell over the country, and there were many men—some great, some small—who felt that life could never again be quite the same for them'.[8]

The new king, it was felt, would not match his father. The aristocracy distrusted him. What they knew about him they did not care for; he was a Victorian in an Edwardian setting, and had drawn his friends from his own social level. There had been no alliance with continentals or American millionaires. He had carried out his duties as the Prince of Wales, visiting outposts of the Empire, opening this and that, with aplomb, and because his private life had never been open to criticism scandal had to be invented to fit him into the pattern of the Georges. It was widely circulated and believed that during his service with the Mediterranean Fleet he had contracted a marriage in Malta with the daughter of an admiral.

In the inner ring of Edwardian Society malice was not wanting. There were many in or on the fringe of the circle of King Edward who felt that his death was the death-knell of the good times and marked the end of the 'great days' or the 'happy days' of Society. In a narrow sense perhaps they were right.[9]

It was a tradition for lampoons to be devised when a new king took over, but there was a venom about those distributed in 1910. The new court, it was considered, would be drab and vacuous, and the sparkle would go out of society life. The topics that had interested Edward would be barred from polite conversation; and George conspicuously lacked his father's interests in horse-racing.

The country gentry, however, welcomed his accession. He was one of them and had one quality that particularly endeared him to them—he was a crack shot. On one occasion he brought down thirty-nine pheasants with thirty-nine shots. On 18 December 1913, when George V was one of the seven guns, there was a record bag of 3,937 pheasants. Such facts did much to comfort the country squire, who waited with eagerness for the ejection of the moneyed middle classes from their pedestals.

There were a few who realised that towards the end of his life Edward VII had not been the man he was. 'It was well that he died in 1910. He died before his decline had become too conspicuous, and he has left a name which will stand for many generations as a synonym for all that is best in constitutional kingship.'[10]

Although George V had not had the long apprenticeship of his father, he was now forty-five and appeared older. In a wordly sense he was naïve, and diplomacy of the kind Edward had indulged in was clearly not his forte. When in 1911 King George went to India for the Coronation Durbar he was oblivious to the gathering storm in Europe, and when on 18 March 1913 the assassination of the king of Greece pushed the great powers nearer to war, George's sentiments were almost parochial: 'Beloved Uncle Willie has been assassinated at Salonica, while walking in the streets . . . Too horrible, I was devoted to him and he will be a great loss to Greece. Mother dear is fearfully upset by this fresh sorrow'.

In May 1913, King George and Queen Mary, and the Tsar of Russia, were among those present at the wedding of the kaiser's daughter, but the kaiser prevented private conversation between the British and the Russians, and despite the growing European tension no move was made to use the occasion politically. Somewhat relieved, George V returned to England, where he visited the Potteries to meet the people over whom he was somewhat bemusedly ruling. The opening of 1914 saw him doing what he was best at—shooting pheasants.

Events were building up to a climax. Germany and France were unmistakably preparing for war, yet the social life in London—contrary to expectations—continued as before. In May, Prince Henry of Prussia came on a visit to the king, who had great faith in the good sense of the kaiser. Late in the afternoon of 28 June 1914 the king received the news of the Sarajevo murder. Its implications were lost on him, and he merely reported in his diary, 'Terrible shock for the dear old Emperor'. The shock was in fact sufficient to inspire Franz Josef, the 83-year-old Austrian despot, to attack Serbia to avenge his nephew's assassination.

Towards the end of July Prince Henry of Prussia returned home. It was believed in Germany that on 26 July the king and the prince had an interview in which the king stated that in the event of war England would remain neutral. On 29 July Austria declared war on Serbia; on 1 August Germany declared war on Russia, and on 4 August Britain was brought in. 'It is a terrible catastrophe but it is not our fault,' the king committed to his diary. On 10 August the kaiser sent a telegram to President Wilson reporting the alleged statement of the king to Prince Henry. The tone was aggrieved. Of course, the statement was denied. The text of the telegram was quoted in a book by James Garrard, American Ambassador to Germany at the outbreak of war; *My Four Years in Germany* was published in 1917 and serialised in the *Daily Telegraph*. A categorical denial of the story was issued, but the repercussions did not die down. In 1938 Captain Erich von Müller, the German Naval Attaché in London in 1914, repeated the allegations, which brought forth a spirited reply from the Keeper of the King's Archives. And there the matter rested.

Was the British involvement in World War I the result of a chat between royalties, a misunderstanding? King George V was certainly a good deal more out of touch with the time bomb that was 1914 Europe than some of his subjects. Arthur Conan Doyle, for one, brought to the matter an insight that one would expect from the creator of Sherlock Holmes:

> I can never forget, and our descendants can never imagine, the strange effect upon the mind which was produced by seeing the whole European fabric drifting to the edge of the chasm with absolute uncertainty as to what would happen when it toppled over.[11]

Many were glad that the days of unease were over. When asked when war would start one army officer said that it would be on the first pretext after the Kiel Canal was widened—to facilitate the passage of German battle-cruisers. The canal was widened on 14 June. Certain politicians wanted war, to divert interest away from troubles at home, and in Ireland where there was open warfare. There were unscrupulous left-wing politicians who thought that a war would bring down the established society and bring in communism.

And there was the man in the street. 'It will be the most popular war this country ever engaged in', declared Ramsay MacDonald, leader of the Labour Party. 'Look out of your windows now, and you will see the people beginning to go mad.'[12]

The Men at the Top

When Edward VII came to the throne the prime minister was Lord Salisbury, who was over seventy, and clearly due for replacement. Once described by Disraeli as 'a great master of gibes and flouts and jeers', all he now wanted was a quiet life. In the so-called 'khaki' election of 1900, Salisbury's party, the Unionists or Conservatives, had got in with a huge majority and there was no wish for a new broom. Salisbury remained at

A 1908 cartoon of Balfour with Campbell-Bannerman. Balfour, 'an old maid in a frock coat', is on the right

the head of the government throughout the Boer War, and then retired in July 1902.

His successor was his nephew Arthur Balfour, who was 'made prime minister because it is desired by the ruling families that the minimum of change should be made,' wrote J. L. Garvin of *The Observer*.

Balfour was born in 1848, educated at Eton and Trinity College, Cambridge, and entered parliament in 1874, becoming private secretary to Lord Salisbury in 1878. Apart from a brief flirtation with the ebullient Lord Randolph Churchill and his Fourth Party, Balfour's political career was subdued and unsensational. For him politics was a polite game; the House of Commons may have been the best club in London, but to Balfour it was slightly vulgar. He was ethereal and somewhat vague. At school he had been known as 'Pretty Fanny' and the connotation stuck.

> Balfour never reads the newspapers, is as ignorant of popular agitations, demonstrations, and all such vulgar things, as an English judge of a burlesque actress whose name and features stare at him from every hoarding and every printed sheet.[1]

It was suggested that the real prime minister was his secretary, J. S. Sandars, and that Balfour, though not bad in himself, was a typical product of his class, the social function of which was 'the manufacture of old maids in frock coats'. Balfour was a bachelor and lived in Carlton Gardens, with small blue and white pots with ferns on the dining tables, fine furniture and pictures, and the absence of that luxury that was so much a feature of the Edwardian scene. His bedroom was dark and bare, and by the bedside was a lectern. However, it was typical of Balfour that on the lectern was a manual on bridge.

Beatrice Webb, whose left-wing politics were the antithesis of his own, has left in her diaries a summary of Balfour:

> A man of extraordinary grace of mind and body, delighting in all that is beautiful and distinguished, music, literature, religious feeling and moral disinterestedness, aloof from all the greed of common human nature. But a strange paradox as a prime minister!

Balfour was too subtle by half for Edward VII, who complained that 'he is always so vague that probably he is wrong'. On his part, Balfour depreciated and undervalued the king's intuitive soundness of judgement. The two men belonged to different worlds. Balfour had been a member of the group known as 'the Souls', which included the vivacious Margot Tennant (who later married Asquith), Lord Curzon (Viceroy of India 1899–1905), George Wyndham (Chief Secretary for Ireland 1900–5), fragile eccentrics such as the patron of opera and ballet Lady de Grey, so fey that the cry of a cuckoo made her feel ill, and the most literate of the aristocracy. Many of the men who belonged to the Souls found places in Balfour's administration.

The feature that struck everyone about Balfour was his charm; this concealed a vein of ruthlessness, and the 'silk-skinned sybarite, whose rest a crumpled rose leaf would disturb'—as the *Irish Times* had it—could be as savage as the next man, if the occasion arose. The occasion did not often arise, though had the socialist 'menace' been stronger no doubt it would have done. Balfour had no interest in the plight of the working man, and whether or not the question attributed to him, 'What is a trade union?', is apocryphal it is the kind of thing he would have said. He had little time for democracy, and it was a matter of indifference to him that cabinet ministers held directorships and had financial interests that might very well clash with government intent.

The Duke of Devonshire, for instance, the Lord President of the Council, was chairman of a steel company that made armour for British warships at a time when the rebuilding of the Royal Navy was a sore point. Balfour even defended his ministers' involvement in outside affairs, and in a speech in the House of Commons in February 1903 he declared that public life would be poorer if ministers were prevented from holding directorships.

Balfour was unquestionably one of the most intelligent of prime ministers. He was a writer as well as a statesman, and his *Defence of Philosophic Doubt* (1879) and *Foundations of Belief* (1895) were cogent well-written books that were treated with respect. He had his eccentricities. He and his brother Gerald (who was also given a job in government) were obsessively interested in the artificial drying of peat for use as fuel, and between them they lost a quarter of a million pounds.

Balfour did not think the time ripe for democracy, the whole concept of which was under a cloud. In *Democracy and Reaction*, L. T. Hobhouse wrote that 'the golden radiance of [democracy's] morning hopes has long since faded into the light of common day'. Balfour had an aristocratic temperament; his government was languid. He had been forced to inherit some of Salisbury's colleagues, such as the Duke of Devonshire, described by the *National Review* as 'a statesman in the last stage of political ossification', and Lord Lansdowne, who had been secretary of war at the outbreak of the Boer War and held responsible by the press for the army's inept showing. Balfour's main defect was that he was afflicted with that 'specially British curse—the lenity to well-connected muddlers'.[2] And all his muddlers were well connected.

Behind Balfour was the old but immensely energetic Joseph Chamberlain. The stormy petrel of the 1880s was obsessed with the idea of tariff reform. The antithesis of free trade, tariff reform involved financial protection for the products of Britain and the Empire. To Chamberlain the introduction of an entirely new and far-reaching tariff system would protect and inspire British businessmen, and bring the colonies into a close economic union. The supporters of Chamberlain's scheme thought that protection would guarantee employment for the workers, and provide sufficient revenue for social welfare. Chamberlain himself had been interested in the provision of old age pensions since 1892. Although he had retired from industry with a fortune as early as 1874, he had seen the tragedy of the poor when they got too old to work. Acquaintance with the poor was not Balfour's forte. He was grateful to Chamberlain for not offering himself as an alternative premier when Salisbury went, but the crusade for tariff reform was inconvenient; not only did it threaten a split in the Conservative party but if it were implemented there was a good chance of trouble with the United States.

Hemmed in between the rival factions, for and against free

THE SOUTH AFRICAN CAMPAIGN—BIGGER GAME IN SIGHT.
Joe Chamberlain: "Here, I've wasted my powder on that pesky Boer, and look at what's a'comin'!"
—*Minneapolis Journal.*

Joseph Chamberlain had an international reputation as a firebrand, and his frequent discomfiture was noted with glee, particularly by the Americans

trade, Balfour prevaricated, hoping that, like so many topics, the issue would drift away. He admitted in the House of Commons that he had 'no settled convictions on the subject'. His main aim was to keep the party together. If anything he had a slight preference for tariff reform, but he could not understand the venom with which the topic was discussed, and when Chamberlain left the government in 1903, Balfour being too luke-warm for him, open war was waged between the free traders and the protectionists.

To some, tariff reform was the One Simple Answer to all the ills of the age of apprehension. This enthusiasm overflowed into verse:

When wealth and mirth refill the earth,
Let each man tell his neighbour:
All this we owe to Chamberlain.
Hurrah, hurrah, hurrah. [3]

To others, Chamberlain represented all that was worst in modern politics. That he had lived and made his money in Birmingham was an added exasperation. The Bishop of Hereford protested about 'this raging tearing Protectionist propaganda manufactured in Birmingham'; the left-wing former engineer John Burns spoke of 'schemes projected by a political bankrupt in the interests of a distressed bankrupt'; and Frederic Harrison, lawyer, expert on trade unions and a doctrinaire Liberal, resorted to personalities: Chamberlain was 'a tawdry charlatan and impudent demagogue'.

In largely irrelevant debates about the pros and cons of tariff reform the class war erupted, and it was up to the Liberals to make the most of this. Opposition to Chamberlain closed their ranks, and three figures began to emerge as possible Liberal leaders—Herbert Asquith, Lord Haldane and Sir Edward Grey, with Lord Rosebery (Liberal prime minister 1894–5) hovering in the wings. The nominal leader was Sir Henry Campbell-Bannerman, who had somehow acquired this unenviable job in 1898. The joker in the pack was David Lloyd George, as unpopular with his own colleagues as with the Conservatives.

For Balfour there was an ominous sign of the times when, in a by-election at Norwich in January 1904, the Liberals won a seat that they had not even contested in 1900. The same thing happened in Whitby in 1905. Balfour was aware that the Liberals were divided; Asquith, Haldane and Grey being reluctant to serve under Campbell-Bannerman. The Liberals were very busy investigating the conditions of the poor, and exploiting their findings, but how would they shape in office, with the mediocre Campbell-Bannerman having a hard job to put a government together, and with Lloyd George and the envious Rosebery undoubted liabilities? Balfour decided to try them out.

He resigned, anticipating a muddled period of Liberal quasi-rule followed by a general election in 1906, in which the Conservatives would sweep the board and be set for another long period in power. There was also a good chance that Campbell-Bannerman would refuse, in view of the schisms in his own ranks, to take office, throwing the ball back into the

Conservative court. It did not turn out like that. Campbell-Bannerman became prime minister in 1905 and proved a much stronger man than anyone believed, while Asquith, Grey and Haldane showed themselves more anxious for office than principle. Campbell-Bannerman also brought in Lloyd George and John Burns, and Winston Churchill, who had providentially moved to the Liberals from the Conservatives in time to become colonial secretary at the age of thirty-one.

The issues of the general election of 1906 were fuzzy-edged and ambiguous, with both sides speaking of the need for efficiency, greater cohesion in government departments, and the evasion and dishonesty of their opponents. The Liberals shelved the Irish Problem (Home Rule and Catholic v. Protestant)—there was nothing in it for them. To the Independent Labour Party, both Conservatives and Liberals were the same—parties for the rich whose joint aim was to keep the working classes down. All parties were compelled to talk of social reform, old age pensions and compulsory national insurance; the only difference

There was little communication between Members of Parliament and their constituents, and the twenty-nine Labour members who were elected in 1906 did little to alter this

was that when the Liberals got in on a massive land-slide they did something about it. The welfare state dates from 1906.

It was a traumatic year for all those on the right wing of British politics. When the new parliament assembled there were only 157 Conservatives, instead of 402. To the distress of the old order, there were twenty-nine Labour members plus twenty-four 'Lib-Labs'. The *Edinburgh Review* saw ominous signs of socialism even in the Liberal members—'the spirit of socialism pervades the whole House'. In 1906 Joseph Chamberlain retired from politics on grounds of ill-health.

The most important thing about Campbell-Bannerman, it was said, was his taste for French novels. He was heartily in favour of a closer relationship with France, and did a good deal to bring nearer Franco-British military co-operation. He distrusted the Germans. The kaiser, he said at the end of 1905, was 'a dangerous, restless, mischief-making man'. Campbell-Bannerman was deceptive. Generally thought third rate, he proved to be good second rate. He was the man without a face, whom everyone expected to find boring and whose astute guilelessness would appear crude after Balfour's savoir faire. Edward VII was one of those who dreaded the thought of meeting Campbell-Bannerman, expecting him to be even more trying than Balfour. To his surprise, he found him companionable and much to his taste. And so did the military people. The Duke of Cambridge, who had been commander-in-chief of the British Army, 1856–95, thought him 'very nice, calm and pleasant'.

Without the subtlety of Balfour, Campbell-Bannerman nevertheless fitted in with the pattern of Edwardian prime ministers. If anything untoward arose, he would rather do nothing. Like Balfour he would have approved of Lord Melbourne's dictum, 'Why not leave it alone?' He was 'easy-going to the point of laziness', commented Margot Asquith, but no doubt Campbell-Bannerman thought that there was enough energy being employed by Lloyd George. Campbell-Bannerman paid lip service to the common man. England, he declared when coming to power, would be 'less of a pleasure ground for the rich and more of a treasure house for the poor'. Lloyd George

Insult to Injury

MISS B-LL-NGT-N : "Free! but I don't want to be free—besides, I'm
fearfully dangerous—and determined—and—oh! you *are* mean!"

Asquith was suave and civilised, and even the suffragettes found him difficult to cope with

was more committed and more vehement: 'There are conditions
of poverty, destitution and squalor that would make the rocks
weep'. On one occasion Campbell-Bannerman asked Lloyd
George, 'Are you feeling cooler now?'[4]

In 1908 Campbell-Bannerman died, and Herbert Asquith,
as the new prime minister, had to take on the task of governing
the country and coping with Lloyd George. Asquith had many of
the qualities of Balfour; he was suave and civilised, and moved
amongst the same people. Born in 1852, Asquith's first memory
was walking with a Sunday school procession to celebrate peace
after the Crimean War. At school he won all the prizes, and at
Balliol College, Oxford, was nurtured by the benign Master,
Benjamin Jowett, along with his parliamentary contemporaries
Sir Edward Grey and Lord Curzon. Jowett saw the successes of
his famous pupils as college trophies, and Asquith was one of
his best buys: 'Asquith is the one pupil of mine for whom I can
most confidently predict success in life . . . he is so direct'.[5]
Jowettism might be summed up as the philosophy of getting on;
as his pupils were scholars and gentlemen the worship of the
main chance was robbed of its grossness and materialism.

Asquith was President of the Union, and took a first in classics. Called to the bar in 1876, he became a QC in 1890, four years after he had entered politics. Between 1892 and 1895 he was Home Secretary under Gladstone and Rosebery, and Chancellor of the Exchequer under Campbell-Bannerman between 1905 and 1908. He and Lloyd George were a good team, though in 1916 Lloyd George unsaddled him, holding the premiership until 1922. Lloyd George was the power house, Asquith was the dynamo, and between them they upheld free trade, inaugurated national insurance and old age pensions, payment of MPs, and a Parliament Act that cut the power of the House of Lords.

Asquith usually escaped the torrent of abuse that was directed against Lloyd George and his sensational 'People's Budgets'. He went placidly along with Lloyd George's frenetic crusade against drink. The nation's liquor bill was £200 million, twice that of the United States, more than the National Budget. There were 160,000 convictions a year for drunkenness.

Rabble-rousing in the East End became a recognised sport. Fortunately for the parties in power, it was greeted with apathy

A nation that is suckled on alcohol is doomed . . . as long as Drink is allowed a free hand on the hearth the result will be that although you may convert your slums into garden cities, your garden cities will in a short time be reduced to slums. [6]

Lloyd George was given a free hand to rabble-rouse in Limehouse. 'Why should I put burdens on the people?' he asked. 'I am one of the children of the people.' And he proved it by trying to put the burdens on the rich, with increased death duties, duties on undeveloped land and minerals, a levy on unearned increment, and a supertax on incomes above £5,000. Not surprisingly the rich wished to throw Lloyd George to their hounds.

It might be supposed that a rapport would be made between the working classes and the rejuvenated Liberal Party, that with Lloyd George the existence of a Labour Party was unnecessary. But Lloyd George was not altogether trusted. He was Welsh for one thing, but more important was the fact that, although he claimed to be a man of the people, he was not. John Burns was; he scorned Lloyd George, and spoke sardonically of the housemaid's knee that the Welshman had acquired from a too frequent kowtowing to royalty.

David Lloyd George, born in 1863, was the son of a schoolmaster, and had started life as a solicitor. Nothing could be more middle-class than his background. Despite his enthusiasm for improving the lot of the poor, he was alien to them, nor did his crusade against drink help his image in the back streets of the East End. Insurance, old age pensions, these only scraped at the paintwork of poverty. In 1908 there was a higher level of unemployment among the wage-earning population than there had been in any year since 1886. Dividends were flowing into the rich man's coffers, but prices continued to rise proportionately to wage increases. Trade union membership rose; these were different unions to the defensive cringing unions of the nineteenth century. The members were harsh and aggressive, and contemptuous of those who sported the Labour label in parliament, and there was a growing militancy in the ranks.

Against this background Asquith was an irrelevancy, even though he

> had in his character every traditional virtue—dignity, honour, courage and a
> fine selflessness. In temperament he was equable and generous. He was a
> most competent head of a traditional Government and a brilliant leader of a
> traditional party.[7]

He was impercipient, his mind was not open to new ideas, and he had no overall scheme. His motto was 'wait and see'. General elections in 1910 had not altered the parliamentary picture very much, though middle-class people sighed with relief when it was found that Labour representation in parliament was slightly down. The Liberals seemed to be set for a long spell in office. Balfour stepped down as leader of the opposition and his place was taken by Bonar Law, another honourable man, upright, straight, uncomplicated, of whom it was said: 'The construction of his mind has no shadows, or ingle-nooks, or cosy corners'.[8] It was also said that he had a hot head and cold feet. It needed more than efficiency and a cool common sense to set a spark to the chill opposition benches. With his pessimism and Scots Presbyterian ancestry, Bonar Law reminded Lord Beaverbrook of a sombre raven among the glittering birds of paradise. Bonar Law, who eventually became prime minister in 1922, was one of the few politicians who saw things coldly. Lloyd George, he thought, was 'the most dangerous little man that ever lived'.

Lloyd George, who had never been abroad before, went to Carlsbad and Berlin, and laid down the law on foreign policy. Edward VII watched his antics with alarm. Clemenceau, wrote the king, had been amazed 'by the *crass ignorance* which L. George displayed concerning foreign politics'.[9] Winston Churchill was also causing problems. He was canvassing methods for reaching a naval understanding with Germany. On such matters the king considered that no one except the prime minister and the foreign secretary was qualified to speak, and resolved to consult Asquith about it. The king's secretary, Lord Knollys, said that Churchill and Lloyd George did not behave like gentlemen, were disloyal to their colleagues, and spent most of their time in unprincipled intrigue.

Fortunately Lloyd George had formed a friendship with King Edward's mistress, Mrs Keppel, and the king had a soft spot for Churchill, as he liked Mrs Churchill. There was also some excuse for the two offenders in that Asquith and Sir Edward Grey were only too pleased not to talk of foreign policy.

Grey was a good deal younger than most of his colleagues, but the energy associated with youth was never much in evidence. He was in his early forties when he was given the job of foreign secretary, and carried out his work in a conscientious manner, proud of being an amateur, an aristocrat in politics who played by the rules. When he took over in 1905 he promised that he would pursue the policy laid down by the previous administration under the conservative Balfour. This involved friendship with the United States, the alliance with Japan, and the Entente with France. 'He had no prejudices, class or otherwise, and always approached every problem of public or private life with the question "what is right?" and having decided on his answer he held unswervingly to his convictions'.[10] But this was hardly enough.

Grey handled small things well, but lack of imagination prevented him grasping the enormity of what would happen if things went wrong. His inflexibility meant that he was misunderstood, not least by the Germans, whom he appeased and conciliated, who referred to him as 'Liar Grey'. Many of his colleagues thought that he could have avoided the war by concession; others thought that he should have been bolder. In any event, he was perfectly set up as a scapegoat for both factions.

It was held that no man could be so wise as Grey looked. His prestige was bound up with his Roman profile, his aloof manner, and his economy of speech. His attempts to reach an accommodation with the Germans was looked upon as half-promises to betray France or Russia. The German statesmen took him to be a subtle conniving man, for they could not believe that anyone so scrupulously honest could be the spearhead of British diplomacy.

For a foreign secretary he was astonishingly naïve. He did not even trouble to read up foreign countries and did not go abroad, preferring to fish (he has a book on fly-fishing to his credit). The only language he understood was French, and that imperfectly. He did not believe that Britain was immune from attack or strife; he knew it. He was a Victorian of the old school, and any suspicions of Germany were lulled by the honest and straightforward attitude of the German ambassador in London, Prince Lichnowsky, who, as it happened, was not in the confidence of his own government.

Right up to the outbreak of war, there was no concerted foreign policy. Actions were taken on an *ad hoc* basis. Things would get better if they were left alone. But Europe sidled into war in 1914, and though Grey displayed an unusual energy in trying to avert it at the last minute, the combination of circumstances was too much for him. He was not a Palmerston, ready to make off-the-cuff decisions. Today he is known by one epigram: 'The lamps are going out all over Europe; we shall not see them lit again in our lifetime.' The date: 3 August 1914.

Notes to this chapter are on page 292.

CHAPTER TWO

LONDON—THE GREAT SPRAWL

DURING THE nineteenth century London had spread out alarmingly, and this expansion accelerated during the dozen years preceding the First World War. The rising young novelist Frank Swinnerton idly wondered if the growth would spread across the whole of the southern counties, leading to the ultimate disappearance of rural England. He saw no cure except the demolition of all the tall houses near the heart of London and the erection in their stead of enormous blocks of flats and dwellings 'built with some beauty'.

The paradox was that, although the 8-per-cent unemployment rate was reaching a height that would today shatter the nation, there was an increasing demand for male and female workers in factories, shops and offices. The amazing industrial development of the city's outskirts called for skilled and semi-skilled labour which could not be found in the stock of unemployed, compounded of the work-shy, of rural labourers unadapted to industrial life, and elderly men programmed for a different age. London industry wooed Birmingham, Coventry and the north, and the provincial engineers and artisans flocked into the city in their thousands.

Hotels and restaurants were springing up to cater for the

Edwardian London was rich in hotels and restaurants. It was the age of the Piccadilly Hotel and the Ritz

wealthy. It was the age of the Piccadilly Hotel and the Ritz, and the great West End emporiums, the most famous of which was perhaps Selfridge's. Gordon Selfridge had learned his trade in Chicago and had assimilated American promotional methods, spending £36,000 on advertising before the store was opened in 1909 with stock of more than £100,000 and a staff of 1,800. It was boasted that it was not a shop, but a social centre. Victorian shopping habits had been based on the small store, usually undercapitalised. The shopocracy, Maple, Heal, Selfridge, altered all that, pouring thousands into advertising and lavish window displays, made into fairylands by the wonders of the electric light. Although Paris was creaming away some of the custom, London was rich in dress shops, milliners, and all those pandering to conspicuous consumption.

Hustle, bustle and confusion characterised the life of central London. Motor buses, horse buses, motor cars, horse cabs, taxis, bicycles, and private carriages, all vied for road space, and the air was redolent with exhaust fumes and the smell of horses. The congestion was partly relieved by the underground railway. The switch to electricity made the tube train a viable proposition, and when the Bakerloo Line was opened in 1906 37,000 passengers used it on the first day, making nonsense of the *Railway Engineer's* statement that 'this tube railway may now be regarded as a beautiful failure'. It took only seven minutes from Piccadilly Circus to Baker Street, whereas an omnibus took twenty minutes and a horse cab a quarter of an hour. The tube train was phenomenally cheap—all fares were twopence, though this was later altered. The movement of passengers was facilitated by the introduction of the escalator, only possible with the invention of the electric motor. This was initially alarming, and at Earls Court a man with a wooden leg was employed to show how safe and easy it was to use.

There were no junctions between the underground railway and the overhead system until 1913, when the Bakerloo Line was connected with the Great Western Railway. The railway companies resented the new rival, realising that their own great age was departing; between 1900 and 1913 only 1,200 miles of track were laid, and the last major station in London,

There was great congestion in London, and accidents of this nature were bound to happen

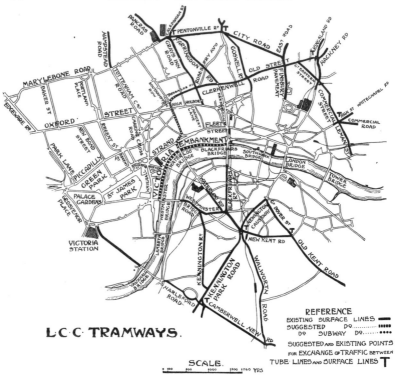

L·C·C· TRAMWAYS.

REFERENCE
EXISTING SURFACE LINES ▬
SUGGESTED   Dº ▪▪▪▪▪
Dº SUBWAY Dº ●●●●
SUGGESTED AND EXISTING POINTS
FOR EXCHANGE OF TRAFFIC BETWEEN
TUBE LINES AND SURFACE LINES **T**

SCALE.

The electric tram revolutionised London transport. This map of 1902 *depicts existing and projected routes*

Marylebone, built in 1899, had an air of obsolescence almost as soon as it was opened.

The build-up of suburbia might appear to have been the answer to the railway dream of fresh custom, but transport between the outskirts and the centres of London was catered for by electric tram. The electric tramcar speedily eliminated the steam tram, first run in London in 1873 along Vauxhall Bridge Road; the compressed air tram, an abortive 1883 venture along the Caledonian Road, and the short-lived gas tram of 1896. The tram ran on rails or by means of overhead wires (the trolley bus). In 1900 340 million tram passengers were carried in London, and in 1903 the 8½-mile route from Westminster Bridge to Tooting was opened. In the same year Hampton Court was incorporated into the tramway system; in 1904 it reached Uxbridge, followed in 1906–7 by Kingston and Wimbledon, Lewisham, Dulwich and Peckham; in 1909–10 by Hampstead, Highgate and Norwood, and 1911–12 by Parliament Hill Fields and Herne Hill. Eventually the railways regained the custom when the tramways and the trolley buses ceased to run, but although the tram lines were a hazard to cyclists and motorists, something was lost when these clanking monsters were withdrawn from the London streets. Impervious to fog and the elements, the trams kept running when the rest of London's road transport was at a standstill.

The tramway system was democratic, used by the occupiers of aesthetic Hampstead and the jerry-built terrace houses of Tooting and Peckham. Where the tramway reached, ribbon development followed, untrammelled by planning considerations. Lovers of London were aghast at what they considered the vandalism of the speculators, with acres of the old city being replaced by huge stores and commercial buildings. The

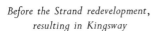

Before the Strand redevelopment, resulting in Kingsway

After the Strand redevelopment

most startling 'improvement' was carried out near the Strand, where the new thoroughfares of Kingsway and Aldwych, arguably two of the most uninteresting streets in London, were thrust through a maze of mean but picturesque streets and alleys. Holywell Street, the centre of the pornographic book trade, was one of the streets to disappear completely in this £4.5 million project. Quaint riverside London was also disfigured by a new stretch of embankment between the Houses of Parliament and Lambeth Bridge. Tunnels under the Thames at Rotherhithe and Woolwich proved an admirable answer to the bottlenecks of its bridges, and the contemporary byelaws· governing their operation have their own period charm: 'No person shall take into the tunnel any loaded fire-arm, gunpowder, dynamite, nitro-glycerine, gun-cotton, Nobel's explosive or other explosive . . . No person shall drive or conduct into the tunnel any cattle or any animal forming part of a menagerie, or any wild animal'.

Surprisingly, despite the tram, the trolley bus and the tube

train, horse-drawn vehicles remained strong contenders as public transport. In 1912 there were still 567 hansom cabs on the London streets, and 576 horse omnibuses. In the more exclusive residential quarters of London there was a concerted refusal to let motorised public transport run. Small traders continued to use horsepower, and livery stables throughout London saw little diminution in their trade. The breweries in particular were reluctant to change over to the motor, and their shire horses were for many years to remain features of the London scene.

The good living of the fashionable suburbs and the gaiety of the West End depended on the prosperity of the City. Extravagant life styles were based on trade, banking, shipping and overseas investment—investment that, had it been used to benefit British industry, might have increased home production and halted the decline in the living standards of the less well-to-do by holding the pound steady and keeping prices down. The various facets of London were more distinct than they had been in Victorian

Despite the motor-car and the tram, the trolley bus and the tube train, the horse cab remained very popular until the outbreak of World War I

times, when boundaries tended to blur, when rich residential areas rubbed against centuries-old rookeries. This can be seen in the gradual supremacy of Oxford Street over the Strand; in the Strand all types and classes met, and the shops of instrument-makers abutted upon chop-houses and public houses of dubious reputation.

It has become traditional to look upon Edwardian London as gay and uninhibited. John Buchan thought it 'dull and mercantile' after Oxford, Max Beerbohm declared that it was 'too awful—fogs—depression—inanimation', and D. H. Lawrence wrote: 'London seems to me like some hoary massive underword, a hoary ponderous inferno. The traffic flows through the rigid grey streets like the rivers of hell through the banks of rocky-ash'.

The 'banks of rocky-ash' were the buildings that were being erected, which, like the age, were flatulent and intended to impress. The Ritz hotel, built in 1904, with a steel frame covered with Portland stone, emulated a French château; the Royal Automobile Club in Pall Mall (1909) seemed to reflect ennui rather than the dash and abandon that characterised contemporary

Houses for the rich were built regardless of expense, (left) 12 Hill Street, Berkeley Square, with its monstrous facade

(right) a more sedate house in Chelsea

motoring; the redesigned front of the Piccadilly Hotel was an insult to nearby Burlington House, and a new low was reached in the cavernous and gloomy design of London County Hall (1908).

The public buildings of the period were products of lazy thinking; the styles used were consciously 'English Renaissance' (the London County Hall), 'Classical', or what Osbert Lancaster termed 'Pont Street Dutch', favoured also for dwellings of the *nouveaux riches*. As the editor of *The Builder* wrote at the time: 'Many of the new residential streets in the west end of London present a really picturesque *ensemble*. . . .' Houses in Pont Street Dutch in Buckingham Gate, and Georgian Revival (with extra sculpture flung at the façade) in Margaret Street, strove for status, along with Harrods, a terra cotta monstrosity with dome of 1901, and Selfridge's. At the same time, the Edwardians were doing their best to destroy the Nash curve of Regent Street, a continual act of vandalism dating from 1910.

Perhaps the common denominator of Edwardian public building was a vaunting of tastelessness; whereas life was trivial and ephemeral, architecture was joyless and sombre, appropriate perhaps for the Old Bailey of 1902 but hardly for the new music halls, the architects of which were as devoted to red brick and terra cotta as the speculative builders of suburban terrace houses. There were few attempts to make use of the techniques or motifs of *art nouveau*, and when architects did try their hand they were a good deal more timid than their contemporaries on the continent. The Horniman Museum in Forest Hill was one of the architectural successes in the *art nouveau* style.

In ecclesiastical and commemorative architecture the Edwardians were at their most aimless and lazy, and, although an eye-stopper, the Central Hall, Westminster, has few religious connotations. The Victorians managed to do something new in their revival of Gothic styles, but Edwardian Gothic plumbs the depths of insipidity. Not surprisingly the death of Victoria called for a quantity of statues, the most grandiose of which is the one set in front of Buckingham Palace, and now rightly treated as nothing more than a traffic island.

The trouble with Edwardian architects was that they tried to be artistic. Their heads were full of unassimilated styles. They were much better when they got off their dignity or were faced with eccentric projects. They were obliged to be monumental in carving out Kingsway or Millbank, but when it came to designing cinemas with names such as the Olympia, the Bijou, the Jewel or the Picturedrome, then they were able to use their talents in an uninhibited way. John Belcher was a typical architect of the period, responsible both for the deadly dull Holy Trinity church in Kingsway (1909) and the exotic fantasies built to house the Franco-British Exhibition of 1908—the White City in Shepherd's Bush, a virtuoso performance only fragments of which survive; this vast complex of buildings was an early example of built-in obsolescence, being constructed of fibrous plaster. In the illustrated review of the exhibition it was stated that 'every building is white without shade, and under the ardent sun it has looked like some brilliant Oriental fantasy—a dream of a virgin

The movement of the Victorian rich from the immediate environs of the City accelerated with the Edwardians. This photograph shows horse-drawn omnibuses, soon to be replaced by trams and motor buses

city bathed in light'. It is a pity that the enthusiasm that permeated the concept and construction of the White City did not infiltrate into the drab world of public buildings. Great chunks of Edwardiana still remain in central London, and no doubt will be with us for many years to come, for they are functional and well-constructed, and with their steel frames and massive foundations they are not so vulnerable to the developers' bulldozers as their Victorian predecessors.

There were parts of London that the Edwardian improvers left untouched. The exodus of the Victorian rich from the immediate environs of the City had meant that the Georgian houses left vacant were taken over by the poor, turned into lodging houses, filleted for apartments and flats (a word, surprisingly, dating from 1824), and filled to bursting point. Nineteenth-century philanthropists, such as Angela Burdett-Coutts and George Peabody, had done something to relieve the congestion of these slums by financing model working-men's dwellings, but they were only scratching at the surface. Nothing was so out of fashion in the early years of the twentieth century as disinterested philanthropy, and the anticipated rent from such dwellings did not warrant their erection. The squalid seedy areas of London were left much as they were, and although there was a building boom between 1901 and 1910 the products were concentrated in the newly accessible suburbs, fashionable districts such as Chelsea and Kensington, and the business and trade areas.

But at least old London was alive. 'The West, like all things of fashion, is but a corpse electrified'.[1] Kings and queens came and went and no one in the East End bothered, and the 'unfortunate classes' fought out their lives in filth and decay without realising that things had changed, that they were now living in the age of extravagance and ostentation. In Limehouse the Chinese were still in their ghettos, and not all the opium dens had been replaced by fish and chip shops. Few London County Council inspectors visited the Asiatics' Home, where there were stone beds, caged cubicles, and no bathrooms.

The unimproved parts of London were still villages, each

The unimproved parts of London were still villages, with their own atmosphere. This snapshot of Whitechapel was taken early in the reign

with its own character and inhabitants. The Jews were scattered over London in fiercely antipathetic cliques; the French Jews were in Soho, the German Jews in Great Charlotte Street, the Italian Jews in Clerkenwell, while those in Whitechapel were Russian emigrés or were long established. It was customary for the Whitechapel Jews to move to Highbury, Maida Vale and, especially, Golders Green, when they had made their money. The Irish settled around Southwark and Bermondsey, areas with the highest unemployment. Journalists considered that the two worst streets in London were Dorset Street and Hoxton Street, though others chose Duval Street, Spitalfields, full of common lodging houses and which held an unenviable record for the number of suicides occurring there.

The most self-contained of the villages was Soho, with its restaurants catering for suburban pleasure-seekers; with the exception of Maxim's, most of the snob restaurants were outside the area. Soho posed as the Bohemian quarter of London, and was dominated by the French. There were stories of Parisians who had left their native city, had come to Soho, and had never afterwards left that square mile, whose world ended at Piccadilly Circus. Shadwell, today an indeterminate district edging on the Thames, was populated by Danes, Norwegians, and Swedes, as well as Mr Jamrach, London's leading dealer in wild animals who had his menagerie there. Shadwell contained what had been the most notorious street of early Victorian London, the Ratcliffe Highway, though the name had been changed. The speciality of Shadwell was providing girl prostitutes for the Scandinavian seamen, a trade that had been publicised in the nineteenth century but which the Edwardians were keen to keep covered up.

Street musicians were very much a feature of Edwardian London. A large number of these were Italians centred in Clerkenwell, who hired out their barrel-pianos from mini-tycoons. The Italians lived mainly in the huge blocks of Victorian tenements that still stud the district, and vendettas were commonplace. Clerkenwell had a faded air of once being of importance, an air that was totally lacking in Hoxton, a place of fish and chip shops, cast-off clothing stalls, and beer-houses. Hoxton contained one of the last of the old-time music-halls, the Britannia, a world apart from the vast new music-halls raised by syndicates. Hoxton was a no-man's-land to the Edwardian spirit, a place beyond reformation that one would sooner forget. The Edwardians did not systematically try to improve such areas as Hoxton or Stepney as their fathers and grandfathers had done, and the projected new city of Eastminster was an idle pipe dream. They looked with indifference on the spectre of the demon drink, the providers of which were everywhere in evidence (London had more than 30 per cent more pubs then than today). Willing to lavish huge sums of money on prestige projects such as Kingsway and Aldwych, they stemmed any financial aid to the slums; to do the Edwardians justice, no one else bothered for forty years.

Notes to this chapter are on page 292.

CHAPTER THREE

EDWARDIAN LIFE

Society in Jeopardy

MANY MEMBERS of the landed gentry cordially disliked King Edward, whom they found as uncongenial as his mother. His concept of what constituted society was not theirs. The king's friend and confidant, Lord Esher, asked:

> . . . what is called 'society'? Too much attention is paid to the word, which is really an anachronism now, and rather common! In fact, there is no such thing. Society is dead and died with d'Orsay and Lady Blessington. There are people 'who give dinners' and people 'who give balls.' That is all. It is open to you to choose whether you will go or not, as you please. This was not the case when society existed. Then, you could no more refuse than you could now refuse to dine with your Colonel. Either you were 'in society'—and in that case you kept its rules, quite simply—or, you were not in society, in which case (if you were anybody out of the ruck) you were generally considered to be some sort of swindler; or to have disgraced yourself.[1]

Nevertheless many people disagreed with Lord Esher. The social round continued, with tennis and garden parties, days on the river, presentation at court, the Eton and Harrow match at Lord's, and all the extravagances of the London Season. The rules of the game were frequently involved and intricate, and some were so obscure that they perplexed even the upper

The subtleties of society etiquette could precipitate disaster. A 1908 cartoon of a party to which no one came

echelons of society. At one dinner Arthur Conan Doyle took in Lady Curzon, simply because he was nearest the door. He had no presentiments of anything out of the way, until she said to him: 'Do you know that you have established a precedent and solved one of the more difficult and debatable matters of etiquette that has ever caused ill-feeling in British Society?'

Why was this? Lady Curzon was the wife of the Viceroy of India. She went on: 'There has never been so vexed a question as to whether a Vice-reine when she is away from the country where she represents royalty shall take precedence over a Duchess. There was a Duchess in the room, but you by your decided action have settled the matter for ever'.[2]

Medieval sophistry as to how many angels can dance on a pin-head was nothing to the subtleties of society etiquette.

At one great country house a footman kept a meticulous record of all the bad English and 'ignorance' he heard while waiting at table, and related the choicer items, with names and dates, to the servants of later visitors. Weekend visits and dinner parties could be, observed H. G. Wells, 'as unbracing mentally and as pleasant as going to a flower show and seeing what space and care can do with favourite strains of some familiar species',[3] but they could also be extremely daunting especially when members of the old order were intent on proving to newcomers that they could snub and patronise as expertly as in the old days.

Licensed eccentrics were still at large in the great country houses of the aristocracy. When one of them slid with abandon down the whole length of the banisters, Sir George Sitwell reproved his son Osbert with the words, 'Don't laugh! These Great Men have their Little Idiosyncrasies'. Sir George himself was not free from eccentricity—'if he *must* meet the living, to him as insubstantial as were the dead to others, he preferred them to be in a trance-like condition of subservience and astonishment'.[4]

But he did not compare in oddity with the Scotsman George Thomas, who carried with him a strap to chastise the children of any friends or relations who happened to be near at hand, and who fined his domestics—and the cat Sambo—if they displeased him. When he died he was buried in a wicker coffin, as this, he considered, was more convenient for the resurrection.

Arrogance and irritability marked many of the old gentry in both town or country. It was as if they were aware that they were a dying breed. Arnold Bennett commented on this in his diaries: 'In Bond Street this morning the main thing to be seen was the well-groomed, physically fit, male animal: a sort of physical arrogance with it'.[5] In the women there was a note of petulance when confronted with the changed conditions. 'The lavish expenditure and the feverish pursuit of pleasure that constitute Society do not appeal to me any more than the restaurant life, which did not exist in my day . . . Nowadays money shouts, and birth and breeding whisper!'[6] So declared the Countess of Cardigan and Lancastre. Lady Dorothy Nevill was at one with her:

> Society to-day and Society as I formerly knew it are two entirely different things; indeed, it may be questioned whether Society, as the word used to be understood, now exists at all . . . Society as it used to be—a somewhat exclusive body of people, all of them distinguished either for their rank, their intellect, or their wit—is no more.[7]

Lady Dorothy commented acidly that in the old days the desire of the *nouveaux riches* was to get into society; now they bitterly complained that they could not keep out of it. All was changed. Society was on the make. Lady Dorothy thought that money was the root of the trouble. In the old days £10,000 a year was considered a decent income; now the millionaires who were buying themselves into the favoured circles would spend as much on a picture. Not that £10,000 a year was to be despised; it was still 'a snug fortune, sufficient to have a little shooting, some hunting, a modest house in the country, and a small *pied-à-terre* in town'.

The keynote of Edwardian high life was enjoyment, the pleasures of the flesh rather than those of the mind. There was a great emphasis on food. Breakfast went on until half past ten, a solid luncheon was followed a few hours later by a substantial

There was a great emphasis on food, well illustrated by this early cartoon by H. M. Bateman, the poet of social embarrassment

tea, and then there was dinner which, even without guests, seldom consisted of fewer than twelve courses.

Notwithstanding the regular meals, one of which would have provided sufficient sustenance for a working family for a week, well-off Edwardians were great nibblers, and in some households dinner was capped by massive suppers (Edward VII thought that for supper nothing could beat oysters). On the piano in the drawing-room there would be a bowl full of crystallised violets, and for any activity calling for extra energy there were snacks at a minute's notice. King Edward favoured a lobster salad or cold chicken to fill in the hours between breakfast and lunch.

Elizabeth Robins-Pennell wrote a weekly column on cookery in the *Pall Mall Gazette*; she was on the side of the gourmet and not the glutton. 'Dish follows dish, conceit is piled upon conceit; and with what result? Before dinner is half over, palates are jaded, "fine shades" can no more be appreciated, every new course awakens fear of the morrow's indigestion'. It was not surprising that at regular intervals the indulgent paid visits to Marienbad or Ems to 'take the waters' and try and restore some order to their bloated and ill-used stomachs. At these fashionable spa towns they underwent the rigours demanded—mile walks from pump to hotel, mud baths, bed at ten—knowing that soon they would be back at their troughs. There were compensations; the spa towns were ideal places for picking up women and offered uninhibited entertainment. The fact of Maud Allan dancing before King Edward VII wearing only two oyster shells and a five franc piece was not news-worthy; it only became so when it was decided to bring her to London for her performance.

Newsreels of the period give the impression that the Edwardians were constantly jigging about, moving in sharp strutting actions. The difficulty in matching the film speeds of the early 1900s with modern projection speeds has made the denizens of the period look a good deal smarter on their feet than was the case. Too often, the Edwardian rich were slow in thought and action, and their intellectual demands were too few to admit of ennui. They encouraged those about them who provided easy entertainment.

Frank Lawley of the *Daily Telegraph* was welcomed in royal circles, because there was cockfighting at his house in Mayfair; the Marquis de Soveral, Portugese Minister in London, blue-chinned and known as the 'blue monkey', because he was a dashing roué; the marine artist Eduardo de Martino, because he was amusing and agreeably sycophantic. There were other hangers-on, such as Sir Herbert Maxwell, who had a habit of entering rooms 'like an elastic ball gently propelled by some invisible hand'; and the gossip Herbert Gardner, 'pleasant of face, agreeable of manner, with a pretty turn for small talk, and good connections'.

The relative inactivity of the men contrasted sharply with the energy of their wives, who flew from boredom with dash and vigour. A new variety of women emerged, termed enigmatically 'the married bachelors of the fair sex', who frequented clubs for women only, such as the Ladies' Army & Navy in Cork

The hall of the Lyceum Club, sacred to women

Street, the Empress in Dover Street, and the Empire, presided over by Lady Jersey. Here they indulged their passion for the in-game of the period, auction bridge. For many leisured women this game became an obsession; by three o'clock they would be waiting impatiently to begin; they would play throughout tea, eat a light club dinner talking bridge all the time, and were back in the card room immediately they had choked down their food, eventually leaving in the early hours of the morning.

The days of the rich women, whether or not they were in society, were spent in passing time, with a languid obeisance to 'duty' in the form of running, or rather being distantly associated with, whist drives and jumble sales. Afternoon calls would take up some of the hours, and when the time was hanging rather more tediously than ever they would pop in at the Law Courts and savour the latest juicy divorce case.

A good many hours were spent in dressing and undressing; there were tweeds for being sporty in, a frock for luncheon, diaphanous tea-gowns, long dresses with trains for dinner. Officially cosmetics were 'fast' though many women used them. As a different dinner gown was considered essential for each evening, a weekend in the country could not be undertaken without a mountain of clothes. The new sport of motoring obliged women to supplement their wardrobes with heavy sealskin coats, goggles, veils, and appropriate hats.

A great deal of time was spent in having their hair done. Extravagant coiffures were built up on pads and with the aid of wire frames. Consequently tall women looked grotesque and short women top-heavy. The ideal woman was shaped like a swan, but crowned with their outrageous hats many ladies gave the impression of being dolls that had been put together in an odd sort of way.

The energy which society women had in abundance, an often desperate attempt to escape from a meaningless round, could result in indiscretions, and adultery was indulged in to enliven an otherwise insignificant existence. Victorian country house gatherings were notorious for the way in which bedrooms were allotted for the convenience of the various occupants, and this trend gathered momentum during the Edwardian years. Adultery in society was made easier by the motor-car revolution, and the tendency of the rich to escape to the riverside or the seaside at weekends, where opportunities for misbehaviour, with or without the tacit consent of married partners, were legion.

There was a dichotomy in Edwardian high society that had been lacking in the Victorian. King Edward VII had strengthened the ceremonial of the court, and the etiquette and decorum in the externals of society had been kept up, and even augmented. Yet the fabric was cracking. The fashion scene offers an indication

The motor-car revolution made it possible for the well-off to escape to the seaside, where opportunities for misbehaviour were legion. Southend, as shown in this photograph, was not yet downgraded

of this. Although nudity was not accepted, and the décolletage in evening dress was less sensational than in Victorian times, the use of lace and chiffon reached new heights of suggestion. There was a completely new attitude towards underclothing. Victorian underclothing had been functional, and even the most expensive prostitutes wore flannel drawers. Edwardian underwear was renamed lingerie, and its basic function was to attract and tantalise the men. Garments that previously no one had seen except the wearer and the dressmaker were now openly labelled 'seductive', drawers were replaced by knickers, the shift had passed through the late Victorian phase of chemise to a slip, and petticoats became frillies. It was the age of frou-frou from the knees down. The most sensational new undergarment was the brassière introduced in 1912. In late Victorian times the cult of the breast had been sly and seemingly accidental; the breasts had been pushed up by tight-lacing. The brassière concentrated attention on the breasts, and combined with the 'temptatious teagown which absolutely defines the figure in a manner which is insinuating' unquestionably set men's pulses racing. The 'pneumonia blouse' was another innovation, a transparent promise of muslin and lace. Everything was in pastel colours, later ridiculed as 'nuances of nymph's thigh, lilacs, swooning mauves, tender blue hortensias . . . all that was soft, washed-out, and insipid'.[9]

The rich could spend a good deal of money in conspicuous display; a petticoat could cost as much as £50, 'evening confections' were priced at £200. The rich brocades, velvets and satins of the Victorian dresses did not cost so much as the lace fripperies of the Edwardian age, in which detail was picked out with a precision and a delicacy that reflect great credit on the dressmaker's art.

Edwardian beauties there were in abundance, and their appeal was brought out by the elaborate dresses of the period, so pointedly that, as Cecil Beaton wrote, 'there was an intriguing perversity about such excessive prettiness'. The demarcation

The house of Worth, favoured by the rich

A rational dress had arisen for sporty women. A surrealist drawing of Princess Victoria with her Beeston-Humber bicycle

line between the professional beauty and the society lady was nearly lost. In Victorian times, wrote one cynical observer, 'the natural goal of professional beautydom proved to be the stage; that of the she-gambler and turfite of the twentieth century is quite as inevitably the divorce court'.[10]

The women treated the men with an affectation of indifference notwithstanding the incessant teasing implied by the new attitude towards underwear. There was a conflict between the introduction of see-through blouses and dresses, and frilly knickers, and the continuation of the long floor-sweeping skirt and high neck-line. The high neck-line was influenced by the decision of Queen Alexandra to always wear such. The reason for this has been maliciously assigned to the debatable fact that the queen contracted syphilis from her husband, and needed a high neck-line to cover scars (vide the unexpurgated version of T. E. Lawrence's

The Mint). Others maintained that these were scars resulting from small-pox.

Looking at the wide picture, it might be postulated that the sex appeal of high Edwardian dress arose instinctively from the demands of mother Nature that the nation must breed, to counteract the falling birth rate due to the increasing use of birth control methods, though perhaps it would be too extravagant to say that women were instinctively preparing their organisms for replacing the casualties of World War I.

There was a clash also between femininity and function. A rational dress had arisen for sporty women, and though still cumbersome by present-day standards the costumes worn for fashionable sports such as tennis and cycling were reasonably suitable. Yet these costumes, outlandish as they were to the reactionaries, were derived from the ordinary clothes of the period, and this cannot be said of the sudden switch in fashion design that followed the introduction of the Russian ballet to western Europe. Many women were more interested in the décor and costumes of the Russian ballet than in the music. *Modernisme oriental* threw a few buckets of bright paint over the pastel shades that had dominated fashion, and the French houses siphoned off the custom of Jay's and Liberty's. One of the leading couturiers was Poiret, who hobbled the acquiescent Englishwomen in harem skirts, hung them with fox furs, draped them in pearls, and enveloped them in wired tunics and jewel-laden capes. 'It was strange', wrote a reporter from *The Queen* in 1910, 'to find oneself wafted into a world of beauty, ease and luxury, and for a moment or two the Puritan in me rebelled'. But not for long. Oriental and Russian barbarism was more amusing than pastel seductivity.

The harem skirt was laughed into obscurity but the hobble skirt caught on to an amazing extent, and the frilly underpetticoats were abolished. 'The narrow skirt of 1910 was an astonishing change from the flowing skirts which had prevailed for the last fifteen years', wrote James Laver in *Taste and Fashion* (1937). 'No longer was it necessary or even possible to lift the skirts when crossing the streets'. The hobble skirt, superbly

With the prevailing fashions, it was often difficult for a woman to lift her skirts when crossing a street. In this illustration to a magazine serial, it even seems painful to walk

named, was as anachronistic in the Edwardian environment as the crinoline had been in 1850 or the bustle in its day. It was anti-sexual, inconvenient, and meaningless; it was said that a staircase called for gymnastics and that it was impossible to stoop without disaster.

It may be that the crying out for novelty, for something different, resulted in these curious phenomena; it may be that society, ashamed by its voluptuousness, was wearing apparel as near as could be got to the hair-shirt, that the hobble skirt was symbolic. Its one sexual charm was that it permitted only little tripping steps. The hobble skirt was harsh and realistic, and to some fashion experts the dissolving fairyland of frillies and chiffon was being replaced by a more masculine spirit in response to the shadow of approaching war. Apprehension was beginning to have its effect on clothes, and when towards the end of 1913 the neck-line began to drop as if to start another age of breast-orientation it was treated as scandalous. Society might be immoral but it was never permissive.

Suburban Life

The Edwardian age was the period of the garden city, the small country house, and artistic suburbia. It saw the coming of Port Sunlight (1905), Bournville (1908), Hampstead Garden Suburb (1907), and Letchworth Garden City (1903), and anticipated Welwyn Garden City (1920) of which Dailymail model village, sponsored by the newspaper of that name, was part.

The nostalgia for the past, the flight from the anxiety that pervaded the era, found expression in the re-creation of village life. As John Betjeman put it, 'Each garden village had houses graded carefully to income—but no rich man's palace nor poor man's hovel—a leafy, happy medium instead, with communal grass and clubs and institutes and a choice of churches'.[1] The gaunt reality of Victorian town life was thrust into the background, and the chilling symmetry of council housing estates was still in the future. The garden cities and newly discovered suburbs brought into action by improved urban transport—the

The suburbanites rejected the clutter of the Victorians, but many replaced this

By this!

tram, the trolley-bus, the motor omnibus, and the tube train—reflected the new life.

Snug, seemly, practical, the houses in the commuter belt were machines not exactly for living in but for being cosy in. The clutter and profusion of objects that marked the Victorian home were rejected out of hand. A few acute observers recognised the implications of suburbia. In his book *Democracy and Reaction* (1904), L. T. Hobhouse wrote: 'Suburban villadom is a political and social portent the meaning of which has never yet been analysed . . . Politically it is a greater burden than the slums'.

Suburban cultural life was replete with operatic and dramatic societies, madrigal singing, and folk song; suburban sports were golf, cricket and tennis. The suburbanites adored the gramophone and phonograph, and played intellectual games such as Styles, Epigrams, Consequences. The more class-conscious changed for dinner, and the more emancipated invented a vocabulary in which teagowns were 'teagies', nightdresses were 'nighties', in which 'deevie' meant divine and 'diskie' disgusting. There was a fad for Italianate endings (partnerina, dansares, dinnare) and

The rich suggestive life of Wimbledon

10.30 whisky replaced the end-of-day cup of tea. The houses were too small to boast a billiards room, and apart from card games the favourite indoor sport was ping-pong, yet to be christened table-tennis. C. F. G. Masterman wrote about suburbia's 'vicarious sports and trivial amusements', but in the cause of middle-class unity the suburbanites managed to encompass a great many participant sports and pastimes.

Those who lived in the suburbs did not go much for religion. The Church of England was still confusedly grappling with the problems of modern life, and the only sector where it was holding its own was in High Church, now renamed Anglo-Catholicism. A fillip to fundamentalism was given by the arrival in Britain in 1905 of two American revivalists, Torrey and Alexander, who tried to recapture the successes of Sankey and Moody of a previous generation. Would Edwardians, they asked, like to have Christ find them in a ballroom, or at the card table, or playing ping-pong on a Sunday? Initially their audience answered with a cowed 'No', but the impact of the American revivalists rapidly wore off.

Mr Kensit, a draper's assistant, also came forward to tackle godlessness. Torrey and Alexander were at least positive; Kensit and his followers were negative, and they saw it as their principal role to create scenes in Anglo-Catholic churches, by brawling and shouting. Kensit's vogue was short-lived, for while carrying out his duties in Liverpool a fellow-Christian threw a chisel at him and killed him.

The hold of Anglo-Catholicism was disturbing to the establishment, and in 1906 a Royal Commission on Ecclesiastical Discipline produced a bulky report predictably casting scorn on Popish ritual and threatening retaliation. The suburbs were not interested. Although they still married in churches rather than registry offices, many suburbanites indignantly rejected anything that interfered with their week-ends, those week-ends consecrated to what G. K. Chesterton termed 'the rich suggestive life of Wimbledon'.

The upsurge of Edwardian suburbia has probably never received the attention it deserves. For the first time the middle classes were branching out without taking a lead from the upper classes.

The suburban husbands were basically white-collar workers. Between 1900 and 1911 the demand for office workers had

The middle-class picture of the working man, given to drink, sport, and lewd pursuits

gone up 50 per cent in the public services, 33 per cent in commerce, and 17 per cent in the professions. Although they did not earn much more than the manual workers, their attitude towards those whom they considered their inferiors was harsh and patronising, and although they did not have much more money to spend, they knew how to spread it around, and the necessity of a fairly frugal and austere life style was made a virtue. They indulged in respectable but inexpensive pursuits, and as their new homes were labour-saving (with dining-nooks instead of dining-rooms) there was no need to employ domestic help. By and large they were fairly gregarious, and in the summer they went on cycling holidays—very few of them owned cars.

Their common factor was a fear of the working classes and democracy, which they considered synonymous. Their collective image of the working man was, considered C. F. G. Masterman, 'a loud voiced, independent, arrogant figure, with a thirst for drink and imperfect standards of decency, and a determination to be supported at some one else's expense'. When Lloyd George produced his 'People's Budgets' he became the most hated man in the canon, the person who would take their money from them and turf them out of Eden.

The image of the working man was mixed with that of the 'man in the street' :

> He knows already all about any appeal you can make to the better side of him, and he has long ago chopped it up in his mill of small talk and catch phrases and reduced it to such a meaningless patter that the words which must be used have acquired trivial and lowering associations. [2]

The white-collared classes moved self-consciously away from any identification with the man in the street and, aided and abetted by their wives, lived lives of overpowering gentility. The living-room was renamed the hall, and had much of the Spartan qualities associated with such a room, and the bedroom was renamed the bower or the boudoir. The houses were furnished in two styles: reproduction, especially sham-Georgian and Regency, and debased 'Arts & Crafts', deriving from William Morris, with art nouveau graftings. Sometimes the art nouveau element predominated, sometimes the cottagey and hand-made.

An art nouveau interior by the firm of Goodyers

Art nouveau was the perfect background for the artistic and genteel life of suburbia, and, like the reproduction styles of furnishing and décor, suburbia got it second-hand, for by the time it reached England from France the momentum had run out of the movement. *Art nouveau* in Britain centred around the store of Liberty's in Regent Street, and so prominent was this firm that the style itself was called the Liberty style even in the country that instigated *art nouveau*.

The style itself was stigmatised by a cynic as the concentrated essence of a wriggle; an art critic spoke of it as abounding in squirming lines and blobs, and said the source of *art nouveau* inspiration had been found in entrails. There were no hard and fast rules, and supporters found in the movement beauty of line, grace of form, and freedom. T. G. Jackson, an artist, thought that the main motive of the designs was a conscious striving after novelty and eccentricity, that the forms of the objects obscured and ignored the lines of the construction, that the natural quality of material was not respected, and that throughout there was a fidgety vulgar obtrusiveness. 'Perhaps I am old fashioned', began Alfred Gilbert, a sculptor best known for Eros in Piccadilly Circus, but *art nouveau* struck him as decadent and nonsensical. The architect C. F. A. Voysey thought that the movement demonstrated atheism, conceit and imitation.

None of these opinions prevented the march of *art nouveau* to commercial acceptance, and the twisting swirling furniture on which was grafted motifs of lilies and other appropriately decadent plants, the 'art pewter' and copper banged out in a variety of shapes and sizes, all fitted in remarkably well with the products of the arts and crafts movement, the angular furniture and the general air of rusticity. The smaller *art nouveau* objects fitted in equally well with perhaps the only piece of furniture invented by the Edwardians, the cosy corner, which combined settee, screen, bookcase and cabinet, all in one. 'Much advertised in ladies' fashion papers, and recommended in journals which profess to give advice and instruction to the enquiring housewife, it is a type of unstable and ill-balanced structure which, so far from conveying any sense of cosiness or comfort, to my mind always seems to be threatening to topple about one's ears'.[3]

The products of the movement also merged into the new houses of the period, in which the round window was a particular feature and there were innumerable artistic nooks and crannies. The trend of décor also facilitated the introduction of what some saw as monstrosities but others as reflections of a new spirit; there was an emphasis in décor on white paint and waxed unpainted or unvarnished wood with designs in low relief, and on fabrics that were self-coloured or gave the impression of being hand-woven.

Many observers saw the fad as the pursuit of novelty for its own sake, and the more acute as a commercial gimmick. George Haité, President of the Society of Designers, drew attention to 'the insatiable desire of our manufacturers for novelty at any cost, and the facilities offered through the illustrated journals for flattering personal vanity by the reproduction and publication of immature efforts'.[4] This last point is important. For the first time modern advertising methods were being used to promote a style; this had not been done for the arts and crafts style, and the aesthetic movement of the last quarter of the nineteenth century, with its emphasis on flimsy pseudo-Oriental furniture and blue-and-white china, had come too soon for the full exploitation treatment. The 1880s had seen a revolution in illustrated magazine techniques, and photographs of the latest consumer goods were widely circulated via the illustrated press and the quality women's papers.

AIDS TO ART.

Reuben : "WHAT YER DOIN' WID DAT OLD DRAIN-PIPE ?"
Phil : "SELLIN' IT TO DE DECORATIVE ART SOCIETY FER UMBRELLA STANDS !"

It was easy to be original if beauty was no object, declared Gilbert Scott in 1903. *This* 1907 *cartoon shows this admirably*

The suburban market, though not specifically rich, was a wide one. But other people were buying *art nouveau*, especially those who were made wealthy by the upsurge in profits and dividends that marked the Edwardian period. Although the poor were getting marginally poorer by the lowering of real wages, the middling rich had never had it so good and could afford to spend a great deal of money in quality *art nouveau*, the kind promoted by Liberty's, Goodyer's, and Story & Co, who set out rooms in the style for the edification of their customers. The suburbanites had too often to be content with the trade versions, which were either ludicrous or timid. The purists resented the bedroom suite, a fairly new term, in which a motif, quite acceptable initially, became overbearing and monotonous when repeated *ad nauseam*.

It was fortunate that metal-work was ideally suited to *art nouveau* decoration, and with items that had not existed before in the private home—such as electric light fittings—the designers could really indulge themselves with hammered brass and hand-wrought copper. The results were novel and interesting, though, as Gilbert Scott, the architect, remarked in 1903, it was very easy to be original if beauty is no object.

The establishment was set against *art nouveau*, which lent itself to ready wit. Gerald Moira, the artist, thought there should be a law against people perpetrating 'such abortions as the kidney and the squirm for a wall decoration, or the dining table with legs that start in the corners of the room, and terminates some eighteen inches above the board in a thing that is half a muffin and something of a quoit. The embroidery, the design of which consists of telegraph wires, at one end an emaciated head, and ending in caterpillar wriggles at the other, the motive of such a design being "A Lost Soul's Thoughts Finding No Resting Place" or something of that sort'.[5] Professor Moira, indeed, put his finger on the crux of *art nouveau*. It was inclined to be intellectually pretentious. Its devotees liked mottoes on beams and over fireplaces, preferably high sounding, not altogether legible, and perhaps in a foreign language; they were the logical replacement of the religious mottoes that had for so long hung above bed-heads;

'God is Love' was no longer the message that the suburbanites wanted to see.

The astonishing acceptance of *art nouveau* by perhaps the only new social class to arise for more than half a century is understandable only if one sees it as the aftermath of the aestheticism that flourished around 1880, when women clad in the long shapeless dresses of the movement asked their escorts, 'Are you *intense?*' The trial of Oscar Wilde gave the thumbs down to the movement, but the mood of the fin-de-siècle infiltrated into respectable life in suburbia. If a sociologist had asked that same question again, the answer in a thousand twee, mullion-windowed homes would have been 'yes'.

The main difference between the aestheticism of 1880 and the suburbanism of 1905 was that aestheticism was certain of itself, and the suburbanites were not. The sinuous lines of their furniture, the freakish metalwork, objects 'in which solid forms disappeared in amazing twists and contortions, ornaments of glass dripped cloudy tears, ashtrays looked like spent dum-dum bullets',[6] all these were directly relevant to their possessors. The one attribute of *art nouveau* that by chance no one mentioned was spinelessness. This was a strong characteristic of suburbia, no matter how the men tried to demonstrate their masculinity on the golf course or at the tennis net, or the women their forward-looking tastes in buying from Liberty's. They had souls to let, and no amount of ping-pong or intellectual word games detracted from this. The triviality could be interpreted by some as an amiable philosophy; as is seen in the 'little man' heroes of H. G. Wells' Edwardian novels, such as *Kipps* or *The History of Mr Polly*. The thwarted desire for romance and the escape from being the insignificant creature who was something, but not much, in the City, these elements play a vital part in the emergence of the Edwardian suburbanite.

Crouched up in their cosy corners, striving to forget the anxieties that pressed down upon them—the falling value of money, the unpleasantness of the working classes, talk of wars and the threats of wars—the occupants of neat houses in Surbiton or Harrow-on-the-Hill read, if they were women, Ella Wheeler

"I SUPPOSE, LIKE ME, YOU HAVE YOUR TROUBLES?"
"OH, YES, MUM; JUST LIKE YOU."

(*Drawn by* JOHN HASSALL.)

A variety of household aids had reduced the need for servants, while those servants who were available belonged to a numerically decreasing species

Wilcox's *Poems of Passion* ('favourites with all cultured persons') or Florence Barclay's *The Rosary*, the best-seller of 1909. The men read A. E. W. Mason's *The Four Feathers* (best-seller of 1902) or Edgar Wallace's *The Four Just Men* (1905). One of the most prolific writers of the period was Nat Gould: by 1909 his healthy extravert novels had sold more than six million copies.

The inner uncertainty was reflected by an uneasiness about one's role. The new woman, emancipated and hard-drinking, pedalled from point A to point B like a mad thing, occasionally flirting with the suffragette movement, enlivening an afternoon by throwing half a brick through a cabinet minister's window. Yet femininity erupted in great billowing dresses and elaborate corsages, and waists of the utmost waspness were achieved by rigorous tight-lacing that harked back to Victorian days.

It may be that things were moving too fast in the early 1900s for anyone to comprehend; the internal combustion engine had revolutionised passenger transport, the electric motor had brought the vacuum cleaner and other household gadgets into the home, reducing the need for a servant, and the wireless telegraph and the first fluttering indications of cinematography— the first London cinema was in Bishopsgate in 1906—promised a revolution in life styles, a challenge that many were reluctant to meet. Such a challenge had been offered nearly a century earlier by the Industrial Revolution, and had been met by a reversion to pre-industrial modes of living, which in its literary form was known as the romantic revival.

Some writers have claimed that the dabbling in *art nouveau* by suburbia was ephemeral, but it is equally arguable that this strange movement, culled from the fag-ends of aestheticism and various outlandish continental movements (especially the odd style known as the 'Vienna Secession' movement), was ready-made for the apprehensive and self-conscious denizens of outer London and the garden cities. It is curious that socialism found an audience there; but it was socialism with a small 's', the easy-going version of the Fabian Society and their high-minded supporters who were as shocked by the brusque attitude of the workers as any timid member of the middle class.

Sir Ambrose Heal tried to emancipate the suburbanite from the 'pretentious stuffiness' of the villa. This advertisement for Heal & Son's 'toilet wares' dates from 1906

Another feature of Edwardian suburban villadom was that it was inconsequential. The inhabitants thought that they had something to contribute, but deep down they knew that they had not. They were a ready market for any new entertainment or diversion, and could be unmercifully snubbed by their tradesmen, especially those representatives of the new shopocracy who, thanks to the patronage of King Edward VII, were being assimilated into society. Ambrose Heal, who had entered the family business in 1893, considered that it was his patriotic duty to emancipate the suburban dwellers from their childish adherence to the gaudy and meretricious absurdities of *art nouveau*, which he made sound sillier by anglicising it.

In the Heal catalogue of 1909, promotion of his own sane no-nonsense products co-exists with a crusade against the style which he hoped to supplant: '. . . all the pretentious stuffiness of the suburban villa, the "new art" overmantel smothered in rococo photograph frames, ineffable green grotesques of cats and other depressing forms of pottery'. Whatever its merits, the Heal furniture of the period is certainly of less interest today than the products of *art nouveau* at its most 'ineffable'.

It was easier to escape, both metaphorically and physically, in the first decade of the present century than it had been. The bicycle had given all but the very poor personalised transport. Escapist literature was abundant; readers could identify readily with one of the best-known fictional detectives of the time, Trent, created by E. C. Bentley:

> A man not yet thirty, with an air of irresponsible good humour, and an easy, unceremonious carriage of his loose-knit figure that struck his visitor as pleasing in general . . . His features were regular; his short, curling hair and a moustache, and, indeed, his whole appearance, suggested a slight but not defiant carelessness about externals. [7]

There was, and is, no better way of escape from the trivial and

Typical of Edwardian crime fiction heroes was E. A. Freeman's John Thorndyke

the incomprehensible than in deliberately allowing oneself to be lured into a doom-laden atmosphere, and this was supplied by a number of skilled practitioners of fiction. Algernon Blackwood in 1908: 'Forces rose all about him, transforming the normal into the horrible, and the spirit of craven fear ran through all his being, bringing him to the verge of collapse'.[8]

E. F. Benson in 1912:

> An awful shuddering and nausea of the spirit rather than of the flesh had seized me, and more than once he had to place my feet upon the steps, while every now and then he cast glances of terror and apprehension up the stairs.[9]

The haunted and the macabre could even be modelled to suit the woman reader, as is evident from Ford Madox Ford's *Riesenberg*, published in the *English Review* in 1911:

> He caught her in his arms. She screamed, a shrill and violent sound like the cry of an eagle, that dissipated itself in the tenuous and desolate air. 'Do not touch me', she cried out. 'I am mad. I have gone mad. Do not touch me! Look down! What do you see?'

The awful and the occult always appeals to a readership that is out of tune with the times, and there is no surer way to gauge the mood of an era than to sift through the tales of mystery and horror that were served up in the weekly magazines of the time (*Strand Magazine*, the most typical of these, sold 400,000 a month). It was significant that when the topic was too near reality even the most accomplished cliff-hanger did not receive its due—this happened to the novelist William le Queux when he described the 'horrid and thrilling invasion' of London by the Germans in 1910, driving home the message by having the book advertised by sandwich-board men dressed in the uniform of the Prussian infantry.

Escape through fiction was highlighted by the increased use made of public libraries. Between 1901 and 1914 library stocks doubled. It is interesting to note that the most popular novelists were those who wrote for the women's market. The number of books per library written by M. E. Braddon (1837–1915), the author of *Lady Audley's Secret* (1862), was 109 in 1907, and she was followed by Mrs Henry Wood, ninety-one, and Emma Jane Worboise, seventy-seven.

To cater for the self-conscious literary suburbs, there was an upsurge in the reprinting of the classics, and the firms involved in this laudable trade must strike chords in all those who haunt second-hand bookshops. World's Classics, originally published by Grant Richards and taken over by the Oxford University Press in 1909, date from 1901; Collins' classics from 1903; Everyman's Library from 1906, and Cassell's People's Library from 1909. The important thing about all these books is that they were cheap. The large sales of these reprints demonstrate that the demands by the suburbs for quality literature was more than skin deep, and that to some extent the literary pretensions were justified.

It is easy to patronise suburbia and all that that implies, but Wimbledon and Surbiton produced a simulacrum of the civilized society that was in welcome contrast to the self-indulgent lives of many rich people. The inhabitants of the custom-built villages that were neither town nor country did not rage and bemoan their condition, and their eagerness to create their own modes of living and culture, shallow and superficial as they may have been, can be seen in retrospect to be pathetic rather than irritating.

It is certainly true that without the patronage of suburbia and the professional middle classes, Edwardian 'culture' would have been very thin indeed. One of the greatest achievements of the suburbanites was to hand down their not undistinguished ethos to their children.

Many of those desperate to acquire a veneer of culture took their text from Edward Carpenter, an apostle of the refined life:

> Life is an art, and a very fine art. One of its first necessities is that you should not have *more* material in it—more chairs, and tables, sevants, houses, lands, bank-shares, friends, acquaintances, and so forth, than you can really handle . . . It is so much better to be rude to needless acquaintances than to feign you like them, and so muddle up both their lives and yours with a fraud.[10]

The desire for the intellectual life was fed not only by
Carpenter, but by the Book Club and the subsidising of the
Encyclopaedia Britannica by Lord Northcliffe; not only by the
cheap reprint of the classics but by the fad for folk dancing and
singing, and the resurrection of ancient music under the aegis of
the Dolmetsch family. A. C. Benson gave an amusing picture of a
concert in Cambridge, with Dolmetsch saying, 'What I am going
to play to you is awfully beautiful, awfully simple, but really
beyond the reach of the modern people'.

> Then some odd tinkling things were played on virginals and lute—sounds as
> if one had shaken up a cage of mice and canaries together . . . The collection
> of people listening with grotesque earnestness to these very odd sounds,
> the deliberate antiquity of it all, the sweeping aside all the progress of
> the art . . . [11]

Garden-city life tried to approximate to that of a university
town with rustic trappings, but no matter how strenuously the
intellectual ideal was pursued there was a lack of depth, and
although externals were grasped there was a superficiality about
the appreciation. It was the idea of ancient music that appealed,
not the music itself. Suburban interest in philosophy was in the
idea of philosophy rather than in the meat and substance, and
for every dozen persons who professed an acquaintance with
G. E. Moore, the fashionable philosopher of the period, hardly
one would have been able to be more specific. They were at one
with the auctioneer of George Eliot's *The Mill on the Floss*, who
brought with him from school 'a sense of understanding Latin
generally, though his comprehension of any particular Latin was
not ready'.

Fortunately the Edwardian arts readily gave up their secrets
without any great intellectual effort, and the writers consciously
or subconsciously wrote for middlebrows who saw themselves
as highbrows. Pseudo-classics such as Edward FitzGerald's
Rubáiyát of Omar Khayyám were gift-wrapped and presented in an
overwrought frenzied manner and left lying on coffee-tables,
tokens of membership of the elect. Although G. K. Chesterton
betrayed a talent for close analysis in his journalism, it was his

essay-writing, light and whimsical, that was enjoyed, and his slim volumes of *pensées* rubbed shoulders with equally quaint books of essays by E. V. Lucas, Hilaire Belloc and Robert Lynd.

This literature was cosy and flattering, and politely shut out the horrid world outside; if one wanted to peer into this outside world, one preferred to go to the fashionable commentators. George Bernard Shaw explained it to one in a simple jovial manner and even made socialism sound friendly. There was no lack of filters or the makers of filters against reality.

This was true also of art. Until 1910 painting was comfortable and comforting, and techniques had altered little over the last twenty years, though if anything paint was being handled in a freer manner by such artists as Wilson Steer, Sickert, and Charles Sims. Subject matter had changed little, and historical scenes were still being churned out by the academic professionals. The 1905 Royal Academy exhibition included *St Agnes in Prison receives from Heaven the Shining White Garment* by Frank C. Cowper and *For He Had Spoken Lightly of a Woman's Name* by John Lomax, works that would have found a place in exhibitions of forty years earlier. *The Cheat* by John Collier was a typical Victorian genre scene; the only contemporary characteristic was the Edwardian dress.

These pictures would not find wall space in the suburbs, which had little money to spend on such luxuries. The Royal Academy catered for the rich for whom expensive pictures were frequently status symbols and not life enhancers. More to the taste of the middlebrows were the products of the New English Art Club, first given an airing in 1906, though there was never much enthusiasm for fine art as such; applied art was another matter altogether. The lack of interest was reflected in the small number of private galleries in the West End.

The suburbanites scorned the affection that the rich had for portraits. The new rich were desperately anxious to get hold of portraits that they could specify as being of their ancestors. In 1903 a Raeburn portrait fetched 14,000 guineas, and a Romney 9,400 guineas (in 1877, forty-nine Raeburn portraits sold for a total of £4,707). In garden city and suburb, artistic products were valued more than art works, and there was a big market for aesthetically designed book-plates. This mood was fostered by the first numbers of the new magazine *The Studio* which sponsored *art nouveau*, and if the intellectual suburbs did buy pictures they were inclined to choose those by artists of that persuasion (artists who have only recently begun to be evaluated and whose work now sells at high prices).

The Studio did much to bolster up the garden city ethos. It gave support to the devotees of the arts and crafts movements and imitation rusticity, and piloted art into the perspective enjoyed by its readers. Lack of confidence was the prevailing malaise of suburbandom, and directly relates to the apprehension that was ever present. It can be seen now that their fears relating to the coming dominance of the working classes were unjustified; working-class leaders doffed their aggression with miraculous ease when they became members of the establishment, when they took their seats in parliament, and the bureaucracy set up by the pioneers of the welfare state proved less damaging than the middle classes dreaded.

This self-consciousness made the suburban middle classes an easy prey to the communication media. One of the key men in the principal medium—newspapers—was Kennedy Jones of the *Daily Mail*. His personal motto was 'Nothing really matters', but in the interests of mass circulation Jones was prepared to play on the nascent anxieties of the newspaper readers (it is worth mentioning that the story by William le Queux of the German invasion of London was serialised in the *Daily Mail*, with the technical details supplied by Lord 'Bobs' Roberts, hero of the Boer War). Lord Northcliffe, the owner of both the *Daily Mail* and *The Times*, was directly involved in creating middle-class worry about world events. When he bought *The Times* Northcliffe stated: 'I shall leave the Editor unrestricted control unless he should—which is quite impossible—fail to warn the British People of the coming German Peril'.[12]

The German Peril and the bogey of socialism—these were the two factors that prevented the apotheosis of the Good Life in the suburbs as expounded by Mrs Miniver in H. G. Wells's

Ann Veronica (1909): 'Everything was "working up", everything was "coming on"—the Higher Thought, the Simple Life . . .'

In retrospect it can be seen that suburban apprehension was not justified. Its loose-limbed culture was interrupted but not destroyed by the war, and in 1918 garden citydom continued where it left off. As a class they suffered less during the war; the upper classes provided the officers and the lower classes the cannon fodder. Suburbia provided the new bureaucracy of the war machine. In the evenings the white-collared hordes returned to their artistic homes, to their cards and their reading and the crackle of the gramophone. Socialism had been averted and the peril was not so bad as they had anticipated. Furthermore, life now had a purpose and was even exciting what with Zeppelins and Russian soldiers with snow on their boots. Whatever confidence the suburban dwellers had gained they had not lost their gullibility.

The Condition of the People

The years preceding World War I were strong in consumer spending and conspicuous display, and notably short on compassion. The poor were getting poorer and the rich were getting richer, but, as T. H. S. Escott, under the pseudonym of 'a Foreign Resident', wrote in his *London Society in the New Reign* (1904), 'Nothing is so out of fashion today as genuine emotion of any kind'. The poor, it was considered, were poor because they deserved to be, and were largely made up of idlers and scroungers who could get jobs if they were less work-shy. Their existence was ignored as much as possible, and the danger of a rising of the submerged classes was repressed despite the warnings of H. G. Wells, who said that Great Britain was in a dangerous state of social disturbance, and that the discontent of the labouring mass of the community was deep and increasing. In 1912 Wells prophesied that 'we are in the opening phase of a real and irreparable class war'. C. F. G. Masterman was even more explicit: 'That vast portion of the working-class which, raw and half developed, has long been half hidden amid its

The existence of the poor was ignored as much as possible, but this was sometimes difficult, such as during the 1912 troubles. A photograph of East End children waiting for food

poverty and squalor, is now issuing forth from its hiding place to assert an Englishman's heaven-born privilege of doing as he likes, meeting where it likes, breaking what it likes'.[1]

Fortunately for the well-being of the rich and the passably well-off, the poor were deliberately kept under, and their apathy was unscrupulously worked on. From the evidence of Poor Law reports and Parliamentary Commissions, there is no question that they were kept below the poverty line by the establishment, and made to wallow in degradation. At its most Machiavellian this can be seen in the organisation and running of the workhouses.

The workhouse, or 'union', was run by a Board of Guardians. These boards were frequently corrupt. They had as their agents relieving officers, men of no training or necessary ability, who doled out money as they thought fit. The goal of the relieving officer was to have an easy life, and this involved dispersing the money with as little inconvenience to himself as possible. The Guardians looked on their terms of office with Public Assistance Authorities as a necessary step to more significant employment in local government. In 1909 there was a commission of inquiry to look into the whole operation of the Poor Law, and its members attended numbers of meetings of Boards of Guardians. At one meeting 'the relieving officers and the chairman stated the cases so confusedly and so incompletely that it was almost impossible to form any opinion as to the methods on which out-relief is distributed . . . There was practically no enquiry as to the resources of the applicants, and with the old people the amount of relief was determined solely by age'.[2]

Relief was distributed without principle or knowledge of the facts. Applicants were bullied and roughly treated according to the mood of the Guardians or the relieving officers, and amid the babel, the slamming of doors and the general air of inquisition, the commission found it difficult to understand what was going on. On one occasion:

> The Board, as a whole, seemed slack, uninterested and unintelligent . . . In one case where the woman was reported dirty and the man given to drink, one of the Guardians mentioned having seen him at the public-house that morning. Relief was, however, granted at the instance of the Guardian of the parish, *who was also the publican whose house the man frequented.*[3]

Blame for the poor quality of the whole machinery for distributing relief was laid at the doors of the general public, who were not interested in the plight of the poor and could not be bothered to elect suitable Guardians. The people who put Guardians in office were the very ones who would benefit from the selection of some particular men. One of the Guardians was quite open about it: 'We are sent here to give outdoor relief to our relations, our fathers, and our mothers, and our sisters and our cousins, and our uncles, and our aunts, and if we did not do it we should soon be sent about our business'.[4]

With this degree of corruption, almost rivalling that of the old Metropolitan Board of Works in the days before the formation

Itinerant workers were always on the verge of the workhouse. A young billposter photo-graphed about 1914

of the London County Council, it is not surprising that those who deserved help failed to get it. The poverty of Edwardian England was no whit less than that of Victorian England; if anything it was more pronounced, for the rich philanthropists who had done much to relieve poverty were now replaced by the money-grubbers.

No one seemed astonished that Boards of Guardians were made up of estate-agents, owners of slum property, and publicans. On one board there were thirty-five members; seven of whom were publicans. The common denominators Boards of Guardians were meanness (the money came out of the rates and low rates would guarantee their success in local government) and discrimination (the money was given to friends and relations, those who spent money at Guardians' pubs, and those who were inclined to cause trouble if they did not receive their beer-money). Occasionally such Guardians were prosecuted for fraud and 'conspiracy to defraud the ratepayers', and although strictly speaking the Guardians were only supposed to serve three-year terms, when they were making money out of their position they were happy, and indeed eager, to stay on. This was also true of workhouse masters and matrons.

The workhouses were no better than their nineteenth-century counterparts. Women and girls were huddled together in filthy dormitories, with aged prostitutes and twelve-year-old orphans sharing beds. The worst conditions were in the infirmaries, essential sections of every workhouse, where beds were pushed close together, clothing and utensils lay about anywhere, and where the inmates themselves had to drive nails into the walls to hang their paltry possessions on. In the infirmaries there was usually only one nurse, and when she had a day off the inmates were left to their own devices; it was rare for a doctor to be in attendance.

The existence of workhouses can be seen as the failure of civilisation. They were the repositories of the old, the infirm, and the unwanted. The 'union' was, to many of the poor, the ultimate in degradation. In 1906 Ellen Regan, who was starving, cut her own throat and died rather than go into the workhouse, and one

The workhouse was, to many, the ultimate in degradation, and many of the poor struggled to hold down jobs for which they were physically ill-equipped

of the jurors at the inquest commented 'Oh, what a shocking thing in this country!' In the same year Andrew Mullen jumped on a wall of Regent's Park canal, and spun a penny, saying to a witness, 'Heads I drown myself; tails I don't'. It turned up heads; he threw his cap to a witness, and jumped. Even suicide was preferable to the workhouse.

Reliable statistics about the poor were hard to obtain, for there was always a certain amount of perambulating poverty. Summer pauperism was always considerably lower than the winter, but averaging out the figures, the paupers of 1907 numbered 793,519—2.27 per cent of the population of England and Wales. These were the people right at the bottom of the heap. The number of people who received relief was 1,706,592, 4.7 per cent; a third of these were in workhouses, two-thirds received what was called out-door relief. Poverty was more pressing in the towns than the country. Rural labourers had fled from the country to London and the big cities, only to discover numbers of unemployed already there. Rural poverty was less obtrusive, for although there was just as much it revolved mainly around the old and the infirm.

London had the big problem, maintaining 15,800 more paupers in 1907 than in the 1880s. In the East End, and in such boroughs as Southwark and Walworth, there existed a residuum of people doomed to perpetual unemployment. The poor married too young, had large families, were riddled with venereal disease, and drank. They were also hindered rather than helped by indiscriminate charity, the donors of which salved their conscience by dealing out money to those who were most insistent—the idlers and the drinkers. The demon drink was used as an excuse for doing little—the poor must take their punishment for giving in to the temptation. In some workhouses nearly half the inmates were there because of intemperance.

The incidence of venereal disease amongst the poor was high. In the Leeds workhouse infirmary between sixteen and twenty inmates were always under treatment. The disease was non-notifiable, and rarely cured. 'Syphilis once, syphilis ever' a British surgeon had said, and this epigram was respected by

Casual labour was a prime cause of basic poverty, and street traders and coster-mongers often barely scraped a living

those whose duty it was to administer treatment to the workhouse
population. Venereal disease was considered a just reward for
immoral behaviour. The treatment usually consisted of mercury
pills, and the recommendation to live a simple life without
alcohol was usually rejected by the patients.

Tuberculosis brought many to the workhouse, and although
it was known to be contagious the authorities persisted in
crowding people together, the fit and the sick, emulating the
conditions of the slums and lodging houses. Some lodging houses
contained 200–300 beds, often let out in eight-hour shifts.

Many observers saw the prevalence of casual labour as a
contributory cause of basic poverty. In the days before labour
exchanges, supply and demand of workers was haphazard, and
employers used the uncertainty as a means of utilising a cheap
work-force. For the most part, work at the docks was carried
out by casual labourers, taken on 'by the day, half-day, quarter-
day, hour, or job'. The example set by the London and India
Docks Company, which employed 72 per cent of its labour force
on regular weekly wage, was not followed. Port employers
considered that the poor were there to be profitably used.

On every side the poor were battened on by employers
desirous of cheap labour, by do-gooders who relieved their own
minds by indiscriminate charity, by nepotism in office, by
patronising relieving officers operating under the aegis of the
Boards of Guardians, and by the clergy. The relieving officers,
going from slum to slum, dished out their sixpences and shillings
with scant regard to need. 'Cases are seldom discussed with
reference to their needs. "She will be content with that", or
"That is what the other old women are getting", or "She is
over eighty, give her another sixpence", were the sort of
considerations brought forward'.[5]

A typical case was the widow living alone who received
3s 6d a week, out of which she paid 1s to a girl to attend to her
room, as she was helpless. Coal and rent cost her 1s 4d, leaving
her 1s 2d a week to live on. The relieving officers considered
themselves both judge and jury; if there was any suspicion that
there were what was termed 'undisclosed resources' they

withheld their shillings. One observer stated: 'There is no doubt whatever that a large number of the outdoor paupers are living in an environment of filth and immorality, and in many cases I fear they are participants in, and abettors of, these foul, insanitary, and degrading conditions'.[6]

In the slums, cleanliness and ventilation were not considered important, furniture consisted of straw palliasses and orange boxes, and the inhabitants defecated in passageways or in corners of rooms as there were no lavatories. A typical slum in the East End of London was described as not a room, but a den. Measuring 8 ft by 7 ft, it contained a sagging couch with ragged coverlets, a rickety table, a chair and two boxes. On the walls were blood marks, the remains of bugs and other insects. Even the respectable poor lived in similar conditions, though their standards of cleanliness were higher. Many did the best they could in atrocious circumstances. In Bermondsey in 1900 one water closet and one stand pipe served twenty-five houses; water was switched on for two hours a day, but never on a

A slum interior of 1912. All the food in the house is on the table

Sunday. In Manchester lavatories had not been introduced until 1898, and in Blackburn and Wigan less than half the houses had them.

The poor were also badly treated by the capitalists of their own class, the small shopkeepers. At its simplest level, 'the poor buy their food in small quantities and thus pay a higher price for it'.[7] They also bought their food 'on tick' and thus had no opportunity to shop around for bargains.

In 1903 21s 8d was considered the minimum living wage for a family of five. Yet in 1914 nearly a quarter of male wage earners earned less than 25s a week. With unemployment averaging about 8 per cent, there was no choice but to work for a pittance. It was either that or the dreaded workhouse. The most ghastly conditions were found in the 'sweated industries'. Jack London in his overwritten but sincere *The People of the Abyss* (1903) tells of the old woman, dying and broken, who supported herself and four children making match boxes at 2¼d per gross. In her

Many slums did not have their own water supply. Water was obtained from stand pipes in the street or alley

98-hour week she made 7,066 match boxes, earning 4s 10¼d. Out of this she had to pay for her own paste and thread. At one sweat shop, little girls were employed licking adhesive labels from early in the morning to late at night, and in the Nottingham lace trade children's eyesight was remorselessly destroyed and few of the juvenile work-force lived past thirty. Outworkers were just as badly off. In Leicester old women did glove stitching; their earnings for a full week averaged 1s 4d. The benevolent authorities supplemented this by 3s 6d all round. A London widow aged 79 working from 5 am until 10 pm at steel-covering earned 2s 11d a week, plus 4s from the parish and a loaf of bread from the local clergyman. In Glasgow an old woman worked ten hours a day at shirt-finishing, and earned 1s 10d a week.

The better off did not want to know about the condition of the poor. One attempt to bring the matter to their attention was made by the Fabian Society and its associates, though most of them had no idea of the plight of those whom they were supporting. Among these do-gooders was Lady Warwick, described by H. G. Wells as 'that remarkable intruder into the class conflict' and who always appeared too well-dressed for the gatherings of 'dingy earnest people'. Many people were appalled by the awful conditions of the poor when they happened by chance to come across them. When Winston Churchill visited Manchester, he commented to his secretary, Edward Marsh, 'Fancy living in one of these streets, never seeing anything beautiful, never eating anything savoury, never saying anything clever.'

The poor did not want to help themselves, nor did they particularly want their betters interfering. They did not want to be cleaned, enlightened or inspected. They did not want their drink regulated or their intimate organs examined for venereal disease. They wanted their rights. They were contemptuous of the well-meaning efforts of the paper socialists, and ignored such attempts to help them as that given to nursing and expectant mothers by the School for Mothers in St Pancras where 1½d dinners could be obtained.

Foreigners were shocked by the spectacle of the poor sleeping in London parks. This drawing of vagabonds sleeping in St James's Park was done by a visiting French artist

It was impossible for the rich to visualise the depths of squalor that existed east of St Paul's, and the moral turpitude that resulted from hideous living conditions. Occasionally the well-off were brought face to face with the denizens of this other nation, when the workers came 'up west' to demonstrate in Hyde Park, or in the persons of the homeless who slept rough. In most cases their reaction was indignation, not against the authorities particularly, but against the poor who dared to bring themselves to their attention.

The London parks were shut at night, but Green Park had the reputation of closing its gates earlier than most. 'It was Sunday afternoon, the sun was fitfully appearing, and the well-dressed West Enders, with their wives and progeny, were out by thousands, taking the air. It was not a pleasant sight for them, those horrible, unkempt, sleeping vagabonds . . .'[8]

To the rich, socialism was equated with the supremacy of the poor. To Lord Rosebery, it was 'the end of all—the negation of Faith, of Family, of Monarchy, of Empire'. The People's Budget

introduced by the Liberals in 1909 to alleviate the condition of
the aged poor was treated as creeping socialism, not least of all
by *The Times*. The budget was 'a chaotic welter of half-ascertained
facts, half-thought-out arguments, half-sincere sentimentalism'.
The paranoia that surrounded the first tentative gropings of the
welfare state reflect a strange attitude of mind, a cynical selfishness. The poor were not only poor because they deserved to be,
but the old were indigent because they had not scraped any
savings together from their miserable past earnings. A cartoon in
Punch, on 5 August 1908, was decidedly ambiguous. Lloyd
George, the chancellor of the exchequer, was depicted as a
highwayman at a cross roads, holding a pistol in one hand and
clutching a box on which was inscribed 'Old Age Pension Fund'.
The caption read, Mr Lloyd George: 'I'll make 'em pity the
aged poor!'

In his peroration in the House of Commons, Lloyd George
said:

> This is a War Budget. It is for raising money to wage implacable warfare
> against poverty and squalidness. I cannot help believing that before this
> generation has passed away, we shall have advanced a great step towards that
> good time when poverty, and the wretchedness and human degradation which
> always followed in its camp, will be as remote to the people of this country
> as the wolves which once infested its forests.[9]

The old age pension thus introduced was more of a token than
a bonanza, and the small Labour Party representation in parliament
was more concerned with the tax on cigarettes. The pension
was 5s a week for those with less than £21 per annum, and this
reduced by 1s for every 2½ guineas. The result was not grate-
fulness on the part of the working classes, but a wave of strikes.
These were alarming not only to the Conservatives and the
Liberals, but also to the Labour contingent, who reluctantly
shelved their abhorrence that twenty-five Wild Woodbine
cigarettes were likely to cost more than 5d.

Strikes did more than anything to convince the timid that their
inchoate anxieties had a basis in fact. As early as 1905 the Welsh
miners had struck, followed by railwaymen, cotton spinners and
engineers. In 1911 there was a seamen's strike, starting in

Southampton and spreading to Liverpool and Cardiff. At Hull, dock labourers joined in; there was looting and rioting, and warehouses were burned. Shortly afterwards Manchester dockers and carters came out, and the trouble spread to London where there was danger of bringing in the military to clear the docks. While the strike raged in London, an unofficial strike in the north erupted into a general rail strike. A mob attacked the police, many of whom were injured, and the troops were called out. They opened fire, killing two of the rioters. The incident was given wide publicity by the press, and an analogy with the Peterloo massacre was drawn.

Trouble at power stations plunged cities into darkness, and gangs of hooligans taking advantage of the labour troubles roamed the streets. There was active support from the intelligentsia which had for so long confined itself to the lecture hall. The London dock strike led to a procession of 100,000 through the City, joined by women workers in Bermondsey. In Liverpool,

Poverty in Wales was acerbated by strikes and lock-outs in the mines

Tom Mann, a firebrand with ominous attachments to the syndicalist movement of the United States, was pressing for a general strike. Some measure of the reaction to these manifestations of organised labour can be gauged by the rise in membership of the trade unions from 2,369,067 in 1910 to 3,918,809 in 1914.

The potential of organised labour had been seen in 1893 in the mining industry. The owners had demanded a 10-per-cent reduction in wages, and their employees had retaliated by withdrawing their labour for fifteen weeks. Not all mines were involved, those in South Wales being kept open. It was here that the most ominous events happened, so far as the general public were concerned. The Miners' Federation, under whose auspices the strike was held, tried to close the South Wales pits by provoking a hauliers' strike. 'Marching gangs' of hauliers moved from pit to pit, intimidating and beating up the Welsh miners, and were only stopped when 2,000 miners at Ebbw Vale fought a pitched battle with the gangs.

At Featherstone, near Pontefract, when troops were brought in following a mob riot, two miners were killed; trade union officials never let the government forget this incident.

More comforting to the middle classes and the employers had been the result of a strike by the Amalgamated Society of Engineers in 1897–8. The engineers wanted a working day of eight hours, and their strike was countered by the employers banding together to form a solid front. The Amalgamated Society of Engineers was the most powerful union in the country but against the forces of organised capitalism it was ineffective, and the strike ground to a humiliating halt. Employers hoped that their defeat of the engineering union would register with organised labour.

Capital knew that the law was on its side. In 1898 a court judgement laid down that picketing was lawful only if confined to 'communicating information', and that picketing to 'persuade', for example, others to strike was actionable. No one could say how a strike could be conducted lawfully. The employers seemed to have all the cards on their side, and could hardly contain their jubilation when in 1901 the manager of the Taff

Valley Railway determined to sue the Amalgamated Society of Railway Servants for loss suffered by his company as the result of a 'wrongful strike'. The trade unions thought that they were protected by the 1871 Trade Union Act. They were wrong. The Taff Valley Railway was awarded £23,000 damages against the union, plus costs, and what has since been known as the Taff Vale Judgement cast a gloom over all unions, who now knew that their funds could be sequestered by a hostile court.

The Taff Vale Judgement encouraged the high command of the Trades Union Congress into politics. Only by representation in the House of Commons could the unions be protected, or, indeed, survive. Fortunately there were many in the Liberal camp who were disturbed by the implications of the Taff Vale Judgement, and the Miners' Federation succeeded in 1906 in returning twelve MPs to Parliament, some of them without Liberal opposition. The representation of Labour in Parliament was largely by courtesy of the Liberals, and the Conservatives have never wholly forgiven them for it.

Unfortunately for the militants of the trade union movement, as soon as their candidates became MPs they seemed eager to join the establishment, to ignore their brief, to emulate their betters, and the waves of strikes that marked the Edwardian age illustrate the failure of capital and labour to come together— a failure that, with rare exceptions, has persisted until this day.

The strikes and associated violence mirrored the feelings of hysteria that prevailed in the years leading up to the war. They can also be seen as an indication that the traditionally submerged classes were breaking surface. They were still poor, but now, goaded and exhorted by larger, more powerful unions with spokesmen in parliament, they wanted to know why.

The Rural Exodus

In terms of the picturesque the countryside was at its best during the period, and townees sought succour and inspiration amidst flora and fauna, the artistic recording the gently decaying villages in water-colour and prose poems. 'A sunset of quite extra-

*Inspiration was sought in the countryside by amateur artists, and this cartoon of 1908
cannot have been far from the truth*

The countryside was at its best during the Edwardian years, though the suburbs of the big towns were encroaching on it

ordinary beauty', wrote A. C. Benson in his diary on 10 December 1905, 'the leafless trees, seen over bare fields, the hamlet roofs, the world beyond, and the sun sinking orange into smoky wisps of cloud, which he seemed to draw with him. We watched the crimson orb slip behind the hill'.

The countryside was treated as a phenomenon especially laid on by the almighty for the edification of town-dwellers, who were somewhat indignant that many country people could not see the beauty and the charm of rural Britain, and much preferred the towns. 'Nature has little meaning for most of them, and no charms; but they love a gas lamp. Nature, in my opinion, only appears to the truly educated'.[1] The rustics, in fact, were in flight from the countryside, where the easily-discerned comeliness of village and hamlet directly related to the stagnation of rural life.

Throughout the nineteenth century agriculture had slowly been losing ground, and in the last thirty years acreage set aside for wheat had fallen by half, following imports of large quantities of cheap grain from America. In 1894 wheat prices were at their lowest point for more than a century and a half. Between 1891 and 1913, about 45,000 acres per annum went out of cultivation in Great Britain, of which half was lost to rough grazing and half to non-agricultural uses.

The 1880s and 1890s were locust years, and although the position became somewhat stabilised by 1900, the impact of those two decades had reduced agriculture to a chronic state of depression. A 700-acre farm in Wiltshire that sold for £27,000 in 1812 came on the market again in 1892, when it fetched £7,000. In 1874 one farmer rented his land at £600 per annum, and paid tithes of £196; in 1901 he paid £250 rental, while the landlord paid the tithes. The farmer stated that he made much more money when he was paying nearly £800 a year than in 1901. In the same county, a 1,600-acre farm had warranted a rent of £2,100 per annum in 1870, but in 1901 this had decreased to £825.

This pattern was repeated throughout the country, and the average fall in rental of land between 1875 and 1901 was 33 per cent. A number of factors contributed to this trend. The great future that had been forecast when steam power was applied to agriculture was never realised, and many farmers almost bank-rupted themselves by buying the new-fangled machinery. In 1877 herds were decimated by cattle plague (rinderpest) and although this was the last year that farming was hit by this disease its financial effect was felt for a decade. Even more disastrous was 1879, when persistent rains and a sunless summer ruined the crops and reduced many farmers to destitution; the floods led to an outbreak of liver-rot in sheep, which for a time crippled sheep-rearing. A royal commission was appointed to look into agricultural distress; it took three years for the report to come out, and then merely stated the obvious—that landlords, yeoman farmers, and tenants had all suffered, and that rents would continue to drop. No policy was framed for helping agriculture; and farmers became disillusioned. Grain was pouring in from abroad, and now that there was refrigeration in ships it was cheaper to import beef and mutton from Australia and New Zealand than produce it at home.

At harvest times women and children were able to contribute towards the family income, and in real terms agricultural labourers were probably better off than town workers

Many farmers turned to dairy farming, but the sequence of bad seasons ruined the hay, and early experimentation into methods of preserving green fodder (ensilage) only partly relieved the situation. In 1883 there was a particularly virulent outbreak of foot-and-mouth disease. Towards the end of the 1880s, farming prospects seemed to improve slightly, but any alleviation was cancelled by the drought of 1893. Another commission of inquiry was appointed, but by the time their report came out, a sequence of droughts had confirmed their view that agriculture was in a bad way.

These years were the yesterdays of the Edwardian farmer, who took the vicissitudes of nature with characteristic British phlegm. Their greatest problem was labour. Before 1871 the supply of farm labourers had always exceeded the demand, but from then on they began leaving the land for the mills and factories of the industrial towns. By 1901 the shortage of farm labour was desperate. In the old days, a farm hand was usually sure of a roof over his head, but with the decline of agriculture landlords could not afford to replace cottages that had fallen into ruin. A cottage cost £550 to build, and with a rent at £10 a year this represented a profit of 2 per cent per annum; with other pressing demands on capital it is not surprising that few were built. Some labourers who kept to the land found themselves living in derelict shacks which were often no better than city slums.

In 1850 the average weekly wage of the agricultural labourer was 9s 3½d; in 1903 it was 14s 7d. These wages were low compared with those obtainable in the city, but there were additional perquisites, such as farm produce, free beer or cider, tied cottages, plus extra earnings at harvest time, when wives and children would also contribute towards the family income. In real terms the agricultural labourer was probably better off than the town worker. Leaving the country for the town, 'he does not think of the rent of the squalid rooms, of the cost of the tramcars, and the music hall'.[2]

A Sussex farmer in 1901 speculated that if he could afford to pay his workers 50 per cent more he could keep them. But most farmers could not, or felt that they could not. They were conditioned into taking what labour they could. Country boys could now read and write, and even when they did not go to the cities they preferred to be shop-boys rather than work on the farms. Hedgers, ditchers and thatchers were dying out and most of those engaged in this essential work were over fifty years of age. Farm labourers in the mid-Victorian period had been happy to work seven days a week, knowing no different, but now they demanded, as their right, a six-day week. On dairy farms it was found almost impossible to get the cows milked on a Sunday, and many farmers were forced to turn their land over to beef cattle (Guernseys fetched between £17–£20 and calves £1). Between the wars, with mechanical milking, the position reversed. In 1937 the dairy herd in England was 36 per cent higher than in 1913.

There were few gilt-edged propositions for Edwardian farmers. Hops in the past had been a reliable produce, but in 1901 they cost £60 an acre, and on this £10 an acre profit was

Many landowners suffered from the agricultural depression, and some of them sold their land to the nouveaux riches who turned farmland into hunting and shooting territory

realised. One Kent farmer was philosophical: 'Hop growing is just like a rubber of whist. I have lost £1,000 a year at it, and have made £1,000 a year'. Fortunately the hop-growing counties were within easy reach of London, and every year by tradition the East Enders left the city to pick the hops. Farm labourers in the home counties had sampled the delights of London and found them wanting. Thankfully they reverted to the land and were willing to put up with conditions that farm labourers further afield would not countenance. In Essex in particular, the absence of cottages forced some farm hands to live in shacks made of orange boxes.

Tenant farmers were in some way compensated for their lower incomes by paying less rent than they had been paying, but landowners suffered unceasingly from the agricultural depression. They were, as one of them cynically mentioned, 'like the eels which are said to grow accustomed to being skinned'. Many were forced to sell up, and thankfully relinquished their heritage to the *nouveaux riches* who turned good farm-land into hunting or shooting territory and fancied playing the squire. The shopocracy, made wealthy by trade, were prominent in this field, and increased the labour problems by hiving off the more useful rustics for service in their retinue.

The decline of agriculture was watched with complacency by successive governments and, although there seemed a future in smallholdings, nothing of moment was done until 1906. By 1914 some 14,000 holdings covering 200,000 acres were created, but these did not alter the general downward trend. Co-operative ventures foundered because of the doggedness and independence of farmers. One such typical experiment was inaugurated near Northampton, where Earl Spencer provided 300 acres for co-operative farming, backing this generous gesture with £3,000 at 3 per cent. For two years the community lost heavily; the next year a profit of £30 was made, and then a run of ill luck finished the project, into which Lord Spencer did not feel inclined to inject any more money.

One curious venture in co-operative farming was carried out by Edward Carpenter. He arrived in the north of England with great ideals, glorying in the environment he found: 'It was all in the old rural style—the leisurely long day with its varied occupations and interests, the life of the open air and the fields, the cattle and the crops, the barn and the public-house'.[3] The only snag was that when Carpenter mentioned the Land Question to the locals their eyes glazed over and their conversation reverted to pigs and potatoes.

Nevertheless Carpenter did see that the great drawback of country folk was their want of initiative, for which he blamed the incubus of landlord and parson. Certainly the farmers did little to rethink their operations, and preferred to place the blame on shortage of labour, the inactivity of the government, and the high price of transport of their produce. In Kings Lynn it cost £400 per annum to send £1,200 worth of market-garden produce to London. Farmers looked back to the good old days when farm labourers were eager to work for a pittance, instead of reappraising the whole pattern of farming.

Village life, which depended on the prosperity of agriculture,

With the agricultural situation many country towns, such as West Malling, in Kent, fell into decline

languished with the departure of so many young men to the towns. There were few of the old festivals, and social life became unenthusiastic and drab. Village inns lost much of their trade, but to some extent were kept going by the passion of suburbia for the country life and by the cycling boom. Rural activities were pepped up by injections of arty-crafty culture. The widow of the bursar at Eton collected a village chorus together in Stanhoe, and claimed that the whole life of the place had been quickened, or, more guardedly, that decadence and dullness had been arrested. Some communities became self-conscious and trivialised for the benefit of the tourist interest; villages were seen as 'quaint' and pretty, and were benevolently defended by the clergy together with a way of life that no longer existed. Wrote one clergyman: 'It is easy to pick holes in the theory of Squire, Parson, and Tenants, but when you have the right people on the spot it is found to be the best society of the kind yet devised by man'.[4]

Creaking attempts were made to keep the old order going, to pretend that village life was flourishing as it had done fifty years before. Bemused and apathetic, villagers were dragooned into acting out their predestined roles. At Mayfield in Sussex an attempt was made to revive the old mummers. Kenneth Grahame, author of *Wind in the Willows*, watched the charade cynically: 'Hardly any of the good old "St George and the Dragon" play left. Instead cheap comic songs from the London music halls'.[5]

It was easy to wax lyrical about the English countryside—'The sedged river, with the fragrant smell of the river-water bubbling, through the sluices, into a pool where a teal was diving, made up for me a scene of great sweetness—so English, so serene, so utterly unaffected'.[6] The writers of *belles lettres* and slim volumes of verse could always be turned on by village and country life, where it seemed that nothing was altered except the replacement of the blacksmith by the garage. The Edwardian essayists echoed with Wordsworth their appreciation of 'splendour in the grass, of glory in the flower', and believed that it was all for them. The countryman's sardonic wit and underlying pessimism they considered quaint, and not the expression of defeat. Nor did they enter these so picturesque cottages, in which were conditions more akin to those of the Middle Ages than those of the twentieth century, where rags and sacks did duty as bedding and straw was used as floor covering.

And what did the occupants of these cottages want with a wage well below the primary poverty level announced by sociologists when they had fresh air and a beautiful view from the window (admittedly the window measured 2 ft square, the glass was broken and replaced by cardboard, and the landlord did not have the money or the inclination to replace it)? Lack of communication between town and country was never so evident as during the golden years of Edward's reign.

Notes to this chapter are on pages 293–4.

CHAPTER FOUR

THE COMING OF THE MOTOR CAR

THE MOTOR car was the supreme status symbol of the Edwardians, and in 1909 *Punch* printed a humorous article on this theme which begins: 'I was tired of pedestrianism and being poor, so I waved imperiously to the passing taxicab. "I will now," I said to myself, "be rich. To be properly rich I must be in a motor".' When the taxi is flagged down, the driver is suspicious of his fare, and asks what the idea is. The narrator goes on:

> I had some idea that you and I might go to Regent's Park together. You shall sit in your little armchair and turn your wheel as you will, while I gracefully recline inside upon the larger seat and dispose my feet carelessly upon the smaller one. *En route* we will observe the life of the great metropolis, and mark the ambition, misery, and vice stamped upon the faces of its inhabitants. Perhaps we may even enter upon some interesting discussion with a motor-bus driver on the way.

Motoring in Britain dated from 1895, when the Honourable Evelyn Ellis brought the first petrol-driven car from France, a 4 hp Panhard & Lavassor machine. This make of car had done well in the first of the long-distance races in Europe and had completed a 732-mile course in 48 hours 48 minutes, proving the definitive victory of the petrol-driven car over the steam car. Ellis backed motoring in Britain to the extent of £20,000 of his own money, and although he was a pioneer in daring the authorities to prosecute him (the 4 mph speed limit plus a man with a red flag syndrome was still in operation) he was soon joined by J. A. Koosen in a Lutzmann and Sir David Salomons. An exhibition at Tunbridge Wells late in 1895 and another motor show at the Imperial Institute, London, in 1896, thrust the motor car into the public domain. In November 1895 *The Autocar* magazine was created, in confident confirmation of the future of motoring. The speed limit was pushed up from 4 mph to 12 mph in 1896, and the first London to Brighton run on 14 November that year commemorated the victory of the motor over the law.

Ellis's 4 hp Panhard & Lavassor motor created a stir wherever it appeared. On its maiden run 56 miles were covered in 5 hours 32 minutes, exclusive of stoppages, averaging 9.84 mph, and whole villages turned out to look at the vehicle, making rustic jokes. Occasionally it was stopped by the police, but they were satisfied by Ellis showing them his carriage licence.

J. A. Koosen had bought his car at the behest of his wife, who conveniently kept a diary:

1895
Nov 23—Took train to Lee and tried to make our motor work; wouldn't; came home at five.
Nov 24—Awfully cold; played with our motor—no result.
Nov 25—After luncheon saw to our motor, but didn't get it out of shed.
Nov 26—Drove to Lee and took Smith and Penning (engineers); Penning spent the day on his back without results.
Nov 30—Motor went with benzoline for first time; awfully pleased.
Dec 2—Waiting for new oil from Bowley & Son.
Dec 9—Drove to Lee at 10; motor sparked at once and went well. After lunch started for home in motor-car; came round by Fareham; had lovely drive; police spotted us; awful crowd followed us at Cosham; had to beat them off with umbrella.
Dec 10—Policeman called at 1.30, took our names re driving through Fareham without red flag ahead.
Dec 13—Went drive round common; tyre came off; sent her to Penning (engineer).
Dec 27—Frightened an unattended horse attached to a milk-cart, which bolted and sent the milk-cans flying in all directions.

That archetypal figure, the motor salesman, arrived on the scene. As the trade-in value of cars was only fifteen per cent he was forced to be exceptionally persuasive

Jan   4—Lost nut off air valve; pushed home.
Jan   14—Motor got stuck; made noises; sent her to Penning.
Jan   19—Moted [sic] to Eastney Lock; Jack got out to hold unattended
            horses, and I drove the car into the curb and smashed frame.
            Shoved into a stable close by.

Koosen goes into motoring history as the first man to be fined for a motor traffic offence: 1s plus 15s 7d costs; the second was a Scotsman in Berwick-on-Tweed, who was surrounded by all 13 of the local constabulary, and subsequently fined 6d with 19s 6d costs. Despite a country parson filling his petrol tank with water and asking if it mattered, and oiling the engine with a bicycle oil-can, the way was set for the Edwardian motoring boom.

The Edwardian car was expensive to buy, complicated and

costly to run. Turn-of-the-century cars were underpowered, and could not exceed 4 mph up hills. Any gradient more than 1 in 9 beat them, and a recommended test ground was Petersham Hill near Richmond, which averaged 1 in 15 with one steep bit 1 in 9½. The salesmen were already fly and glib, maintaining that the best of all test grounds was Savoy Hill, leading to the Embankment, which they claimed was 1 in 8½, though really it was 1 in 13.4.

No gentleman could be expected to mess around in the crude smoking interior of a motor car, and the new domestic was introduced, the motor servant—'He is a new type of man, and will require the wages of other engineers'.[1] Motoring in vehicles without hoods or windscreens called for special clothing. Tweed and cloth were out, for the air whipped them out into balloons; perforated leather was recommended, with the stipulation that the coats should button closely round the wrist. Trousers should be bound tightly around the ankles; and the

Motoring called for a new type of clothing, for men and for women. The artist here knew more about fashions than about cars

experts advised the adoption of a garment shaped like a bell tent from which the rain would run. Peaked caps, as used on the continent, were not recommended, as these were 'only seen on the heads of the drivers and conductors of electric tram-cars &c'. Goggles were a must.

One kept one's car not in a garage, which was French and therefore rather naughty, but in a motor stable. Green motorists who thought that machinery *per se* was strong and robust put their vehicles in damp motor stables, and were rapped sternly over the knuckles by their betters. Motor stables had to be on the large side, for no gentleman would think of having fewer than three cars. As for cheap cars, it was a disgusting notion, and the Automobile Club should be ashamed of itself for running an exhibition of cars priced at less than £200 at Hereford.

The new race of motorists were not particularly considerate or good drivers, though the 1896 act demanded that if anyone in control of horses lifted up a hand to stop a car, the car must stop (if possible). Side-slips (skids) were unfortunate, but there was not likely to be another car about, and horses and people were soft anyway. 'Lady cyclists were formerly a great danger, as they were apt, when a motor was heard approaching them from behind, to fall off their machines, apparently in terror; but this distressing spectacle is now [1906] comparatively rare'.[2] A driver was respectfully recommended, if he and not his motor servant was at the wheel, to practise reversing, for it was undignified to have to push a car out of a hotel yard because there was no room to turn. The early cars were fitted with something called a 'sprag', which if the gears failed when going up a hill, would come into operation, and hold the car.

In 1903 a 10 hp Panhard, a small car, cost 4d a mile to run. The price of petrol varied enormously from a copper or two to 1s 3d a gallon, depending on the cupidity of the garage proprietor. A doctor with a 10 hp car maintained that it cost as much to run as two horses, but that nevertheless the motor car was invaluable. The medical profession was the first to use the car for anything other than sport or gallivanting around. Sportsmen found the car a delightful toy, and used their twelve-bores from moving cars; if they hit anything with their cars they were advised to go back in case there was a stew or a soup to be made from some broken creature.

Part of the expense of motoring revolved around the price of spare parts. As tyres cost £24 15s a pair and were always bursting, the more economically-minded motorist kept to solid tyres. It was a brave man who went out without his motor servant, for things could go wrong very easily, and the only way the engine could be got at was from underneath. There were few instruments, and the first sign of an engine over-heating was the smell of burning paint. Pistons were easily ruined (and were painted with aluminium paint by unscrupulous second-hand car dealers), and some of the more powerful cars used as much oil as petrol. A motorist who drove every day and did his own maintenance would need to spend an hour a day cleaning, oiling and adjusting.

To many people, the very uncertainties of motoring were part

By 1911 the motor bus had displaced more than 2,000 horse-drawn buses, though there were still a few horse-drawn 'pirates' on the London streets

Victim: "WHAT HAS HAPPENED. WH-WHERE
AM I?"
Doctor: "YOU HAVE BEEN KNOCKED OVER BY A
MOTOR-CAR; BUT IT IS ALL RIGHT—YOU WILL
RECOVER."

Motor cars were a source of humour. Although not particularly funny, this cartoon was typical of the genre

of the charm. Icy roads, rain, clouds of dust, these made the adventure more exciting. There was a passion for fast cars, shared by King Edward, who was proud of having exceeded 60 mph on the Brighton Road as early as 1906. The king favoured the Daimler and the Mercedes, which were painted a rich claret colour, and he enjoyed choosing new cars. Like many motorists he hated being overtaken or, indeed, having any car in front of him, and would urge his driver to pursue and pass as though the honour of England were at stake.

In 1904 there were 24,201 cars in the United Kingdom, one third of them in London. British makers had come late on the scene, and the bulk of the cars were German or French; American cars were not recommended. Motor cabs, known as 'Clarences', had just come in. There were few motor buses as yet, but the possibilities of the internal combustion engine as a transport aid was seen as early as 1906 when home county farmers sent their produce to London by road.

The roads were terrible; the widespread use of the railway had caused the neglect of the fine highways brought into being by the stage coach. The decline of the turnpike system meant that no one was much interested in keeping the roads in good order. The poor quality of road surfaces, however, helped to keep car speeds down and reduce the number of accidents.

Many people hated the coming of the motor car. 'It made people independent of their near neighbours, and while it enlivened the lives of the well-to-do it spoiled county society for the less well circumstanced'.[3] *Punch*, as usual, was well-attuned to genteel discontent, and proposed the Anti-Motor Show, featuring the Spiky Turtleback, a huge steel dish-cover studded with twelve-inch spikes and attached to the wearer's back by springs and straps; the Vesuvian Jacket, made of gun-cotton with detonators as buttons and coloured red with yellow stripes, and the Pedestrian's Repair Outfit, containing a wooden leg. The fox-hunting fraternity refused to allow the new-fangled monster near them.

The march of progress was inexorable. In 1905 the chief constable of Guildford had a count taken of the cars that went up the High Street—they numbered 50,000. The most significant thing was that people became casual about cars, mentioning them in passing, and motoring terms took their place in the English language. The journalist W. Robertson Nicoll, though he never spoke of motors or motoring, referred to himself as being 'out of gear'. Between 1905 and 1907, motor prices went down by a third, and in 1908 the era of the cheap car arrived with the importation of the Ford. Nevertheless the small popular family car did not interfere with the prestige of the top names. In 1907 the De Dion Bouton had seven distinct models on the market varying between 8 and 30 hp. The works of the car were immensely improved, though there was less emphasis on the coach work; in the early 1900s it took forty days to paint the coach work on a Mercedes or a Rolls-Royce.

The motoring enthusiast bought a new car as soon as technological advances warranted it, throwing another second-hand car on to the market for another motorist to buy at a fraction of its cost. A three-year-old car was worth only 15 per cent of its original price. There was a good deal of swapping and changing,

as Arnold Bennett records in his diary on 17 December 1907:
'Pett Ridge said Arthur Morrison had sold his Japanese pictures
to the British Museum for £4,000, and bought a motor car.
Also that B. Pain (Barry Pain the humorous writer) had bought
a car off W. S. Gilbert and sold it again'.

The mania for speed and power so manifest in naval matters
produced a variety of monster cars. As early as 1902 on a private
road at Welbeck, Nottinghamshire, Charles Jarrott drove a
70 hp Panhard at 79.25 mph. The Nice Race Meeting of 1903
brought together the fastest models then built, but gloom was
cast over the meeting by the death of the celebrated Count
Zborowski in his racing Mercedes. The first significant entry of
America into the motor-racing stakes was in 1904 at Daytona
Beach in Florida, where W. K. Vanderbilt clocked up 92 mph
in his 90 hp Mercedes. In the same year a French car topped the
100 mph mark. These fast speeds were calculated on the basis of
the flying kilometre.

*The Victoria Embankment was one of the first stretches of road to be treated with tarred
macadam*

Various inventors, many of them of an unpractical turn of mind, began in 1904 to build cars that aroused excitement and acquired notoriety. The hitherto unknown Bellamy produced an 8 cylinder 165 hp car with a projected speed of 115 mph; this was topped by Dobelli of Rome who exhibited in London a 180 hp monster with four massive cylinders, an engineering curio rather than a serious rival to Mercedes or Darracq. In 1905, speeds were reckoned over the measured mile, and in Florida a Napier covered this distance at 105.8 mph and a 120 hp Mercedes at 109.5 mph. Average speeds were much higher than the previous year, and in a 100 mile race a 90 hp de Dietrich machine averaged 76.5 mph.

These great achievements boosted interest in motoring, and by May 1906 there were 44,098 cars registered in the UK. Something had to be done about the roads, and a stretch of the Victoria Embankment was experimentally treated with tarred macadam, which proved extremely effective. In 1909, 2,500 miles of main road were tarred in London alone.

1906 saw the inauguration of the French Grand Prix at Le Mans, and it was felt that motor-racing depended on the success of this meet. Britain was restricted by the 20 mph speed limit of 1903, and in the autumn of 1906 Mr and Mrs Locke King decided to lay out a track in their own ground near Weybridge— Brooklands—with accommodation for 100,000 people.

Commercial vehicles were hampered by limitations imposed on weight; until 1905 no commercial vehicle was legal in England if its unladen weight exceeded three tons. Motor buses were first licensed by the police authorities in 1904, and by 1910 had displaced 22,000 horses and 2,200 horse omnibuses. A few operators retained their horse-drawn buses, and because of their cut rates were known as pirates. These continued to run as late as 1912, as shown by a conundrum published in the magazine *Tittle-Tattle*:

What is the difference between the LGO Co's busses [sic] and the pirates? The former have acetylene lamps, the latter a set o'lean horses.

Although attempts had been made to introduce motor-cabs

The New Cab Tariff

" Oh, constable, the taximeter says we've come between two and a half and two and four-sixths miles. The driver says his taximeter is slow, and we've come between two and four-sixths and two and five-sixths miles. I'm sure we've only come about two and a sixth, so we're going to split the difference. What do you make the fare?"

Cab fares were a cause of much confusion, as reflected in this cartoon of 1906

in London during 1904, 1905 and 1906, it was not until 1907 that the General Motor-cab Co put 100 vehicles on the road, and these proved so successful that by the end of the year there were 723 taxis in London, a figure that quadrupled in the next year. By April 1910 there were 4,941 taxis, though there remained on the streets 1,200 hansom cabs and 2,500 horse-drawn four-wheelers. The hiring rate for taxis was as high as 8d per mile. The word 'taxi' was received into the English language in 1907, and given a certificate of acceptance in 1912 with the stage play *The Girl in the Taxi*, immortalised by the phrase, 'If you can't be good—be careful'.

Parallel with the development of the motor-car was that of the motor-cycle, which was a triumph of logic over preconceptions. Motor car designers took a long time to throw over the idea that the car was an adapted horse-carriage, whereas the motor-cycle was functional from the start. The French were the dominant force in car manufacture until the end of the decade, while the leading motor-cycle manufacturers were British.

By the middle of 1905, 34,700 motor-cycles were registered in the United Kingdom, and became increasingly popular among the young and those who could not afford a car.

The motor-car revolution was seen as similar to the railway revolution. But there was one main difference. The railway had been an instrument of democracy, while the car represented private ostentation at its most arrogant, the final triumph of the haves over the have-nots. Perhaps the ultimate in Edwardian status symbols was the 1911 Rolls-Royce 'Silver Ghost', costing £1,154 (more than most people earned in ten years).

Many of the pioneer motorists were members of the Aero Club, and C. S. Rolls was not only a key figure in motoring circles but a balloonist. 'Balloonacy', as the sceptics called it, became fashionable, with meetings at Ranelagh and Hurlingham. The most spectacular publicity stunt was a race between a balloon and cars, starting from the Crystal Palace; it was won by the balloon, for the cars were forced to abandon their challenge at Farnham when darkness fell, while the balloon went on to Basingstoke.

One of the status symbols of the age, the Rolls-Royce

A cartoon strip dealing with 'Balloon-acy, the Coming Craze'

Like pioneer motoring, ballooning was a rich person's sport, and the magazine *The Car* attempted to convert its readers to the new craze. Ballooning was elegant, exclusive, health-inspiring and full of mild excitement, and although the decline set in about 1909 when aeroplanes became the rage it retained a following until World War I. In 1906 a rich newspaper proprietor, Gordon Bennett, instigated a series of long distance races, the first being won by an American who clocked up 402 miles—from Paris to Whitby in Yorkshire. Sport-loving ladies found ballooning much to their taste, considering it more feminine than motoring, but for the time being left aeroplanes to the men.

As early as 1894 Hiram Maxim had constructed an aeroplane that would probably have worked had he had a light aero-engine at his disposal. In 1900 he complained that he had spent £17,000 on the problem of a heavier-than-air machine. In the event he was beaten to it by the Wright brothers in 1902. In 1906 the *Daily Mail* offered £10,000 to the first person to fly from London to Manchester; this was won by a Frenchman, Paulhan. Blériot had already taken the *Daily Mail* prize of £1,000 for the first cross-channel flight. He and the other aeronauts were fêted by Lord Northcliffe, who in the columns of the *Daily Mail* emphasised the importance of flight; the Blériot plane was set up in Selfridge's in Oxford Street, and the music hall brought the good news to the masses:

> There's a wonderful time coming soon,
>   For they tell us we're all going to fly!
> And we'll take daily trips to the moon;
>   What a picnic for both you and I!

Many Englishmen refused to take the aeroplane seriously. The journalist R. D. Blumenfeld declared that 'these things represent a foolish waste of money. Besides, flying across the Channel means nothing after you have done it. You can't carry goods or passengers'.[4] The preference for the airship owed something to the supremacy of French aeronautics, and it was invested with great possibilities. Illustrations were published of the airship of the future crossing the English Channel, with passengers sitting in deck-chairs on the decks, open to the elements.

Nevertheless the *Daily Mail* prizes acted as an incentive. When a prize of £1,000 was offered for the first circular flight of a mile by a British-built aeroplane, industry roused itself, and on 30 October 1909 the money was won by J. C. T. Moore-Brabazon flying a machine built by Short Brothers. Two years earlier, the first short aeroplane flight in England was accomplished by an American, S. F. Cody, in a 'power-kite' of his own invention, somewhat obscurely named British Army Aeroplane No 1.

British Army Aeroplane No 1 did not indicate a startling anticipation of the role which aircraft were to play in the war, and although the Royal Flying Corps was instituted in 1912 it was pathetically ill-equipped, consisting in 1913 of four squadrons of aeroplanes and one of airships and kites, Despite the pre-1909 enthusiasm for ballooning, the British were well behind the Germans and the French in building airships, known as dirigible balloons. In 1908 Count von Zeppelin had built an airship 446 ft in length with a lifting capacity of well over ten tons. The Zeppelin was to be one of the great psychological weapons of the 1914 war.

Notes to this chapter are on page 294.

CHAPTER FIVE

THE SEXUAL REVOLUTION

Eugenics and Birth Control

THE WORD eugenics was first given currency in 1833, and made respectable by Francis Galton (1822–1911), the cousin of Charles Darwin. Galton had written that the active and ambitious classes deferred marriage until they could afford it, and there was thus a permanent obstacle to the fecundity of the 'more elevated classes'. The improvident and the weak-willed were on the other hand very prolific, and in time this would lead to the deterioration of the race, and civilisation would revert to barbarism.

To resolve this problem in a rational manner, the science of eugenics—the deliberate breeding of the superior person, the first superman—was introduced. The Edwardians pursued the study and propagation of this concept with enthusiasm. They took as their text Galton and his followers, some of whom had gone into eugenics because Galton had founded in 1904 a Research Fellowship at London University. The Eugenics Record Office was started in a room in Gower Street, and a few years later was renamed the Eugenics Laboratory. Galton was a man of many parts, explorer, meteorologist, and doctor. The police forces of the world owe him a great debt, for in 1892 his book *Finger*

SHALL BABIES BE ABOLISHED?

A question asked not entirely for fun

Prints laid the groundwork of that method of criminal detection. But his chief claim to fame were his admirable studies in heredity, *Hereditary Genius* (1869) and *Natural Inheritance* (1889).

One of Galton's strongest supporters, Dr James Crichton-Browne, wrote:

> A recognition of the obligations which man owes to his fellow-men, and the promptings of love's divine self-abnegation, impose restraints on some of the competitors, who, instead of forcing their way to the front, as they are well able to do, stand aside and allow themselves to be beaten by those less fitted to survive.[1]

It need not be asked who were the most fitted to survive. The rich. The eugenists conveniently overlooked the fact that the cream of the rich, the old aristocracy, were theoretically low on the list. In his *Physiology of the Mind*, the Victorian pathologist Henry Maudsley stated that the last members of an old family were nearly always consumptive or insane, the two qualities most deplored by eugenists and discovered with alacrity in the lowest echelons of society. There was only one difference: the upper classes were made insane by in-breeding, the lower classes by drink.

The tone of eugenics in the Edwardian period can be judged by the first shot fired by Galton in 1901, when he read a paper to the Anthropological Institute on the 'Possible Improvement of the Human Breed under existing conditions of Law and Sentiment'. The law took no cognisance of the desirability of only perpetuating an élite, and eugenists looked longingly at certain of the United States, where criminals and the insane were unceremoniously sterilized—especially if they were Negroes as well—the Negroes were breeding 4-per-cent quicker than the whites. The British eugenists also envied the no-nonsense attitude of their American colleagues—the American Breeders' Association was formed in 1903.

Respectability was given to the whole eugenics movement by referring back to the classics, in much the same way as homosexuality was made less reprehensible by keying it in with Plato's *Republic*, the book that also provided a starting-point for eugenics. Plato discussed the possibility of improving the human species by arranged marriages, by letting warriors have the first pick of the fair. In Plato's *Laws* there is a proposal to tax bachelors over thirty-five. Aristotle was also brought into the canon, for in his *Politics* he urges the desirability of arranged marriages for the benefit of the children.

The British eugenists had close ties with Germany, where eugenics was known ominously as 'race hygiene'. The effect of eugenics in Germany was considerable, for the theory of the superman had as a supporter not only the eugenists but Friedrich Nietzsche (1844–1900). His superman was to be developed by giving unbridled freedom to the struggle for existence, in which power and pleasure were the only criteria. Historically speaking, Nietzsche's philosophy was a development of that of Schopenhauer. Both of these men were sick, distraught creatures, seeking for a compensation in their ruthless dreams, but nevertheless Nietzsche was seized upon as a guiding spirit by those advocates of the superman who were contemptuous of the gentility of the eugenists.

It was logical to extend the concept of the superman to include the super race, and 'race hygiene' became not only anthropologically but politically exciting. It is of interest to recall that the two composers most influenced by Nietzsche and Schopenhauer—Richard Strauss and Richard Wagner—were key figures in the iconography of Adolf Hitler (though his own tastes were more for *The Merry Widow*). The Nordic blond hero stalks through Wagnerian opera as if aware that the eugenists were about to make him respectable.

Fascinating as the prospect of the superman was, how could racial improvement be effected? The answer was simple. 'Sexual selection, guided by the eugenic ideal rather than by sordid desires, would seem the surest way'.[2] How could the information be acquired to determine whether a match was likely to produce satisfactory progeny? Eugenists were quite willing to make an off-the-cuff decision. The poor, on moral grounds, were bad risks. If pressed, eugenists mentioned the name of Mendel (1822–84), whose paper on plant hybridisation was published in 1865 but largely disregarded until 1900. Most eugenists, however, did not feel at home among gametes and zygotes, preferring to leave to the geneticists the hard work involved in the study of Mendel.

Galton was more to their taste. He was a lively and interesting writer, but apt to see significances where there were none. He had to decide whether the mental and moral qualities of men are inherited according to the same laws that govern the production of eggs by fowl. He tackled this like a dilettante rather than a scientist. He obtained records of what he termed the good tempers and bad tempers of married couples, and tried to find out what proportion of their children were good or bad tempered. He went through old lists of the results of examinations at Cambridge to see what proportion of the sons of those who had gained distinction in these examinations had themselves done well. It need hardly be added that finding out whether a married couple was good or bad tempered depended as much as anything on whether they liked or disliked the observer. The Cambridge 'investigation' meant little, as a child could inherit brains from a mother as well as a father.

Eugenics thus got off to an unfortunate start, as its founding-father was statistically suspect. Eugenics was also centred on physical characteristics. Those unfitted to perpetuate the race were weedy, undernourished, in poor physical shape. Opponents of eugenics pointed out that the 'big blond beast' of Nietzsche, the unthinking ideal product, was not exactly the most desirable type of person to be turned out by the conveyor-belt. And surely, if physical well-being was a prime factor, what would be done about Caesar, an epileptic?

There were some sharp minds in the eugenic movement, but far too many of its members were sublimating their hatred of the lower classes. Many eugenists would, if attention had been directed towards them, have been weighed in the balance and found wanting.

One of the leading figures in British eugenics was Karl Pearson. Born in London in 1857, educated at King's College, Cambridge, he was called to the bar in 1882, a career that did not suit him. He preferred to enter the new field of eugenics, and was appointed Galton Professor of Eugenics at London University. He was awarded the Darwin Medal by the Royal Society for his numerous contributions to the mathematical theory of evolution and heredity. A statistician of rare ability, he was highly regarded as the expert on eugenics after Galton died in 1911, and in 1925 he wrote the definitive biography of Galton.

But behind the impressive façade Karl Pearson was not all that he seemed. Although he did not die until 1936 at the age of 79, he was under the illusion that he had tuberculosis and doomed to die young, an illusion that was not amenable to the statistical method. As an expert on eugenics it might be supposed that he would choose his love object rationally and according to the dictates of his science. There is an element of high comedy in his choice of the novelist Olive Schreiner, who had a frantic desire to wear men's clothes, who proved too much of a handful to Havelock Ellis, and, the final absurdity so far as Pearson was concerned, was a Lesbian.

One of the crispest of Pearson's colleagues was Major Leonard Darwin, president of the Eugenics Education Society from 1911. Darwin poured ridicule on the ostensible goal of eugenics, the

Nietzsche superman; this was better left to the Germans (who did, after all, carry through the charade). Darwin emphasised that the decisive factor in the struggle for existence was general ability, a difficult thing to measure. Not that the eugenists were particularly keen to measure general ability, as they were now hooked, after the random methods of Galton, on investigating children—and children have their own unpredictable ways of turning out differently to hypotheses framed by investigators. The Binet-Simon tests of 1915 were a kind of Bible to latter-day eugenists.

Major Darwin horrified social reformers in his view that the poor deserve to be poor and that their ranks are continuously swollen by the arbitrary descent of the unfit from the upper layers of society. This was comforting for eugenists; it confirmed their intuitive feelings that the poor had only themselves to blame, and that the pressures of society and the wicked capitalist system had nothing to do with the existence of a wretched sub-stratum of society. For, when the pros and cons of eugenics are finally sifted, the whole movement was a weapon of class, a sublimation of the view that the poor were multiplying so fast as to imperil the bastions of the middle classes.

With few exceptions, the Edwardian eugenists were afflicted with an immense arrogance. This was illustrated by a controversy between Pearson and Havelock Ellis carried on with a rancour that would be surprising if one were unaware that they were both rivals for the masculine hand of Olive Schreiner. Pearson claimed that Ellis 'had done much to perpetuate some of the pseudo-scientific superstitions'. Ellis replied ironically that Pearson:

> . . . is careful to tell us at frequent intervals, before he himself entered the field [of eugenics] all was 'dogma', 'superstition', 'nearly all partisan', at the best 'quite unproven'. I am inclined to think that these terms, which spring so easily to Mr. Pearson's pen, are automatic reminiscences of the ancient controversies he has waged with theologians and metaphysicians. [3]

Eugenists also had a penchant for dashing generalities. In his book *Eugenics*, Edgar Schuster summarises, after some inconsequential tests:

> Whatever are the innate differences between university professors, small tradesmen, and the denizens of the Liverpool slums, by the time they reach adult life there is little question that the order in which they would be placed with regard to their intellectual qualities is the same as that in which they are here written.

Some lunatic fringe eugenists believed in telegony. This means that if a woman had a child by one husband and subsequently another child by another husband, the peculiarities of the first husband would exert an influence not only on his own child but on the other man's. Maternal impressions, the action of external factors on an unborn child, were also treated with some respect.

The eugenists could not agree whether war was a good thing for mankind or not. The commonsense view was held by Havelock Ellis, who flirted with eugenics in his book *Man and Woman* (1894). He maintained that it was a remarkable tendency of the warlike spirit to exterminate itself. The fighting stocks were killed off, leaving the prudent, those who fought and ran away. This was disputed. Reckless fighters would be braver and win more quickly than those who fought and ran away, to be regrouped to fight again, and thus prolong a war. In the context of the time, with war just over the horizon, this was not an academic point.

In France and Germany, 30–50 per cent of conscripts were rejected as unfit for any kind of war service, though standards were speedily relaxed when war began. In 1911, 64,000 men offered themselves for enlistment in Great Britain; 45 per cent were turned down. One eugenist did comment that if war occurred the men who were killed would be on an average physically superior to those in their age group who had escaped the risk. But war, and the prospects of war, were far less important than the eugenic duty to restrict the birth-rate of the poor.

Why should the eugenic movement, which had been created well before the twentieth century arrived, have been so influential in Edwardian England? Briefly, the answer lies in the effect of birth control and the coming of the welfare state. In 1906, taxation was levied for the education and preservation of large families of the poor; no longer would their high birth rate be countered by a high death rate in infancy. This taxation was a double-edged weapon to eugenics, for those taxed would limit their own families to suit their pockets and would at the same time be subsidising the erotic behaviour of the lower classes, who lacked the knowledge, the will or the inclination to limit their own families.

It is not surprising that desperate measures were proposed by the eugenist high command. Major Darwin advocated sterilisation of the poor by means of the 'harmless and painless' X-rays, the new fad. This was called 'negative eugenics'; the encouragement of the superior classes to propagate was termed 'positive eugenics'. Such inducement could be monetary, and the eugenists proposed a rating reform. Big families needed big houses; parliament should subsidise rates on these. No one needed telling that the poor with big families did not own houses to pay rates on. Eugenics should be taught at school; the marriage laws should be looked at with a view to prospective spouses having to obtain a medical certificate, and the poor must be implanted with the ethics of love and marriage. Love was not blind, nor did it laugh at locksmiths. In every heart there should be an image of the ideal lover, to serve both as a guide and a goal. The fact was overlooked that it was unusual for a girl of the lower classes to have retained her virginity past the age of fourteen.

Between 1700 and 1800 the population of Great Britain increased by 30 per cent; between 1800 and 1900 it increased by 300 per cent. Some saw this as good; there was more labour to do more jobs and so create trade and prosperity. Others saw it as too many people chasing too few jobs, drawing an analogy with Ireland in 1846, when there was a peasant population of 8 million, living like pigs. Famine and emigration brought the population down to 4 million. The Irish, engage in internicine wars and quarrel with their English overlords as they may, then became prosperous. The Black Death in the fourteenth century reduced England's population by two-thirds; the fifteenth century was the happiest time for the agricultural workers, before or since.

Victorian Britain managed to cope with the population increase, though in the worst quarters of London unemployment was never less than 25 per cent. The colonies absorbed several millions. In the eighteenth century birth control propaganda had been directed at the man about town, but later the emphasis shifted to the respectable married man. During the nineteenth century more than a million tracts were sold on birth control, and many more were distributed free. Two pioneers were Francis Place (*The Principle of Population*, 1822) and Richard Carlile (*Practical Hints on How to Enjoy Life and Pleasure without Harm to Either Sex*, 1826). An English reprint of an American treatise on birth control, *The Fruits of Philosophy*, sold 42,000 copies between 1834 and 1876.

Notwithstanding the torrent of abuse heaped upon birth control, it became more widely adopted and by increasingly efficient methods: vulcanisation of rubber led to the rubber sheath, and in 1886 the soluble quinine pessary was perfected. In the 1870s, two freethinking reformers decided to republish the by then obsolete *Fruits of Philosophy*, and were involved in a tragi-comic court case, for the law saw birth control literature as obscene. The case drew public attention to the facts of contraception, and from 1878 the birth-rate of the United Kingdom dropped. The middle classes were the most significant converts, followed by the 'improved working class', who saw in the restriction of the size of their families a way to ascend the class ladder.

Birth control, despite frowns from some quarters, became respectable; society ladies distributed large quantities of birth control booklets to maternity hospitals. Though condemned by the bishops, the clergy gave their support. The Reverend Dennis Hurd was very pleased with his findings, as described in his book *A Christian with Two Wives*: 'The two girls are happy; they have three sons each, and they might have had ten, but I think three plenty for one woman; it just develops her nature and character, and makes her more lovely'.

At the Manchester Church Congress of 1888, a Professor Symes said, 'I have the strongest reason to know that the subject is engaging the attention of an immense number of people in all classes in England and elsewhere'. As the old century gave way to the new, more and more people planned their families, though because of the prohibition on the sale of birth-control literature many continued to use old-fashioned methods, such as douching, withdrawal, and the utilisation of the so-called safe period, which varied from authority to authority—one writer specified this as just one week a month.

Official attitudes to birth control did not change very much though the propaganda was more open, and there were advertisements on the 'gates of fields in the deep country' and on the walls of railway station urinals. Advertisements in periodicals and newspapers were bitterly attacked, and readers of *Myra's Journal* in 1905 would soon acquire 'a second-hand knowledge which would place them on an equal footing with an experienced prostitute'. More reprehensible than advertisements for contraceptives were tracts on induced abortion, making use of pills of lead plaster; a liquor in which copper coins had been boiled; quinine crystals, and various salts.

The medical profession closed its eyes to the new wave. The *Lancet* declared that birth control was a 'distasteful subject', but notwithstanding the aversion of the general practitioner to discuss the topic there was evidence of an increased use of contraception by the middle classes. In 1905–6 the Fabian Society found that, out of 316 marriages investigated, 242 couples practised birth control. The most powerful indication that even the most respectable members of the middle class were practising it came with the census of 1911, where it was found that Church of England clergymen, those prolific breeders of Victorian times, were 30 per cent less fertile than the population as a whole.

In 1906 Sidney Webb, the doyen of the left wing intellectuals, declared that between a half and two-thirds of married people practised some form of birth control. A new generation of propagandists emerged, though most of their books were not written until the war and after. The most famous of these was Marie Stopes, whose *Married Love* (1918) became perhaps the most widely read book on birth control, and only marginally less influential was Margaret Sanger, whose *Family Limitations* was published in 1914.

The morals and motivations of the new school could not be reasonably questioned. Generally speaking, the police preferred to leave the propagandists alone, though in 1911 James White was arrested for selling *True Morality* in the market place in Stanley, County Durham; he was fined £20, but chose instead to go to prison. In 1913 the Malthusian League (Malthusianism, drawing its name from Malthus, the eighteenth-century clergyman who foresaw the dangers of a teeming population, was the Victorian name for birth control) organised twice-weekly meetings in Southwark, and within a month had distributed 25,000 handbills to the working classes.

The books on birth control issued during the Edwardian period were considerably better than those produced during the nineteenth century, which were furtive in tone. There was a big mail order business, supplying such books under plain cover. *Hygienic Methods of Family Limitation* (1913) pronounced the safe period risky; withdrawal difficult on the nerves; and advocated sheaths at between 2s and 6s a dozen, which could be washed and used four or five times; and pessaries at 2s a dozen.

There was mutual distrust between the birth controllers, who wished to encourage the poor to practise birth control, and the eugenists, who preferred legislation and force, and were more interested in its benefits to the upper and middle classes than to the poor. Notwithstanding a certain prurience on the part of birth control enthusiasts, there is little doubt that they were considering the welfare of the poor when they took what they termed 'the good news' to the masses.

The rise in the number of respectable advocates of birth control did much to rob the movement of its Victorian reputation, and the support of the popular weekly magazine *John Bull* from 1910 nullified a good deal of reactionary opinion. Those who attacked birth control saw that it could no longer be put forward as an unqualified evil, but the wide sale of contraceptives and birth control literature would, they argued, destroy sexual morality. This was put uncompromisingly by Lieutenant-Colonel Everitt, who told a House of Commons committee on patent medicines in 1912 that 'young people of both sexes are led to believe that they can have illicit intercourse without any fear of detection, and this, of course, leads to what may be called free love, amateur prostitution, and other evils of that sort'.

The overwhelming success of the birth control movement is demonstrated by the 1911 Census, which also makes clear that the eugenists' fears that the poor were breeding faster than the other classes were justified:

England and Wales, 1911 Social Class	Legitimate birth rates in social classes per 1,000 married males
1 Upper and Middle	119
2 Intermediate Class	132
3 Skilled Workmen	153
4 Intermediate Class	158
5 Unskilled Workmen	213

The middle classes had to overcome their scruples before practising birth control; they veered between listening to the strictures of their mentors, doctors and clergymen, and self-interest. Nothing illustrates so well the hypocrisy of the middle classes as their fulmination against birth control propagandists and their consistent use of birth control methods. The upper classes had no such scruples. In an interesting investigation carried out using Burke's Peerage, it was found that marriages among the aristocracy during the ten years ending in 1840 gave an average of 7.1 births to each fertile couple; the ten years ending in 1850 and in 1860 each gave 6.1 births. But from 1871 to 1880 they dropped to 4.36, and from 1881 to 1890 to 3.13. This was reckoned by statisticians to be below the figure needed to sustain the class, and it was facts like this that led the eugenics movement into such contortions in the first ten years of this century.

Edwardian Love and Romance

To a large section of the population the passing of Queen Victoria meant little in the day-to-day business of life. They mourned her, were appropriately enthusiastic about her successor, and then relapsed into their normal routine. Victorianism did not end with the accession of King Edward, and in many middle-class families the old taboos and proscriptions were maintained. If anything, some of the more reactionary families tightened their control on their impressionable young, especially their daughters, when they sensed that the mood of the fin-de-siècle showed no sign of dispersing.

The 'improved working classes' were also concerned about the morals of their children. The Education Act of 1870 was beginning to bite in respect of the child-bearing age groups, and the improved working class was at pains to disown its former drinking, blasphemous image. In the lace-curtained terrace houses of Balham and Clapham there was no shortage of gentility.

Gentility can imply an aversion to looking at facts, the preference of an easy-going ignorance to knowledge, and a fondness for stale archetypes. One of these archetypes was the relation between the sexes. At no time was there a greater interest in love and romance than among the middle classes and improved working classes of the first decade and a half of the present century. Romance was supplied by a host of hack writers and ethereal lady novelists, and figured strongly in such books as Baroness Orczy's *The Scarlet Pimpernel* (1905) and *The Elusive Pimpernel* (1908). Love and romance were therefore seen through the filter supplied by writers, such as the novelist de Vere Stacpoole, whose *The Blue Lagoon* was the best-seller of 1908.

A characteristic supplier of antidotes to apprehension and a copious provider of formulas for the marriageable was Elinor Glyn. She produced a novel almost every year containing heroines who were nicely saucy or haughty, epitomised by Ambroisine in *The Reflections of Ambroisine* (1902). In a passage at arms with a wealthy young man who uses phrases like 'snug little crib' and 'beastly hard luck' (and was thus rather common), Ambroisine is kissed against her will; she repulses the man with 'You are to understand that I will not be mauled—and kissed like—Hephzibah at the back door.' 'Hoity-toity', the man replies, 'what airs you give yourself! but you look so deuced pretty when you are angry.'

Elinor Glyn occasionally turned away from fiction to summarise her philosophy of love. 'The lowest creatures, the worst characters', she wrote, 'are raised when they love—because for the time it holds them under its sway, they cease to be utterly selfish.' Also 'The first thing to learn—and to drum into your head—is that no one can love or unlove at will', and 'Love improves the character: it brings kindness and tolerance for others, and a generosity unknown at other times.' Elinor Glyn was also inclined to see love as an aesthetic process: 'To bring love to perfection is just as difficult as to rear a delicate plant, and every one of its changes must be watched and guided.'

In real life, romance was found to be inconclusive and arbitrary. Guided by pre-set ideas and misled by the fantasies of fiction writers, its followers got themselves into difficulties, turning for help to the advice columns of the women's magazines. Some of these journals were edited by the most inappropriate of men. Frank Harris, whose *My Life and Loves* has only recently been brought out from under the counter to be sold openly, edited *Vanity Fair* from 1907 to 1910 and *Hearth and Home* from 1911 to 1912. The health and beauty column of *Hearth and Home* had Dame Deborah Primrose assuring readers that a prominent bust was not in good *ton*, and although Harris was quite likely to roar out to worried correspondents who called at the office, 'There's only one use for a woman—get out of here before I show you', he knew that the success of a woman's paper depended on the charisma of its advice columns.

Annie S. Swan, a no-nonsense daughter of a Scots farmer, whose hobbies were walking, cycling and golf, edited *The Woman at Home*, and herself replied to correspondents. A surprising number of the letters were written by men. Miss Swan

The fantasies of writers of fiction led many people astray. Romance was not as clear cut as it was in magazine serials

(in real life Mrs Burnett Smith) advised 'Wanderer' to leave his wife alone as, now that she was comfortable and in a good position, he might be accused of ulterior motives were he to persecute her any more. 'Crushed Violets' was advised to dismiss her careless lover from her mind, and console herself with someone else; while 'Her Friend' wrote telling Miss Swan of the case of a friend who had been replaced in a husband's affection by a younger woman. This letter filled Miss Swan with 'a great, sad indignation'. Probably aware that 'Her Friend' was the woman herself, she delicately asked whether the deserted woman was letting herself go in the matter of looks.

She was not afraid to administer a sharp tap on the wrist. 'Looker On' was advised to mind her own business; 'Bobby' was

"Look into my eyes and tell me that you hate me!"

How far could flirting go without being immoral? There was little help from Crosspatch Patty *by E. Maria Albanesi for which this illustration was drawn*

told to write in a different tone; and 'Daisy Darling', who complained that her lover had tired of her and who wanted him punished, was told not to be a bore. She was puzzled by a morbid hysterical letter from 'Budah', whom she told to do some honest hard work; and did not discern the psychological motives behind a letter from 'La Desirée' who 'is afflicted with a mysterious charm which causes every man who meets her to fall in love with her'.

A good percentage of the letters related to suspicions, and her advice was to bring everything out into the open. There were also anguished queries as to how far flirting could go without being immoral, or indeed where could a line be drawn between everyday civility and flirting, at a time when comradeship between the sexes was a great talking point. Miss Swan took a sensible line on platonic friendships; these, she considered, were not possible. She mentioned an instance of one that had lasted seventeen years and then ended in marriage; a waste, she commented, of seventeen years. 'French Marigold' was involved in a platonic friendship, and clearly wished it to be less platonic; she was advised to talk it over with her parents.

A correspondent signing herself 'Revolting Daughter' wanted some share of the emancipation cake, but was too habituated to parental control to do anything about it. She was having a mild affair with a youth who worked in her father's music warehouse and was teaching her the mandolin. Like 'French Marigold', she was advised to tell the whole story to her parents.

Unquestionably Miss Swan was on the side of the establishment, and if all correspondence columns had been conducted with her assurance parents would have had nothing to fear. The main problems of the letter writers derived from their having taken too seriously the facts of life as emasculated by novelists. Most writers, no matter how they conducted their own lives, would not commit themselves in print. George Bernard Shaw professed to be sexually liberated, but when he was expected by fellow socialists to publicly denounce marriage he was obdurate, warning his disciples that disregard of the conventions brought too much friction into private life and that it was troublesome enough being a socialist and agnostic without professing free love. His ethos was based on the motto: 'Do not throw out dirty water until you get in fresh'. In other words, keep marriage until you find something better.

Marriage was the rock on which romance foundered, but it was also the sacred state that preserved the respectability of advice columns in women's papers. Speculations in the daily newspapers about the possibility of introducing 'marriage leases' were treated as the outpourings of atheists or—worse—socialists. 'It would seem', declared Annie Swan, 'that the cancer of selfishness and flippancy is more widely spread through society than we dreamed.' However, the danger was more apparent than real. 'The great bulk of British people are still sound in the fundamentals.'

Nevertheless, even the women's pages recognized that marriage was no longer the religious state that it once had been, and was now tied up with the concept of home and duty. Going into marriage also had an element of the heroic, and proved that the British, eschewing selfish indulgence and happiness, were not so degenerate as many thought.

Bernard Shaw urged his women friends not to burn their boats without the protection and status of legal marriage—unless they were economically independent. D. H. Lawrence was not so circumspect. 'Only through a readjustment between men and women, and a making free and healthy of this sex, will she get out of her present atrophy',[1] he declared. But he did not live up to his convictions and as soon as he could, in 1914, he married a Nottingham lecturer's wife with whom he had eloped. H. G. Wells, another pioneer in the re-evaluation of the married state, defended his own marriage by saying, 'In our period, if we had not married, half our energy would have been frittered away in a conflict of garden-wall insults and slights and domestic exactions'.[2] Yet in a paper read to the Fabian Society in 1906 he stated that, 'I no more regard the institution of marriage as a permanent thing than I regard a state of competitive industrialism as a permanent thing'.[3]

The influence of such novelists as Wells played a part in

"Oh, by the way," you hear him say,
"I wish you'd marry me some day;
"How would next Friday fortnight suit you?
"And—may I (what they call) 'salute' you?"

Marriage was no longer the religious state of the Victorians, but it was not usual to treat it with flippancy

determining attitudes towards marriage, and *Ann Veronica* was treated as a primer by emancipated women and by women who desperately wanted to be emancipated. Today Ann Veronica herself would cause few eyebrows to rise, but to her real-life contemporaries she epitomised a type to be emulated. The book was banned, preached against, and attacked by the editor of *The Spectator*, John St Loe Strachey, as '. . . the muddy world of Mr Wells' imaginings, a community of scuffling stoats and ferrets, unenlightened by a ray of duty and abnegation'.

The old brigade regarded marriage as being under greater pressure than was the case, and literature that tended to degrade the institution was treated in a hostile manner. Duty and obeisance to the will of society kept marriages going even in the saddest conditions, and where partners were, as Carlyle put it, 'gey ill to live with' a pretence was kept up. Divorce was still a rarity. Between 1906 and 1910 an average of 638 decrees nisi were granted each year, and the rate of divorce had hardly altered since Victorian times. Divorce action was extremely expensive; an undefended suit would cost between £50–£60, and a defended case could cost upwards of £500. When it is borne in mind that only 70 per cent of petitions were successful, ill-matched partners were reluctant to go through the traumatic process even when they could afford to. The poorer classes were in no position to engage in divorce proceedings, and in 1909 a royal commission was appointed to look into the laws of divorce with particular reference to the poor.

Adultery was still the inexcusable sin, except among the rich and the emancipationists, and was discussed in hushed whispers unless it could be made to appear comical. On the other hand, a breach of promise action was 'socially a dead letter for all but the ladies of the dramatic profession and the lower classes'.[4]

No matter how hazardous marriage might be, there was no shortage of contestants. Those who could not find their own mates applied to the matrimonial agencies or advertised in the columns of the Sunday newspapers. A number of interesting letters appeared in *Reynold's News* in January 1908:

A superior person would like to marry an honourable man. Would make a capable farmer's wife. Aged 33.

Two friends (30, 32) highly respectable, domesticated, honourable women, would like to meet two friends or brothers, steady honourable men, retiring from navy or mechanics.

Eva, 4' 11", 25, fair, wished to meet a refined dark man, with the added stipulations that he must be an abstainer and a nonconformist (in religion not habits). A Christian gentleman of means, of a loving disposition, sought a wife; an affliction was not objected to. The customs and taboos of society always create outsiders, and although such plaintive and pathetic letters were not by any means uncommon in Victorian popular papers, it is somehow surprising to find them in the Edwardian Sunday press. The call for marriage candidates of an 'honourable nature' demonstrates that the advertisers were well aware that male readers might con the correspondence columns with a view to adventure, though there is some doubt whether the more vulnerable were protected by this stipulation.

The problems of love and marriage can be read between the lines of the agony columns of *Reynold's News*:

PAT—tremendous row. Consequences awkward. Forbidden to play bridge. Happily no blame attaches to you. Say nothing. Be careful. E.

DEARIE—Enjoyed Saturday evening, especially cab ride between Waterloo and Vauxhall. Caught 1.20 am train to Clapham. All right at home. Meet me same time tomorrow. EVENING DRESS.

FAIR ONE—Do be patient, dear. It is all for your good. K. would make life intolerable if he knew. CHIP.

Though there was also promise:

Delighted to see you. Sooner the better. How would Tuesday 3.30 Charing-cross bookshop suit you? Girl in Gray.

Will charming young lady wearing green feather hat with white boa who caught eye of gentleman in Putney bus on Friday last communicate with Admirer? There was then no opportunity of speaking. Address this paper. P.S.T.

Women were able to escape into business. No longer was marriage the only career open to them

The young were often handicapped in their pursuit of love by the resentment and petulance of the old and middle aged. The old would not let Victorianism die. They were envious of the freedom of the young Edwardian woman who was going out to work in one of the professions, such as medicine, opened up to them by the stout pioneering work of progressive Victorian women. An army of young women were recruited to operate the telephone exchanges; in 1901 only 18 per cent of telephone operators were female, but in 1911 this had risen to 32 per cent and rose higher still by 1914, when there were 775,000 telephones in Great Britain. Even more significant was the revolution in business activity caused by the wholesale acceptance of the typewriter. Being a typist was considered a respectable occupation for a middle-class girl, and being twice as well paid as a shop assistant the typist became a person worth the courting by the mass media. The typist also created a new type of life-style, and was wholly responsible for the genesis of the tea-room and the cafeteria.

These well-bred young ladies, set uncertainly in the social structure between the shop-girl and the teacher, were torn between the influences of the home and those of the emanci-pationists—reluctant either to adhere to the moral standards of their parents or throw in their lot with the New Woman. They were therefore very much inclined to seek an answer to their uncertainties in fiction or the popular press.

The high-class newspapers and periodicals took a very priggish tone about the romance that was served up to an eager readership. Of Elinor Glyn's *Three Weeks*, the *Daily Telegraph* wrote that 'the record of these erotic passions . . . only avoids by a hair-breadth the accusation of growing positively squalid', a critique that did the book no harm as two million copies were sold in nine years.

In the end, the Edwardians had to adjust as best they could to their human needs. Only in retrospect can their age be seen as extravagant or ostentatious, greedy or immoral. The people themselves were still in thrall to their Victorian upbringing, and were confused by the diverse promptings of what they recognised as a different age, though in what ways it was different they could only guess. At one time, the bemused had found help and consolation in the Bible; thwarted and hopeless love would find final consummation in the hereafter. The Edwardians did not have this straw to cling to, but sought succour in women's magazines and in the tabloid newspapers pandering to bewilder-ment. Genuine information about love and romance, the counter-feits for sex, was hard to come by, and the glib answers of journalists were not good enough. Although it was the age of Havelock Ellis and earnest studies into the psychology of sex, such works were not for the masses, and middle class and working class investigators had to find consolation in such insipidities as Edward Carpenter's *Love's Coming of Age*.

In many cases it was reassurance rather than information that was wanted. The Edwardian young were vouchsafed glimpses of the ideal love, and built fantasies upon this which toppled before the inroads of reality. It is the theme of thousands of Victorian novels, and the Edwardians had no monopoly on unrequited love, on misunderstandings, or on fickle fate. But unlike the previous age they had nothing to fall back on.

The Feminists

The lethargy and the apathy of Edwardian men in politics, the arts, and everything except the pursuit of pleasure was countered by ferocious energy on the part of their women folk, which reached its apotheosis in the suffragette movement, but which was apparent in a variety of diverse activities. The women of the middle classes and the upper classes played whist and bridge with a concentration and a devotion that their husbands could rarely match, hordes of women cyclists tried to demonstrate that women were no longer the weaker sex, and in hockey, golf, ping-pong, diabolo and Swedish drill women were as active as men. Lady beaglers in masculine garb tore through hedges and fell into ditches, ju-jitsu and fencing were practised by belligerent young women with unyielding verve, and when the British leisured classes made ski-ing in Switzerland an in-sport the women were as much in evidence as the men. In 1912 a Miss Maitland had the temerity to win an all-comers ski competition.

The game of bridge was introduced into London clubs in 1894 as Russian Whist, but the vogue did not really get under way until 1907 when auction bridge was evolved ('Strange game of esoteric charm, Bridge of a myriad sighs and curses'). The power of bridge was such that it all but killed fashionable 'At Homes' and nearly finished musical evenings, though that, declared the *Morning Post*, would be 'a crowning mercy'. Bridge was coincident with the rise of women's clubs. In 1913 there were twenty-two clubs for women in London, including the Ladies' Army & Navy.

IT TAKES TIME.

Miss Weston: "AND HAVE YOU PLAYED MUCH GOLF, MR. JONES?"

Mr. Jones: "WELL—ER, NO, CAN'T SAY I'VE *PLAYED* MUCH, BUT I'VE WALKED ROUND THE LINKS SEVERAL TIMES IN THESE CLOTHES, AND I'M BEGINNING TO UNDERSTAND THE LANGUAGE."

In sport, the arts, and business, women were no longer content to be the weaker sex, and could be formidable adversaries, as this 1901 cartoon makes clear

Women were no longer restricted to their homes and a dull round of social visiting; increasingly, restaurants and tea-shops catered for feminine restlessness. Harrods opened a Gentlemen's Club and a Ladies' Club; in the latter tea was served to the accompaniment of Harrods Royal Red Orchestra. In 1903 the *Daily Mail* referred to the number of 'quick lunch' establishments opening, at which the customers helped themselves, and there was a splurge of vegetarian restaurants, the clients of which were predominantly women entranced by the new fad, nut diets.

The stage was set for women to exert their influence. They were venturing into politics. The Hon Mrs Alfred Lyttelton, author of *Warp and Woof*, a play dealing with the oppression of the dressmakers, was an active member of the Women's Liberal-Unionist Association and the Victoria League; Mrs Brodrick, wife of the war minister, was on the executive committee of the Ladies' Grand Council of the Primrose League, of which the vice-president was the formidable Lady Ancaster, a society hostess in the grand manner.

Some of the women had thrown off not only their stay-at-home ways but their stays as well. They wanted it conceded that not only were they men's equals, but they were their superiors, infinitely brighter, better and finer. Their rallying cry was 'Votes for Women!'

In 1903 the Women's Social and Political Union was formed. This was not another Women's Liberal-Unionist Association or Victoria League; the WSPU was militant and aggressive. Its leading figure was Mrs Pankhurst, widow of Dr Pankhurst who had been prominent in women's suffrage since 1868, when, as a barrister, he had defended women ratepayers in a test case. The Liberals had disillusioned him, and after Gladstone 'had thrown the women overboard' in 1884 the Pankhursts deserted the party and flirted with the Independent Labour Party. Dr Pankhurst died in 1898, and Mrs Pankhurst felt free to leave Labour; the Manchester Suffrage Society was dreary and old-fashioned, and, worst of all, democratic. Mrs Pankhurst deemed herself the king-pin in the 'votes for women' movement, and gathered round her a select group of new women, malcontents and despairing spinsters.

One of these was Annie Kenney, a cotton operative who had lived all her life at Lees, near Oldham, and had started work at ten years old. Thin, haggard, hysterical, Annie Kenney was the stuff of which disciples are made. She tried to join the local committee of the card and blowing-room operatives, but the men were aghast at the prospect of women trade unionists. They told her she would not like it, as textile unionists were a drunken lot, more interested in whippet-racing than anything else, and held their meetings in public houses. Other members of the movement included Miss Kerr, the office manager, whose main motivation for being a suffragette was her hatred of her architect father; Beatrice Sanders, the wife of a Fabian; Aela Lamb, a frail orphan anxious for revenge on society; Mary Home, who kept the newspaper cuttings and the research material, a pale young woman with a hare lip, the daughter of an Indian Army officer; Vera Holmes, a singer in Gilbert and Sullivan opera; and Jessie Spink, a shop assistant who carried a portrait of Mrs Pankhurst on her breast, and who, aflame with aspiration, changed her name to Vera Wentworth to become a novelist.

However, Mrs Pankhurst's two greatest allies were her daughters Sylvia and Christabel, whom she overpowered with her rancour and bitterness. The eagerness of these three women to get the vote became an obsession. The movement was helped because many politicians thought that women should get the vote; these politicians were on the left wing, and did not realise that when women did get the vote they would be the most powerful force against them (if there were no women voters today the Labour Party would always be in office).

The suffragettes' most loyal supporter was the veteran Labour politician Keir Hardie, who lived a frugal life at 14 Nevill's Court, just off Fetter Lane in London. His walls were covered with engravings of socialist heroes of yesteryear, and he had a collection of fossils gathered when he was a coal miner. The prim anti-sexual demeanour of the Pankhursts appealed to him, brought up in a Calvinistic environment. He gave them tea and scones, and saw them and their movement through a veil of sentiment.

The Fabian Society was wholeheartedly behind women's franchise—theoretically. But many of its members were disappointed by the women who were out to achieve it. If women wanted to be free, wrote H. G. Wells, good luck to them; free love and birth control would necessarily replace domestic chains. He was disillusioned. 'It became increasingly evident that a large part of the woman's suffrage movement was animated less by the desire for freedom and fullness of life than by a

The gallery of the House of Commons became a gathering point for ardent suffragettes

passionate jealousy and hatred of the relative liberties of men'. For one woman who wanted to live generously and nobly there were a score who merely wanted to make things uncomfortable for the 'insolent, embarrassing, oblivious male. They did not want more life; their main impulse was vindictive'.[1]

In 1905 the Women's Enfranchisement Bill was talked out ·in the Commons by Henry Labouchere, who objected to women getting the vote on the somewhat obscure grounds that they could not be soldiers; when another member pointed out that he was not a military man, Labouchere exploded in patriotic rage. Mrs Pankhurst had watched the scene from the public gallery, and went down to break the news to her colleagues. There was in indignation meeting, joined by Keir Hardie, at which one of the old timers, Mrs Wolstenholme Elmy, decided to tell everyone about the early days of the movement back in 1865.

Despite events in London the movement was still centred in Manchester. It was clear that the Conservative government was doomed, and when Sir Edward Grey arrived to speak in the Manchester Free Trade Hall in October 1905 it was as a future cabinet minister that he was treated. The suffragettes were present in force, and when Grey refused to answer questions about votes for women, Christabel Pankhurst and Annie Kenney created a scene, spitting and scratching at police officers called to remove them. Manchester made the mistake of making martyrs of them; summoned to court, Miss Pankhurst decided to go to prison for seven days, Miss Kenney for three, rather than pay nominal fines.

The matter received wide publicity in the London press. The *Evening Standard* was for the girls going to prison, the *Daily Mail* declared that this only proved that women did not deserve the vote. Keir Hardie telegraphed that it was a dastardly outrage to send the girls to prison, but it would do immense good for the cause. The implications were seen by Winston Churchill, who was at the Free Trade Hall, and he went to Strangeways Gaol to pay the fine, an offer that was refused by the governor. It is possible that by turning down the fifteen shillings the governor of the gaol cost his country hundreds of thousands of pounds.

The suffragettes realised that by being sent to prison they would win public sympathy. Now that the Liberals were set for power, the future cabinet appeared at the Albert Hall to answer questions. The chance was too good to miss, and the suffragettes created a scene and unrolled a 9 ft banner from the balcony. At an Asquith meeting in Sheffield, Annie Kenney began to wail, and her companion, Sylvia Pankhurst, was uncomfortably aware that the audience would think that Miss Kenney was mad. Men in the audience struck her with fists and umbrellas, and she was ejected, but still not imprisoned. It might be different in London. It was. The *Daily Mail* gave the movement the label 'the Suffragettes', though *Punch* preferred 'the Insuffrabelles'.

Society eccentrics, such as Lady Carlisle and her son the Honourable Geoffrey Howard, backed the suffragettes, and the maverick journalist and half-mad W. T. Stead offered enthusiastic support, having to be forcibly prevented from kissing Annie Kenney.

At this stage the movement began to get substantial financial help, and the Pethick Lawrences allied themselves to the suffragettes. The Pethick Lawrences had founded a co-operative dressmaking venture, a holiday hotel for working girls, and had built a children's holiday home. Lawrence's monthly paper, the *Labour Record*, was a platform for suffragette thought.

The new government was more openly sympathetic than the Conservatives had been towards enfranchisement. Two hundred MPs formed themselves into a Women's Suffrage Committee; these included members of the opposition who had been stead-fastly against the movement but now realised this was a wonderful chance to embarrass the government. Mrs Pankhurst thought that now was the time to jump in and create a major disturbance in the House of Commons, but her daughters dissuaded her. Some idea of Mrs Pankhurst's egotism can be gauged by her tearful reproof: 'You have balked me—both of you! I thought there would have been one little nitch [sic] in the temple of fame for me!'[2]

Keir Hardie remained the spearhead of the 'votes for women' lobby, and in April 1906 the matter was brought up again. The suffragettes in the gallery were over-anxious; when they saw policemen ranged around the wall, they erupted, were ejected, and thus alienated their supporters in parliament. In May a deputation representing 260,000 women was advised to be patient. But the suppressed hysteria was bubbling over, and there was increasing violence on both sides when meetings were interrupted: One suffragette lashed out with a dog-whip at a steward attempting to eject her, while Annie Kenney was again sent to prison, though other suffragettes avoided martyrdom by having their fines paid by well-wishers.

To many people the whole business seemed to be getting beyond a joke. Women, who saw no purpose in getting the

A cartoon strip dealing with the increasingly militant suffragettes

vote and were quite happy with the power they already wielded, banded together to show that the suffragettes were atypical. A petition was presented signed by 243,852 women resolutely anti-suffragette. The male viewpoint was that ladies, whatever their grievances, should behave in a ladylike respectable manner. There was an ironical news item: 'Two suffragettes the other evening made their way into a private house where a reception was given in honour of Mr Asquith, and created an unpleasant scene. They were disguised as ladies'.

The novelist Elizabeth Robins, who was also an actress known for her interpretation of Ibsen, caught the spirit of the time and smartly turned out the play *Votes for Women* and the novel *The Convert*. The Court theatre, never averse to topical themes, put on the play in April 1907. Christabel Pankhurst was becoming the heroine of the movement, outshining her mother and sister, who complained of her 'incipient Toryism' and ruthlessness. Those who spoke quaveringly of the good old days of the 1860s were being ousted in favour of professionals who could raise money. The movement's income was £3,000 in 1906–7; £7,000 in 1907–8; reaching £20,000 in 1908–9, and £32,000 in 1909–10. More than 5,000 meetings were held in 1907–8; the paper *Votes for Women*, founded the same year, had a circulation of nearly 40,000 by 1909–10.

The full militancy of the suffragettes became evident on 23 October 1906 when they held a meeting in the lobby of the House of Commons. Their all-embracing wish was realised; they were all sent to prison. The national press welcomed the strong line of the Cannon Row Police Court magistrate, and amusedly quoted Christabel Pankhurst's statement, 'Four working women from the north went to prison, and their husbands are enthusiastic'.

Women's prison life in 1906 was squalid and degrading. Keir Hardie demanded for the suffragettes the status of political prisoners, which would have meant better treatment, but this was refused. Several women were released by undertaking to keep the peace; Mrs Montefiore considered no cause was worth having vermin in the hair. Sylvia Pankhurst stuck it out and received some of the glare of publicity that had fallen too strongly on her more exotic sister. She made a little money by writing about her terrible experiences in Holloway Gaol. Rival suffrage movements, such as the National Union of Women's Suffrage, headed by Mrs Fawcett, praised the courage of the imprisoned suffragettes— except the Pankhursts. The non-militants did not want anything to do with that family.

The spirit of martyrdom was abroad; every progressive woman wanted to go to prison. The police obliged. Fourteen days in Holloway was as good as a testimonial, as can be seen from an advertisement in the journal *Votes for Women*: 'SUFFRAGETTE leaving Holloway Prison on the 28th inst. desires post as SECRETARY, or would undertake typewriting at home'. The small Labour Party representation in parliament watched developments with disquiet and started their own movement, the Women's Labour League. Keir Hardie was caught in the middle and disowned by the suffragette high command.

Christabel Pankhurst thought her sister Sylvia was getting too much attention, and threw herself into another Houses of Parliament battle so as to get arrested. When suffragettes were released there was joy all round; in addition Sylvia was troubled by the attentions of W. T. Stead who gave every indication of trying to ravish her. In 1907 seventy-five women and one man were arrested in an assault on the Houses of Parliament, the object of which was to seize the mace. Included in the round-up were two lady painters from Norway and Italy who had nothing to do with the show. The Pankhursts went about the country spreading the suffragette message, and Mrs Pankhurst narrowly escaped being rolled in a barrel in Newton Abbot. Cabinet ministers were cautious about open meetings, and audiences were admitted only by tickets. The suffragettes resorted to forged tickets. Accosting ministers at meetings and receptions became a new tactic.

A further attack on parliament was carried out by twenty-one suffragettes hiding in two furniture vans; funds were raised by a week of self-denial; sympathisers rattled collecting boxes at

The Haunted House—a vision of the House of Commons during the Suffragettes' Reign of Terror.

A newspaper cartoon indicating the prevalent attitude towards ' Votes for Women'

street corners; and John Galsworthy donated autographed copies
of his books to help the cause. Winston Churchill was an especial
target for suffragette hatred; he described the suffragettes as
hornets, 'allying themselves with the forces of drink and reaction'.
In the summer of 1908 a great demonstration was held in Hyde
Park. Thirty special trains were run from the provinces. The
organisers counted on an audience of 250,000. *The Times*
declared that the numbers that actually came could be treble
this; the *Daily Express* commented: 'It is probable that so many
people never before stood in one square mass anywhere in
England'. The government was challenged to do something,
faced by this support. It would not. After a demonstration in
Parliament Square, where the women were manhandled by
the police and by roughs, two suffragettes took a cab to Downing
Street and threw two stones through the window of No 10.
It was the beginning of a new campaign.

A schism between militants and non-militants was splitting

the movement, but the former were winning. For the opening of parliament on 13 October 1908 it was decided to rush the House of Commons. Handbills were printed; a 'votes for women' kite was flown over the parliament building; and a steam launch, with posters announcing the forthcoming attraction, patrolled the river. For what was called the Battle of Parliament Square, the police were massed in cordons, 5 ft deep, and instructed to make as few arrests as possible. A show trial with Christabel Pankhurst fizzled out, though she was sent to prison. *Punch* thought of a way to stop demonstrations: pass an act making it a penal offence for any newspaper to publish the names or photographs of any females offending against public order.

Christabel Pankhurst and her mother were now in prison together. Mrs Pankhurst broke the rule of silence and was put in solitary confinement; she obtained the intervention of the powerful C. P. Scott of the *Manchester Guardian*. The government were at a loss what to do; Asquith's motto of 'Wait and see' hardly applied to the mounting energy of the militants. Worse was to come. When an attempt was made to eject another demonstrator from the ladies' gallery of the House of Commons, it was found that she had chained herself to the metal grille and could only be silenced by being gagged. At meetings, violence accelerated. In the streets women would spring out of vans to write slogans in chalk on the pavement before chaining themselves to railings.

The latest weapon in the suffragette armoury was the hunger strike, suggested by Mrs Pankhurst after her release. The first woman to carry out this threat whilst in prison was a sculptor, who was set free after ninety-one hours of fasting. The police combined their forces to keep the suffragettes out of Parliament Square; the women counter-attacked by breaking windows in government offices. In Liverpool, a suffragette armed with a hatchet climbed on to a roof, tore up slates, and hurled them on to the roof of a hall where the war minister, Haldane, was speaking. An iron bar was thrown through the windows of a railway carriage, and there was an epidemic of window-breaking. The offenders were forthwith sent to prison where they went on hunger strike; but now they were not released, but forcibly fed. This created a furore. Public sympathy, which had been waning, was now reviving. Lady Constance Lytton, who had once rejected militancy, was now burning with fervour and anxious to be incarcerated with other stone-throwers; she seized the opportunity to throw a stone at the radiator of Sir Walter Runciman's car, knowing that as she had a weak heart, prison and forcible feeding would probably kill her, making her the first authentic martyr of the cause and eclipsing all the achievements of the Pankhursts in one fell swoop. To her disappointment, she was released as unfit soon after being given a six-week prison sentence.

Disguised as charwomen, two women broke a stained-glass window during the Lord Mayor's Banquet; two others, disguised as street hawkers, threw an empty ginger-beer bottle into Asquith's car, and Lady Constance Lytton made her second bid for glory by dressing up in poor clothes and assuming the name of Jane Warton, seamstress, before getting arrested. Forcible feeding made her very ill, and in 1910 she had a paralytic seizure, but this did not stop her from window-breaking in 1911. In 1912 she had a stroke, and remained bedridden until her death in 1923. She wrote of herself as:

> One of that numerous gang of upper-class, leisured-class spinsters, un-employed, unpropertied, unendowed, uneducated . . . economically dependent entirely upon others . . . A maiming subserviency is so conditional to their very existence that it becomes an aim in itself, an ideal.[3]

Insight of this quality was rare. Lady Constance Lytton was, far more than the Pankhursts, a tragic figure in the comic opera convulsions of the movement. She was thirty-nine when she joined; when she came out of prison she was fobbed off with a £2 a week job as a junior organiser. Unlike many of her colleagues, Lady Constance believed deeply in what she was doing. The sociologist Masterman saw agitation for the vote as an 'outlet for suppressed energy and proffered devotion'; H. G. Wells dismissed the suffragettes as 'a fluttering swarm of disillusioned and wildly exasperated human beings, all a little frightened at what they were doing'.

Militant leaders of 1910. Left to right: Lady Constance Lytton, Annie Kenney, Mrs Pethick Lawrence, Christabel and Sylvia Pankhurst

In 1910 Asquith called a general election to strengthen his hand—a miscalculation as he lost a hundred seats to the Conservatives, though he retained office through the co-operation of the Irish members. The suffragettes called a truce, hoping for a more acceptable posture on the part of the government. It gave time for everyone to review the matter, and meditate upon the impact of the feminists.

Nothing shook the fabric of society so much as the activities of the militant suffragettes. It seemed as though the sex roles were being reversed, that the viragos were gaining control. The government was seen as effete and powerless, incapable of any sensible action, unable to adjust itself to changing conditions,. and more intent on retaining its dignity than making any strenuous efforts to seek for a formula. It was the case of a weak administration refusing to face the fact that it was weak, and unable to go for a compromise as this would be seen as the victory of a group of hysterical women over gentlemanly statesmanship. The extremists on both sides lost sight of the topic. Votes for women was an excuse for anarchy and repression.

The death of Edward VII threw the suffragette movement into confusion, and Christabel Pankhurst, to the distaste of sister Sylvia, proclaimed her devotion to the throne and all it stood for. With this proof that the suffragettes were human, and the prospect of another bill, significantly named the Conciliation Bill, coming before parliament, it seemed as though there was a chance for peace. The bill did not go through. The militants redoubled their efforts and on 'Black Friday' scenes of unparalleled ferocity occurred in Parliament Square, when 115 women were arrested; the police behaved with zealous brutality, striking the women with their fists, kicking them when they were down, twisting and wrenching arms, rubbing faces against the railings, and pinching breasts. The more refractory women were marched down side streets and beaten up.

Police behaviour was as much a cause for concern as the activities of the suffragettes. It confirmed the belief of the

A new phase of suffragette activity began with attacks on property, especially West End shops

working classes that the police were instruments of government tyranny, even though their attitude towards the suffragettes was one of indifference. In previous years it seemed that the police had instructions to take things coolly, to make as few arrests as possible consistent with preserving order. A government inquiry was requested into the actions of the police, but this was refused by Churchill, for whom a confrontation with the suffragettes was becoming an obsession almost as reprehensible as suffragette violence.

Attempts on the House of Commons were self-defeating. In pitched battles the police always had the ascendancy. Attacks on property were less easily dealt with, and the West End shops were a target for women armed with hammers. Among the stores desecrated were Swan & Edgar, Marshall & Snelgrove, Jay's, Liberty's and Burberry's. It is said that in Bond Street hardly a shop window remained intact. The suffragettes turned their attentions to Knightsbridge and Kensington High Street. The frenzy of destruction was the most alarming thing that had happened yet. A desperate attempt was made to tighten the net round the ring-leaders, and Christabel Pankhurst fled to Paris and directed operations from there.

Harsh treatment had resulted in several deaths, but conditions in Holloway Gaol had eased; Sylvia Pankhurst described it as a veritable Liberty Hall. A wing had been given over to the suffragettes, and cell doors were left unlocked. The composer Ethel Smyth had joined the movement and was writing music for it, including 'March of the Women' and '1910, a Medley'.

The new phase of activities involved arson, destruction of the contents of pillar boxes and the giving of false fire alarms. Street lamps were broken, slogans were painted on the seats on Hampstead Heath, keyholes were stopped up with lead pellets, house numbers were painted out, chairs were flung into the Serpentine, cushions in railway carriages were slashed, flower-beds were damaged, bowling greens and golf courses were cut up, telegraph and telephone wires were severed, and envelopes containing snuff and red pepper were sent to every cabinet minister. The glass of a jewel-case in the Tower of London was

An attack on Buckingham Palace resulted in the arrest of Mrs Pankhurst

smashed; thirteen paintings were mutilated in Manchester Art Gallery; refreshment pavilions were burned down in Regent's Park and Kew Gardens; empty houses were destroyed, and an old cannon near Dudley Castle was fired, terrifying everyone within earshot. The bombing of Lloyd George's new house may have had some connection with votes for women, but little else in this roll call of vandalism had. It was destruction for destruction's sake, a vendetta of hatred.

The government's only satisfaction was that it had found the means to counter the hunger strikes in prisons. The Cat and Mouse Act was passed; a suffragette on hunger-strike was released on ticket-of-leave, and picked up again and put back into prison when she was strong enough.

The war between government and suffragette could have gone on continuously, but both sides experienced a sharp shock on Derby Day 1913, when Emily Wilding Davison threw herself in front of the king's horse and was killed. She had made three attempts to kill herself in prison by flinging herself over corridor railings. The movement had found its first authentic martyr. The self-aggrandisement of the Pankhursts, the repressed naughtinesses of the rank and file, the orgy of destruction were brought into perspective. And so was the reason for it all. For it became apparent that female suffrage was not very important after all. Many continental countries had it, and no disaster had resulted. A movement that arose in China demanding the vote for women had had an immediate success; the Chinese government happily passed a bill, and the women went back to their domestic duties.

The suffragette movement was a symptom of a deep sickness in the state of the country. Publicity made it seem more important than it was; indignation was artificially engendered by news-papers realising that they had a series of scoops on their hands, and when the tempers were easing off the militants did something else to incite the government, the police, and the small traders who were more interested in the fate of their plate glass windows than the whys and wherefores of votes for women.

Whether or not the suffragette campaign was, in the words of H. G. Wells, nagging and ignoble, it did prove how vulnerable England was to internal strife. Fortunately the militant workers did not grasp the lessons, nor was there a liaison between the working classes and the suffragettes, who opened an office in Bow to explain the sex war to the poor. Although the government behaved in a thoroughly block-headed way, it was psychologically checkmated by the perverse attitude of the suffragette high command. The Pankhursts simply could not be reasoned with. Their crusade became an obsession, and they were masochistic in the way they gloried over their imprisonment and the hard-ships they endured. The forcible feeding that so shocked the nation was the answer to hunger strikes, but the suffragettes never seemed to realise that this was, by and large, a response by a civilised regime. It did not occur to them that they could have been left to starve. Incarceration in Holloway gave meaning to the lives of scores of insipid, bored members of the traditional leisured classes. It was pathetic that old and sickly enthusiasts should have been conned into bravado, and have paid for it with their lives.

What did the suffragettes hope to achieve by getting the vote? It is interesting that few of them bothered to think about this; if they did, they thought that paradise would be opened to them. Mrs Pankhurst was sufficiently unhinged to believe that when women got the vote they would cease to menstruate. Envy of men and men's liberties had turned in upon itself.

The male supporters of women's suffrage—Shaw, Galsworthy, the poet Zangwill (licensed buffoon of the set)—shirked martyrdom; they stood on the sidelines and cheered. The Pankhursts were woolly suburbanites with an urge to destroy; responsible followers, such as the Pethick Lawrences, who backed the early endeavours and were later cast off, suffered most. Pethick Lawrence himself was held responsible for the attacks of suffragettes on private property and made bankrupt. Conveniently for the Pankhursts, they had no property that could be sequestered.

In later years, confinement in Holloway, mass demonstrations, and the glorious excitement of window-breaking in the West End became nostalgic topics. There was reticence about the fag-end of the great crusade against sex inequality. H. G. Wells dismissed it in a sentence: 'as Europe collapsed into war, the Vote was flung to women to keep them quiet',[4] an unchivalrous statement that was not correct. By mutual consent, hostilities between the militant suffragettes and the government ceased when the real war started. Most of the suffragettes then diverted their astonishing energy into helping the nation, by taking over the jobs of men who had joined up; they became window-cleaners, plumbers and tram-conductors, joined the nursing services or the new munitions industries. Other women succeeded in coping with the flood of refugees from Europe, especially Belgium, and with a measure of government assistance managed to harbour a quarter of million of them.

The suffragettes were too busy to continue campaigning for the vote, and those who had been most vociferous accepted its coming with a disarming casualness; they were amused rather than angry by Lord Curzon's apoplectic speech declaring that women voters would be the downfall of the Empire.

In February 1918 it was all over. Women had the vote. No longer would MPs automatically throw letters from lady constituents into the wastepaper basket, but it is doubtful whether female suffrage was significant for a good many years.

Notes to this chapter are on page 294.

CHAPTER SIX

ALARMS AND EXCURSIONS

The War Lords

BALFOUR, CAMPBELL-BANNERMAN, and Asquith were termed in a previous chapter as the men at the top. But were they? Perhaps it might be more correct to describe these prime ministers as men who were trying to stay at the top in the face of difficulties caused by their own supporters, who were trying to cope with national and international matters whilst striving to avoid the knife in the back. Their worries were dispersed over a range of topics, and the time at their disposal was insufficient to deal with international matters that they may well have been able to solve better than their foreign secretaries. It is not surprising that, with such pressing burdens as the upsurge of the working classes, the menace of trade unionism, the maniacal belligerence of the suffragettes, the Irish problem, and the administrative difficulties caused by the stirrings of the welfare state, prime ministers relegated the anxieties arising from foreign affairs to the lower levels of the consciousness. Why keep a foreign secretary and bark oneself?

Britain's foreign secretaries, though capable and dutiful, were not fitted for the duties that they should have carried out. They lacked percipience and ruthlessness, and strove endlessly to perpetuate the status quo, pacifying and appeasing if need be.

When they did venture into taking a firm posture, there was an even chance that they would be wrong. A prime example was the support of Sir Edward Grey for the Turkish uprising in 1908, which led to the unseating of the old order that had strong links with Britain and the setting up of a Turko-German understanding.

Actions were taken in the realm of foreign affairs before World War I that were unthinking, meaningless and arbitrary, and those who were concerned with the possible results of muddled diplomacy were often contemptuous, brash and explosive. The most ardent and colourful of the war lords was Sir John Fisher, First Sea Lord between 1904 and 1910. Born in 1841, a midshipman in 1854, Fisher had seen action on the China station. He became the protegé of Admiral James Hope, whose motto was 'favouritism is the secret of efficiency'. It was a motto Fisher never forgot.

At the first opportunity Hope promoted Fisher to lieutenant; in 1869 Fisher became a commander and went back to China, and in 1872 he returned to Britain and specialised in torpedo warfare. In 1881 he was appointed to command *Inflexible*, the largest ship in the Royal Navy, built in 1876 with 18in-thick armour-plating. In 1882 he took part in the bombardment of Alexandria, organised the first armoured train and commanded it in various skirmishes with the Egyptians. After being invalided home, he collaborated with journalist W. T. Stead in *The Truth about the Navy*. In 1886 Fisher was appointed Director of Naval Ordnance; five years later he became Admiral-Superintendent of Portsmouth Dockyard, and gradually rose from Third Sea Lord to become First Sea Lord in 1904.

Fisher's background shows that here was a man, experienced in both administration and command, who knew what he was talking about. Arrogant and overbearing, with a delight in making enemies in politics and within the service, he perhaps could have saved Britain from involvement in the war, by the simple expedient of knocking Germany out before she had re-armed, by 'copenhagening' the German fleet in harbour without warning of war. Fisher was an early disciple of the principle of the first strike. His attitude was exemplified by a sequence of

Britain felt safe in the care of the Royal Navy. It was axiomatic that it was the best in the world

apophthegms published in 1919—'Think in Oceans—shoot at sight', 'Surprise—the pith and marrow of war', 'Rashness in war is Prudence, Prudence in war is Imbecility', 'Hit first! Hit hard! Keep on hitting!' 'The three requisites for success—Ruthless, Relentless, Remorseless'.[1]

To his contemporaries, having Fisher about was akin to harbouring Attila the Hun. In the delicate mincing world of international diplomacy he was seen as a savage incomprehensible intruder. The army hated him; he saw the army as an appendix to the navy, and a minor appendix at that.

When he took over the navy in 1904 he decided that he had to be cruel to be kind. Since 1815 the navy had been resting on its laurels; only in 1860 was hanging from the yard-arm abolished, only in 1880 had flogging with the cat-o'-nine-tails been suspended. The fleet was antiquated and obsolete, and the first thing to do was to get rid of the relics of a vanished age, which amounted to 154 ships including seventeen battleships. These were to be replaced with just four types of vessel, battleships with a speed of 21 knots, armoured cruisers, destroyers with a speed of 36 knots, and submarines. The emphasis on future ships was on big guns and speed, rather than on armour plating.

The navy would be disposed differently, with ships being withdrawn from the Mediterranean and placed in the North Sea, directly facing the ultimate enemy, Germany. At a time when many statesmen wondered which nation Britain would fight, Fisher had no doubt at all. He demanded absolute readiness for war; he was disgusted that for a third of the year the navy was in Portsmouth Harbour, disorganised and languishing.

Fisher's most startling coup was to introduce *Dreadnought*, his first super-ship. Built in eleven months, *Dreadnought* rendered obsolete every other warship in the world, including those in the Royal Navy. Fisher's design team did not stop there; it was responsible for the birth of Fisher's second category, the armoured cruiser, which was large and very fast. These vessels, renamed battle-cruisers in 1912, did not live up to expectation as they were used in situations that Fisher deplored, where their speed proved of little avail. The dreadnoughts and the armoured

Lord Fisher declared that the submarine would accomplish a vast revolution in naval warfare, but the Admiralty dragged its feet, and the Germans proved that Fisher was right

cruisers only made complete sense in the context of Fisher's aggressive policies, and historically their evolution was less important than his anticipation of the role of the submarine.

Having studied the naval war between Japan and Russia in 1904, Fisher realised that the Japanese won because their ships were marginally faster than those of the Russians. In one of his cogent angry letters, dated 20 April 1904, he declared that the war would have swung the other way if the Russians had had submarines: 'It's astounding to me, *perfectly astounding*, how the very best amongst us absolutely fail to realise the vast impending revolution in naval warfare and naval strategy that the submarine will accomplish!'[2]

Fisher had been an advocate of the torpedo since 1872, and realised its suitability as a weapon for the submarine. In 1903 he had watched a demonstration in Portsmouth Harbour, in which the old ironclad *Belleisle* had been sent to the bottom in seven minutes by a torpedo, even though the ship had been specially strengthened. By the time Fisher left the Admiralty in 1910, he had achieved the construction of sixty-one submarines. Without him, the navy reverted to its apathy, and when he returned in 1914 the number of submarines had decreased to fifty-three, and of twenty-one being built only five were any good.

The dreadnoughts were a mixed blessing, for they encouraged Germany to build an equivalent fleet. The British naval estimates had risen from £23,778,400 in 1898-9 to £36,889,000 in 1904-5, and although the scrapping of obsolete ships had effected some economies in upkeep, there was a clamour to keep the expense down—a clamour that rose to a roar when the Liberals took over. The Liberals needed the money for their social services scheme. The cutback on the building of dreadnoughts was countered by the Admiralty, and a compromise was reached.

To some extent, the dreadnoughts were status symbols, designed to overawe the Germans. They were seen as the One Simple Answer. Fisher did not see the dichotomy between his own 1904 views on the supremacy of the submarine and the

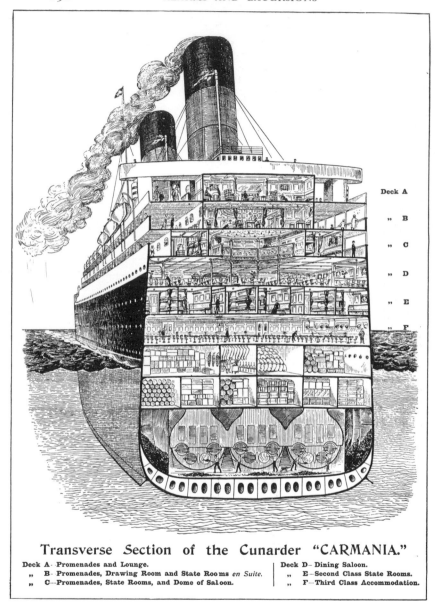

Deck A
„ B
„ C
„ D
„ E
„ F

Transverse Section of the Cunarder "CARMANIA."

Deck A—Promenades and Lounge.	Deck D—Dining Saloon.
„ B—Promenades, Drawing Room and State Rooms *en Suite.*	„ E—Second Class State Rooms.
„ C—Promenades, State Rooms, and Dome of Saloon.	„ F—Third Class Accommodation.

In 1903 German passenger liners crossed the Atlantic in record time; the Cunard Steamship Co Ltd countered this with a massive shipbuilding programme backed by government money. This is a cut-out section of one of their ships

construction of dreadnoughts that were the born victims of offensive submarine warfare. The enthusiasm of the government for the dreadnought is only fully understandable when one considers what was happening in the world of passenger liners. In 1903 the Germans had won two blue ribands for crossing the Atlantic in record time. The instinctive response to this had been a loan by the government of £2,600,000 at a very low rate of interest for the building of two turbine vessels with an anticipated speed of 25 knots, the *Mauretania* and the *Lusitania*. In 1907 a British passenger liner crossed the Atlantic in a time that was not bettered until 1929. To the Edwardians it was inconceivable that anyone but the British could be supreme at anything to do with the sea.

The modernisation of the navy was accompanied by far-reaching reforms in structure and administration, and here Fisher came up against the full forces of reaction, headed by Admiral Lord Charles Beresford, who denounced Fisher's North Sea policy as a fraud upon the public and a danger to the Empire, and demanded an official inquiry into Admiralty policy. This acrimonious situation was much enjoyed by the Germans who realised that Fisher was a very real threat to them, and that while he was in control of naval fortunes the possibility of a first strike was always possible. It was well-known that he had the ear of Edward VII, who relished the rough-talking, rumbustious First Sea Lord. Those with a long memory backed the king against Beresford.

From 1905 to 1907, during the time of the feud with Fisher, Admiral Beresford had been in command of the Mediterranean Fleet. Fisher had little interest in the Mediterranean, as it was too far away from the enemy, Germany, whose only interest in the Mediterranean was on behalf of its ally, Austria, who had a base at Fiume on the Adriatic. Beresford was slightly younger than Fisher, but although he was sixty he preserved some of the qualities of his youth, when he was a bosom friend of Edward VII, then the Prince of Wales. His father was the celebrated rake, the Marquis of Waterford, and Beresford had inherited the family high spirits and penchant for the gay life.

He shared with Prince Edward the affections of the Countess of Warwick. Beresford's wife had got hold of a letter from Lady Warwick to Beresford, and was indulging in a little discreet blackmail. The Prince of Wales became involved in the intrigue, and in 1890 Beresford called at Marlborough House and accused him of being a blackguard and a coward, shaking his fist in the prince's face. Edward was not a man to let such affronts be forgotten. It was perhaps not surprising that Beresford lost the duel with Fisher, and was ordered to haul down his flag.

To Fisher this defeat of his rival was as important as a judicious 'copenhagening' of a foreign fleet, but his boastful demeanour alienated many who had regarded him highly. His dreadnought policy was also showing the kind of dividends no one welcomed. The year was 1909; reports were coming in that the Germans would have dreadnought parity by 1912. Four battleships a year had been planned; the Admiralty now wanted six and, when even more alarming intelligence came, put this demand up to eight, a demand that was refused by Lloyd George and Winston Churchill. To the Conservative opposition, the opportunity was too good to miss, and they instigated a motto, 'We want eight, and we won't wait'. A compromise was reached, but the country looked round for a scapegoat and found one in Fisher. It was claimed that he had been caught on the hop by the German acceleration in ship building. The inquiry that Beresford had called for was granted, and although Beresford was rapped over the knuckles for his ungentlemanly behaviour, and although the Admiralty was exonerated, Fisher was chided for his secrecy, for his policy of keeping his own plans to himself. This chill reprimand encouraged Fisher to resign, and for four vital years he was obliged to sit on the sidelines and fume. When he was recalled, it was too late for his particular strategy: the capture of Heligoland—which had aimlessly been exchanged not so many years previously for Zanzibar and was now an important cog in the German war machine—and the landing of an amphibious force on the Baltic coast for a direct assault upon Berlin.

His concept of the army was as a bullet fired by the navy. But by 1914 France, who had little trust in naval power, had her way—the British Army was to be an auxiliary of the French, to fight uncomplainingly on their left flank.

Fisher had made a prestige navy into a fighting navy. Could anything be done with the army after the Boer War had shown it to be a creaking anachronism? It was an army in which Guards officers based in London lived at home or in clubs, played cricket or tennis, and were regular visitors to fashionable Sandown Park, Hurlingham or Ranelagh. It was considered rather odd if a subaltern could not get four months leave a year, odder still for a captain to spend more than six months in the year anywhere near his regiment. The hunting-shooting seasons saw the flight not only of foxes and various small birds but of Guards officers into the great outdoors. No officer could live on his pay: a Guards officer needed £300 over and above that, and an officer in the prestigious 10th Hussars £500 extra on top of his pay.

It was an army in which the soldiers spent their lives drilling and scrubbing out their quarters, conditioned to blind obedience to an officer élite. 'We make the private soldier in many cases a fool', admitted one officer, 'because we start with the assumption that he is a fool'.[3] The Boer War, said Sir Alfred Milner, had been 'an avalanche of military incompetence'. Staff work had been haphazard, manoeuvres and marches were carried out in a stilted clumsy manner, and the weapons and equipment provided were inferior to those of the enemy. It had taken a long time for the idea to sink in among commanders in the field that the British Army was not fighting half-naked savages with spears but wily white men from a good European stock.

The government at the outset of the South African war did not take the Boers seriously. The commander-in-chief, Lord Wolseley, complained, 'I always come away from these meetings of Ministers in saddened frame of mind when I have listened for some time to the military folly talked by most of those who comprise that Committee . . . The whole time was taken up in worrying over the number of field guns we should order, and the machinery we should erect to make guns, ammunition etc'.[4]

Lord Lansdowne, secretary for war 1895–1900, proved as useless in that role as he was as foreign secretary (1900–5). He had gone to the War Office 'with the comfortable knowledge that nothing was required of him beyond *vis inertiae*. Then unfortunately the South African hostilities supervened. Long before their conclusion Lord Lansdowne had sagaciously removed himself to another sphere'.[5]

Into the post left vacant jumped another time-server, William Brodrick, a man desperately anxious for office. Observers recorded that Brodrick seemed to take a gloomy pleasure in informing the House of Commons that the war was going very badly. Brodrick was diligent in reorganisation; Winston Churchill described how Brodrick made army corps 'by a mental process and a scratch of the pen'. His management was denounced as 'mess, muddle and make-believe'. Six army corps dreamed up on paper, a concession to panic, did not prevent his reluctant departure to the India Office in 1903. The kiss of death had been given by King Edward's confidant, Lord Esher: 'A very capable man, rendered incapable by circumstances—by military officials, all with ill-defined duties, all pulling different ways instead of all pulling together'.[6]

Lord Esher himself wisely avoided being made secretary for war, the graveyard of reputations, and the job fell to H. O. Arnold-Forster, whom the king cordially disliked. He complained to the prime minister that Arnold-Forster lacked polish and was socially uncouth, and Balfour agreed, saying that Mr Forster's manner was not his strong point, 'but though he wants manner, he does not want *tact*'. The prime minister, however, happy that somebody had taken on the post, was too sanguine, for Arnold-Forster went into the job 'with the enthusiasm of the apostle and the spirit of the martyr; he suffers from a superexcitation of the nerves such as six hundred years ago produced the *stigmata* and other evidences of an overheated imagination'.[7]

Arnold-Forster was no more fit to reform the army than the unfortunate Brodrick, and alienated not only the king but the officer class when he abolished inter-regimental polo tournaments. He spent much of his time probing into his predecessors'

files, and undoing what they had done. There was the affair of
the jam. There had been 1,350,816 tins of it, holding a pound
each. Arnold-Forster discovered with triumph that the pound
had been an apothecary's pound of twelve ounces, and created
something of a stir by his diligence in uncovering the inconceivably
uninteresting. His army reform plans were inconsequential and
muddled. The sceptics looked at his background: nephew of the
poet Arnold, and adopted son of W. E. Forster, pioneer of
elementary education. Arnold-Forster did not wear his hyphenated
name with the aplomb of a Campbell-Bannerman. He had also
been unfortunate enough to write schoolbooks, a book called
the *Citizen's Reader*, and the weirdly entitled *In a Conning Tower*,
mistakenly thought by more than one indignant buyer to be
written by a naval officer.

Alternatively arrogant and subservient, Arnold-Forster was
relentlessly doomed as soon as he crossed the threshold of the
War Office. Brodrick had been the butt of Winston Churchill,
who had sardonically demolished the myth of the six army
corps: 'The first three army corps are incomplete, the fourth
consists of Sir Archibald Hunter, the fifth is in the War Office
file, and the sixth Mr. Brodrick has taken with him in his
pocket on his trip to the Mediterranean'.[8] But Arnold-Forster
was more vulnerable. For, unlike Brodrick, he was slightly
common, and his quietus was dealt by the king's secretary,
Knollys, in a letter to Esher, on 1 December 1904, though it
took some time to bundle out the body:

> You will probably agree with me that it would not be judicious for the King
> to press Arnold-Forster too hard, as if circumstances, owing to the way in
> which he is behaving, obliged him to resign, it would be unfortunate if his
> friends (I suppose he has *some!*) went about saying he was got rid of by the
> King, or to please H.M.[9]

These then were the war lords of the first half of the Edwardian
age—Lansdowne, Brodrick and Arnold-Forster, presided over
by the bland Balfour. They were collectively too little regarded
to involve Britain in any dangerous adventure. They were minor
figures by any standard, basking in the glories of state.

Their low calibre was reflected by the attitude of the prime minister, Balfour, who wished to rule with the minimum of fuss and to ignore the threat of Germany. There was no army officer of the quality of Fisher to shake the war ministers into animation. Wolseley and Roberts were old and unenthusiastic. Such re-armament as had taken place after the Boer War, when artillery was re-examined and ground troops equipped with the short Lee-Enfield, had been carried out not by the ministers but by their subordinates, with a vague nod of approval from above.

The man who replaced the unfortunate Arnold-Forster was Richard Haldane. He had met Asquith when he was a barrister, and while recovering from illness Haldane paid frequent visits to Asquith's house in Hampstead, where he met the Liberal intellectuals. Haldane was orientated to German thought—Campbell-Bannerman's nickname for him was Schopenhauer—and he also took an interest in the lower levels of society and flirted dispassionately with socialism. He was on amiable terms with the Fabian Society, whom he expected to find a group of Utopian faddists bent on bloody revolution and instead discovered a bunch of wordy theorists with whom he could swap banter.

Haldane gradually moved into the power centres of liberalism; he and Asquith gave annual dinners at the Blue Posts, Cork Street, at which the coming generation of statesmen were present—Balfour, Rosebery, Curzon and Grey. His private life was less satisfactory, and he was jilted by Miss Munro Ferguson.

A visit to Germany in 1890 confirmed Haldane in his belief in Teutonic organisation, and during the Boer War he was distinctly a hawk. Asquith looked on him as the think tank for the Liberal party, and there was no question that Haldane was destined for high office. Despite their aversion to Campbell-Bannerman as Liberal prime minister, Asquith, Haldane and Grey each served under him, though Haldane did not get the post he wanted. Haldane asked, 'What about the War Office?' Campbell-Bannerman retorted, 'Nobody will touch it with a pole'. Haldane took up the challenge.

His aim was a compact fighting army, and, with the Liberal preoccupation with economy and money for the poor, Haldane

"A Little British Army, etc."

HALDANE, R.A. (or rather R.B.): "There—now I call that a very neat job"

The press welcomed Haldane's Territorial Army, and this cartoon was typical of many of the time

had to consider two factors—saving and efficiency. Out were the expensively-maintained coastal defence batteries that would accomplish nothing, no matter how a war went, and out too were garrisons in such places as St Helena and China. The militia were to be abolished and replaced by a territorial army, and there would be a reduction in the strength of the Guards. This created a furore, but the former prime minister, Balfour, backed Haldane's reforms, having recognised that the War Office had done little when he was in office.

Despite his affection for Germany, Haldane was aware that it was from that quarter that danger would arise. On 8 January 1906 Grey wrote to him, 'Persistent reports and little indications keep reaching me that Germany means to attack France in the spring'. Grey's intelligence service was no more efficient than that of his undistinguished predecessors, but dimly he was discerning the mood. If any of his colleagues sensed the same thing they took care to conceal it, preferably from themselves. The more reactionary Liberals regretted that such an acute, intelligent man had been put in at the War Office, though they were partly mollified by the 1907–8 army estimates, which were down on the previous year.

Grey was happy to see Haldane go off on a visit to Germany instead of him, a trip encouraged by King Edward, who got on well with Haldane. Unlike his predecessors, Haldane was neither awkward nor prickly, and this stood him in good stead in Germany, where he was allowed to examine at close quarters the organisation of the Berlin War Office. He met von Moltke, the nephew of the great German military tactician, who praised Kitchener. The kaiser was impressed by Haldane, and they discussed the new British Army in which the German ruler appeared to take a brotherly interest. By the time Haldane came back, he had reached a *modus vivendi* with the Germans, though this was not to be built upon.

Each in his own way, Haldane and Fisher were creating a modern military machine, but there was no co-operation between the two services. Fisher declared that Haldane had fallen into the 'vulgar error' of imagining that the army and navy were run in more or less the same way, and talked 'twaddle'. Haldane deplored Fisher's method of keeping his plans to himself. Haldane also had his own economy-mad colleagues in the cabinet to contend with, as well as the aged Lord Roberts, who was stomping the country seeking to denigrate the territorial army. The only thing Britain could do to save herself, he maintained, was to start conscription. As things were, the country could not resist invasion. The word invasion triggered off a number of predictable responses, and there was a spate of spy stories. It was said that the Germans had thousands of rifles in a cellar of a bank near Charing Cross, ready to be taken up by German sympathisers when the grey hordes landed on the coast; and the appearance of an airship in the skies over London created terror, though it was only advertising some commodity.

These stories were widely reported in the sensational newspapers. The kaiser got to hear of them and added his own iota of confusion, saying that it would be a good idea to drop mines in the Thames and the Solent when the fleet was congregating, a comment that made its way back to London to create more heartache.

Lord Roberts had been in the army since 1851, starting off in the Indian Army where he had won the VC. He did well in wars in Abyssinia and Afghanistan, and after the set-backs in the Boer War he was sent out to South Africa, being one of the few men to emerge from that mêlée with any credit. 'Bobs' was the darling of the troops, immeasurably better known to the rank and file than Haldane, though Haldane had created an excellent impression among the higher ranks. No one doubted Roberts' worth or his personal courage; he was the 'hero of innumerable adventures that might have been specially enacted to please the boys of a preparatory school'.[10]

There was little question that now Roberts was a liability rather than an asset. He got the ear of the king, warning him that Haldane's model army was the laughing stock of Europe and that the territorial army would be useless in a war because of its defective training.

A more formidable rival was Lord Kitchener, who was mercifully commander in chief in India and thus a long way away. Taciturn and severe, it was said of Kitchener that he had never spoken to a private soldier, that his family treated him with awe rather than affection, and that he was a war machine on two legs. Furthermore, Kitchener did not want to come home as he was hoping to become viceroy. However, it was clear that he did not hold Haldane in very high regard, dismissing him as an unpractical theorist and the territorial army as a bunch of play-boys who would come to nothing. Basically Kitchener did not like civilians; he would have preferred the administration of the army to be out of the hands of politicians. Nor did he like the navy; the navy was an instrument to transport a vast army across the English Channel, and whether or not Haldane wanted a vast army there would have to be one, for the war with Germany would be long and arduous, calling for a degree of endurance only anticipated by the American Civil War. Kitchener had little confidence in the French: the Germans would 'walk through the

French Officer: "THE GREAT THING IS, AFTER ALL,
MY COMRADE, DIGNITY AND ELEGANCE."
(A Drawing by Jean Victor Bates.)

*Lord Kitchener did not like civilians, the Royal Navy, or the Territorial Army. In the
event of war he thought the Germans would walk through the French lines 'like partridges'.
Cartoonists found the French army funny rather than fearsome*

French line like partridges'. But all this was academic; it was
more important to be viceroy of India, a country whose role was
an agreeable subjugation.

Nevertheless, the territorial army arrived. In June 1909 the
king presented colours to 108 territorial battalions at Windsor.
It was the outcome, wrote Haldane, of three years of missionary
enterprise.

The war, when it came, ran according to the grim forecast of
Kitchener. The territorial army provided a cadre after the
British Expeditionary Force—the best trained army in Europe,

thanks to Haldane—had been decimated. Haldane did the best he could under the conditions imposed upon him: limited expenditure and no conscription. Clever as he was, he was no military tactician; he could not have foreseen that the supremacy of small-arms fire and the machine-gun would inaugurate the phenomenon of trench warfare, and that defence and offence would be evenly matched. Bedevilled by opposition from a section of the army and some of his own party, not to mention the Conservatives, Haldane provided a sharply-honed weapon that was too subtle for the situation. Fisher had envisaged a navy that would operate with such a force as Haldane had created. They were both prophets of the next war but one.

The American Threat

Britain acquired her Empire in a prolonged fit of absentminded-ness, and it was a surprise to many that there were profits to reap as well as thousands of square miles to police. The finding of gold in Australia and South Africa enriched the home country, and India was plundered with endless zest. Britain's dominant trade position and her unique geographical location made the policy of splendid isolation possible, but as the nineteenth century drew to a close there were indications that other nations wished to have a bite of the cherry. In a speech at Leeds in 1888 Lord Rosebery said: 'The other powers are beginning a career of colonial aggrandizement. We formerly did not have to trouble ourselves with colonial questions, because we had a monopoly of colonies. That monopoly has ceased'.[1]

By that time the French were out of the race, following their definitive defeat in the Franco-Prussian War, and their falling behind in industrial reorganisation—partly due to the absence of a home supply of coal. France was still the hereditary foe, but she was treated like the grand old warrior who had gone to seed, and if there was enmity it was tepid. She had her empire, a good deal less profitable even on a pro rata basis than Britain's, and although she was hanging on to it, there was a certain despair, as though the Republic was not certain that she could. Germany was another matter. She was a late starter; the assortment of states that had formed Germany before the unification had made a colonial policy impossible.

The Germans were irked by Britain's refusal even to consider that they should have an empire, and in 1885 Bismarck was incensed by the British foreign secretary's insistence that British friendliness towards Germany was incompatible with a German pursuit of a colonial policy. 'We should be curious to learn', wrote Bismarck sardonically to his minister in London, 'why the right to colonize, which England uses to the fullest extent, should be denied to us'. As Germany was becoming industrialised at a faster rate than England, the conditions for a confrontation were already being built up.

But these conditions were already being built up elsewhere—in the United States. The Americans had shrugged off in an amazing way the after-effects of the Civil War, which had killed 600,000 of their young men, and although there was a great slump in 1873 and another one in 1893 (when there were 15,000 business failures and 574 banks went broke) the march of America towards commercial parity with Britain was unnervingly steady.

The first signs of the US colonial mentality were seen in 1878, when the country of Colombia granted a concession to a French company to drive a canal through the isthmus of Panama. President Hayes saw this as a threat to the United States, and that such a canal must be under the control of America and 'virtually a part of the coast-line of the United States'. Shortly afterwards the United States interfered in a conflict between Chile and Peru; this almost caused a war between Chile and the United States when crew from an American ship were killed in Valparaiso.

The key to an overseas empire was a supply of coaling stations. For a fleet that depended on steam, these were vital. America saw the Pacific as its area of influence, and a convenient coaling station, the Samoan Islands, was divided between the United States, Britain and Germany, though this arrangement proved so difficult that in 1900 Britain withdrew from the islands, receiving concessions from Germany in other parts of the world.

But the most dangerous events of the time so far as Britain was concerned occurred not in the Samoan Islands, nor Alaska (bought from Russia in 1867), but in Cuba. Cuba was under Spanish rule, and in 1895 a revolt broke out against the Madrid government, which was not quelled even though 200,000 Spanish soldiers were sent to the island. The Cubans adopted guerilla tactics, and the wire entanglements and blockhouses built by the Spaniards failed dismally to cope with the insurgents. The Spaniards then took to organising concentration camps, in which the death rate arising from brutality and disease was very high.

The Americans watched the situation with unease, for the rebels were burning the sugar plantations, and American business had a $50 million stake in sugar, tobacco and iron. By 1897 Cuba was in a condition of anarchy, and militant Americans were in favour of going in and cleaning up the mess. They were actively abetted by the sensationalist press, which drummed up a war, though for a time it was thought that reason would prevail. An American warship paid a 'goodwill' visit to Havana, to reassure American residents and businessmen that they had not been forgotten, and in return a Spanish cruiser visited New York. These amiable gestures were forgotten when the Hearst press published an indiscreet letter from the Spanish minister in Washington condemning the president of the United States as weak and a bidder for the admiration of the rabble. Yet even this, despite the bellicosity of Theodore Roosevelt, a devotee of war and slaughter and all manly sports, would not have led to war. In February 1898 the battleship *Maine* was destroyed probably by a mine in an explosion in the harbour of Havana, and 260 men died. Although President McKinley and the Spanish government were desperately trying to avoid war, war remorselessly came.

It was welcomed by the Hearst press and by American business. Senator Thurston of Nebraska was unapologetic: 'War with Spain would increase the business and earnings of every American railroad, it would increase the output of every American factory, it would stimulate every branch of industry and domestic commerce'.[2] There were other reasons; the Americans were suffering from a sense of inferiority, a sense of deprivation. They had not fought, except amongst themselves, since they had thrown the British out in the War of Independence. Why should they not enjoy themselves at the expense of the Spaniards, a nation long in decline? Spain had an empire. They would take it away from her and go into the colonial business themselves. Probably the Europeans, who saw all this going on, were distressed because the Americans had got in first.

Not surprisingly the Spanish Government backed down in every conceivable way, willing to let the Americans walk over them in any manner they pleased, but President McKinley, realising that a satisfactory and convenient war would guarantee him office for a second term, did not lay the vital documents before Congress. The Spanish-American War was brief and almost bloodless. It was declared on 19 April 1898 and on 1 May the Spanish fleet was destroyed in the Philippines; an army was sent to Cuba, landing at Santiago instead of Havana, 700 miles nearer the United States, and in August it was all over. The Americans lost in battle 379 soldiers and fewer than twenty sailors, despite military maladministration that vied with that of the British in the Boer War.

It was an easy, if not a particularly efficient way to win colonies. H. W. Nevinson, the journalist, was in Spain covering that end of the operation. There was little for him to do, for the Spanish heart was not in the war; the best Spanish battleships were still in harbour. They had not sailed and they had no intention of sailing.   .

The Philippines, Puerto Rico and Guam were ceded outright to the Americans. Cuba was temporarily occupied until an independent government, more amenable to the Americans than the Spanish administration, was installed. This coup, allied with an incident that occurred in 1895 in Venezuela—the United States accused Britain of attempting to control Venezuela when a difference of opinion arose relating to the border between Venezuela and British Guiana—brought America to the attention of Britain in no uncertain manner.

As a result of the Spanish-American War the Americans found they were treated with a good deal more respect. The militarists decided that they liked empire-building, even though there were inconveniences attached to the acquisition of foreign lands—the Philippinos did not like the Americans any more than the Spaniards, and rose up against them. Unfortunately for the United States, the world had already been carved up between the European powers, and the only way to increase territory was to tackle the empire of some power that had once been great, but was now in decline. It is possible that the French empire was considered, but even the most enthusiastic of imperialist powers blenched at the prospect of acquiring the thousands of square miles of sparsely inhabited African desert, with a doubtful supply of minerals beneath the ground.

But what about Holland, with its rich empire in the East Indies? America had bases in the Philippines for any attack on Sumatra or Java. But there were now political inhibitions about taking the territories of other countries and it would be difficult to find a pretext for annexing the Dutch East Indies.

Suspicion of American motives had been felt in Britain from about 1895. In March 1898 Arnold Bennett was present at a discussion between the owner of the magazine *Woman* and the editor of the *Morning Post*. They 'suddenly began to talk about the chances of war. I was astonished at the eagerness for it, and the certainty with which they predicted where and between whom it would occur . . . We ought to have fought the U.S.A. a year or two ago, when they wanted a war. We should have thrashed them easily, and that would have cleared the air of the war cloud'.[3]

Did the United States want a war with Britain? In December 1895, Theodore Roosevelt wrote to Cabot Lodge: 'Let the fight come if it must. I don't care whether our sea-board cities are bombarded or not; we would take Canada'.[4]

Perhaps the most important factor that prevented a conflict at this time was that although America had most of the hallmarks of an imperialist power she lacked economic incentive. She did not seek fresh markets for her goods. In 1900 the United States exported four per cent of her manufactures, while the figure for Germany was twelve per cent and Britain twenty-five per cent. Had the United States wanted to export more manufactured goods she would have had no difficulty in finding markets, for she was well ahead in the products of the industrial age, such as typewriters, and sewing-machines (in both of which America had the virtual monopoly), telephones and other advanced equipment.

The factor that could have swung the balance in favour of open conflict between America and Britain would have been an alliance between Germany and Britain. It is significant that Joseph Chamberlain, the colonial secretary, gradually dropped his dream of such an alliance; he knew the temper of America well, as he was married to an American. It is interesting to speculate on what would have happened had America gone to war with the combined forces of Germany and Britain, for unlike both those countries the United States only kept a small standing army, numbering fewer than 100,000 men in 1900. It is even more interesting to see that such a war was a contingency, recognised by men who afterwards would have been aghast at such a possibility.

The Edwardian age opened with America emerging as a classic imperialist power, the features of which were laid down by Lenin:

1 The concentration of production and capital, developed to such a high stage that it has created monopolies, which play a decisive role in economic life.
2 The merging of bank capital with industrial capital and the creation, on the basis of this 'finance capital' of a financial oligarchy.
3 The export of capital as distinguished from the export of commodities, becomes of particularly great importance.
4 International monopoly combines of capitalists are formed which divide up the world. [5]

Despite the warlike utterances of a number of American statesmen, there was a greater fund of goodwill in America towards Britain than Britain believed. The US government did not attempt to make capital out of the Boer War, despite the attempts of Irish-Americans to raise an Irish brigade to fight the British in South Africa. Congress petitions for intervention or mediation came to nothing.

There was still sufficient apprehension in Britain, however, to merit comment. In July 1902 the Dutch press feared that a pretext might be sought by Britain for seizing the Dutch East Indies, to prevent them being taken over by America or Germany, both of which had colonies near by. By this time, however, anxiety had shifted from American politics to American business, represented by the gigantic figure of J. P. Morgan.

After the great crash of 1893, Morgan had supplied the United States government with $62 million to avert utter catastrophe, and in 1901 Morgan and his associates formed the United States Steel Corporation, capitalized at $1,321 million, which controlled sixty per cent of the nation's steel-making capacity. In 1902 Morgan bought a number of British shipping lines. British industry was long-established and old-fashioned. It bobbed about on the pond of free trade and was not helped, as industry was in the United States and Germany, by an elaborate screen of protective tariffs. Even such dominating firms in the world of heavy industry as Armstrong Whitworth and Vickers were dwarfed by the American combines.

The uneasiness of Britain was reflected in the popular press. In May 1901 *The King* magazine published a mock proclamation:

Whereas we, Pierpont Morgan I., have now acquired, obtained, and taken possession of the United Kingdom, with all its dependencies, plantations and appurtenances in full suzerainty for US, our Heirs and Successors, till further orders, and Whereas WE are apprised, guess, calculate and suspect that unregistered English persons are still at large in this our Kingdom . . .

And in the gossip column of the same paper: 'Mr. J. Pierpont Morgan is staying in Paris, and will shortly visit Aix-les-Bains, where he is very popular. He has not yet decided which town he will buy'.

It was fortunate that the 'American invasion', as it was known, encompassed not only businessmen:

On the whole, I think the influx of the American element into English society has done good rather than harm, whilst there are many old families which, both in mind and pocket, have been completely revivified by prudent marriages with American brides . . . Bright and vivacious, it may with justice be said that it is by the American girl that we have been conquered . . . [6]

The businessmen, as it turned out, were less alarming than had been anticipated and, even to the old school, presented a refreshing contrast to their English equivalents. The rich Americans had a peculiar penchant for philanthropy, incomprehensible to English businessmen who diligently kept their money to themselves. Andrew Carnegie, a big figure in steel, poured thousands of pounds into higher education in Scotland. In this altruistic field, the Americans were following the example of George Peabody (1795–1869) who gave half a million dollars towards building tenements for the London poor.

As the Edwardian age proceeded, the American threat diminished, until the mere idea of an armed conflict between Britain and America became laughable, though the Germans tried to stir up trouble in the United States when it was clear to them that an alliance with Britain was out of the question. Troublesome matters that arose during the decade was amicably settled; a certain rapport was awkwardly founded between King Edward and President Theodore Roosevelt, who had settled down after his earlier rumbustious days as a fighter for Cuban freedom and an advocate of war. Grey, the foreign secretary, handled the Americans with considerably more ease than he dealt with the European powers. Although a certain bitterness was felt when the American slump of 1907 reacted sharply on the British economy, it was seen more and more that British and American interests coincided. In March 1908, Theodore Roosevelt wrote to Arthur Balfour that he had 'ugly doubts as to what may befall our modern civilization'.[7] Ten years earlier he would not have cared.

In Search of an Ally

England at the start of the Edwardian period was in the position of a neurotic old lady who suddenly feels lonely. She had shrugged off friends for twenty years, and now that she wanted some, whom could she trust? The nicest kind of friends were those who spoke the same language (the Americans) or who belonged to the same family (the Germans), but these were always putting provisos in the way, and in the end she had to settle for someone else, someone who had been a bit of a bother in the past, but who was probably not too bad after all. The French too were lonely and disconsolate.

Genuine friendships were hard to come by in 1901, and British friendship was not especially welcome. Britain was suspect militarily, her economy was static, and her people, as seen from the other side of the channel, were decadent. According to the British newspapers, people would not fight except with their mouths; industrialists, less concerned with patriotism than the main chance, sold arms to the enemy and provided brown paper boots to the army; and there was a commercial policy of absolute indifference and indolence. The only factor that was incalculable was the Royal Navy, seemingly invincible.

When it was clear that the entente cordiale between France and Britain was on, misunderstandings were cleared up. In 1904 a bargain was struck with France that she could have a free hand in Morocco if Britain were allowed a free hand in Egypt. This understanding had been forecast by *The Times* in March 1903:

> Here popular feeling has been altered very decidedly in favour of France, perhaps not without regard to the contrasted attitude taken up by another nation . . . the controverted questions which agitate the relations of France and England are not of the first order of importance . . . quite trifling in comparison with the great interests which both have in common.

The Russo-Japanese War provided a test of the friendship. Britain had previously signed a treaty with Japan, but France had a long-standing treaty with Russia. *The Economist* put the dilemma well: those who were lauding the Japanese victories were advised to 'moderate their exultation over Russian defeats. After all they are the defeats sustained by the friend of a friend'. Nor did the British acclaim too loudly their pleasure that the Russians did not get the terminus of the Trans-Siberian Railway they wanted (ostensibly the reason for the conflict, though Japan was more interested in the acquisition of Korea). The Japanese victory lessened the Russian threat to India. Other nations were not too sorry about the Russian humiliation; although America faced Russia across the Bering sea. As the war went on there was some American rethinking: in August 1905, Cabot Lodge wrote to Roosevelt that it was not in the American interest 'to have Russia too completely crippled'.

It was now felt that Britain could approach Russia, and the way was paved by offering a loan. A convention was held in 1907 in which Tibet, Afghanistan and Persia was recognized by both parties as buffer states. Persia, the tricky one of these three, was divided into a large Russian zone, a small British zone, and a neutral zone in the middle. In 1909 the Persians got rid of a particularly obnoxious shah, and the Russian troops went in and put him back. As a bonus, they shelled Persia's most sacred shrine. But Russia was now a friend, and furthermore a friend who was building up her already vast army, and reinforcing her strategic railway systems with cash supplied by France.

Many cynical politicians thought that with such a friend as Tsarist Russia Britain could well do without any enemies. Russia had watched what was happening in the Balkans with disquiet. The British had not much interest in the Balkans, where there were always wars, and were bored with Turkey, on whose behalf Britain had nearly gone to war with Russia thirty years before, and there was anger towards Grey, who had been on the side of the Young Turk revolution in 1908. The days had long since gone when Turkey was seen as the poor innocent in danger of being crushed by the Russian bear. She was now nothing but a nuisance. The Russians on the other hand were neurotically interested in whatever was going on in the Balkans. When Austria, without warning, parley or apparent purpose, walked in and annexed Bosnia and Herzegovina, Russia was aggrieved, and the bitter animosity excited throughout Russia against Austria was a considerable factor in the chemistry of the start of World War I.

The issues in the Balkans were totally alien to British thought;

each Balkan nation was a virtual land-mine. Since Turkey went into decline, Russia and Austria were the powers most interested in this conglomeration of arrogant and self-opinionated states. The key to them all was Serbia, which was under Russian protection.

Since 1905 there had been a trade war between Austria and Serbia, and even then it appeared that Serbia was an ill-fitting piece in a rather tedious jigsaw puzzle. Germany was also interested in Serbia, for vital to her development as an imperialist power was the railway to Constantinople, part of the projected Berlin to Baghdad railway route which would ensure that Turkey remained under the German thumb, and would alarm Russia and Britain, with their interests in Persia and India. Such a railway had to go through Serbia and, with the Russians alienated, there seemed no prospect of them welcoming the German engineers into the country.

If Belgium was traditionally the cockpit of Europe, Turkey the sick man of Europe, Germany the eagle and Russia the bear, then assuredly Italy was the hyena. In the neurotic quest for allies, Britain had not paid much attention to Italy, to which she had, in the nineteenth century, administered sharp slaps when it seemed as though Italy was going too energetically into the empire-building business. Italy had hoped to get Tunisia with the British nod of approval, but the French had stepped in first. True, Italy did manage to acquire a slice of empire in Eritrea, though her adventure in Abyssinia had turned rather sour. An offer by Britain to let Italy have a modest slice of colonial cake led the Italians to pontificate on a grand Anglo-Italian carve-up of north Africa. This was considered impertinent by the British politicians, and Italy was coolly snubbed. She was forced to stand on the side-lines and watch while Britain and France acquired their African empires.

In the old days Turkey had ruled the Balkans ruthlessly and harshly, and the troubles there related directly to her growing decrepitude. Not surprisingly the Italians, deprived of an empire in north Africa, looked across the Mediterranean at Libya, which since 1835 had been directly ruled from Constantinople.

In 1911 the Italians seized Libya. To their delight this move was approved by France, who had had a good deal of trouble with the Turks, especially in the hinterland where south Libya merged imperceptibly into French territory.

To the surprise of other colonial powers, Italy ruled Libya in a civilised and enlightened manner, building roads, railways, schools and hospitals, and respecting the religious feelings of her new subjects. Detached observers could not help comparing the Italian attitude with that of the British in north Africa, and a scandal that had occurred in 1906 was dredged up to illustrate their differences in colonial rule. In that year, a group of British officers stationed at Denshawi in the Nile Delta amused themselves by shooting pigeons belonging to the villagers. The villagers tried to stop this slaughter, and a woman was shot. The officers were ill-used and one died of sunstroke. The villagers were brought to trial; four were hanged, two sent to prison for life, and eight flogged. 'The arrangements were admirable', wrote the British official on the spot, 'and reflect great credit to all concerned . . . the Egyptian, being a fatalist, does not greatly fear death, and there is therefore much to be said for flogging as judicial punishment in Egypt'.

Technically, the Italians had an alliance with Germany, but this was recognized as not worth more than the paper it was written on, for it was clear that, in any alignment of power, Austria would side with Germany, and Austria was the country most antipathetic to the Italians. In any event, Italy was not worth courting.

In the search for friends, Britain was not only counting the heads but counting the armies. What was there in the way of cannon fodder? Russia had plenty, and could call on a million combatants in the event of war, but she was dreadfully deficient in arms, especially artillery. She was also short of ammunition; there were only a thousand rounds in reserve for each light gun and rifle. After the débâcle of the Russo-Japanese War, the Russians had spent great sums on their navy—expending £24,477,487 in 1913, more than any other country except Britain and the United States. Four Russian battle-cruisers laid down in 1912 had the requirements demanded by Sir John Fisher in his reorganisation of the Royal Navy—speed and fire-power.

Italy, whichever way she turned, did not seem militarily important. Her army, which on paper numbered 289,000 men, lacked heavy field artillery, and what guns there were were old 'rigid' guns. The standard rifle, though excellent, had been in service since 1891. The machine-gun, which was to be the dominant weapon of the war to come, was conspicuous by its total absence. Italy's naval programme was languid, and in 1913 she had only one dreadnought. Though she had a strong torpedo-boat force, the navy by and large was top-heavy with ancient vessels. Of all the maritime powers, Italy had the smallest number of battleships.

In the coming confrontation with Germany, the role of Japan was uncertain, but in the event of a German naval presence in the East the Japanese navy was well qualified to take care of itself and perhaps nullify a German attempt on India or Australia. Japan's was the fifth navy in the world, after those of Britain, Germany, the United States and France.

The understanding that when war came the British would serve on the French left flank necessitated an appraisal of the French army. On a peace-time footing in 1914, it numbered 823,251 men, but the French boast that this could be more than trebled in a short time was warranted by events. French equipment and artillery were immeasurably better than the Russian or Italian. On 1 September 1914 France had 1,135,000 rifles, 25,000 carbines, 106,200 sabres, 2,158 machine-guns, 4,098 field guns, 389 heavy guns, 192 mountain guns, and 200 aeroplanes.

It was assumed that Belgium would become involved in the war, being invaded either by Germany or by France and Britain. In the year preceding the war, Belgium's army estimates were on a par with those of Sweden or Australia, and few believed in her 350,000-strong army (in the event it numbered 117,000). The Belgian army was ill-equipped with obsolete weapons; the standard rifle was an 1889 model. The war caught the Belgians in the midst of reorganisation, when they were thinking about building a fleet.

Britain's appraisal of possible allies was governed by the belief in a short sharp war, with Germany caught between the nutcrackers of the French and Russian armies, her navy destroyed or bottled up, and her industry rendered mute by a relentless blockade. In the event, counting the heads did not do much good; they had to be in the right place at the right time. No one in Britain, except Kitchener and his circle, foresaw the ineptitude of the French war-machine and its pursuit of an *idée fixe*—a strike through Lorraine—although the French knew that the Germans intended an offensive through Belgium and the unprotected north of France.

The Battle of the Marne proved conclusively that something had gone wrong, and the musical-chairs diplomacy of the preceding decade had failed. Somebody had not only shot the pianist and changed the rules of the game, but had dismantled the piano as well.

Notes to this chapter are on page 295.

CHAPTER SEVEN

SPORT AND ENTERTAINMENT

The Sporting Life

SPORT FLOWERED without let or hindrance between 1901 and 1914, and historians never tire of pointing out that it was the golden age of sport, with amateurs rubbing shoulders with professionals, good humour in the grandstands and hardly a trace of bottle-throwing or hooliganism; Britain was triumphant in all fields, walking away with fifty-six gold medals at the 1908 Olympic Games.

Many of the rich gave over their lives to sport. The poor were less fortunate; the only sport they took to their heart was football, with cricket decidedly a second best. In association football there were still amateurs, such as the Corinthians, among the leading clubs. They were not seen by the working classes as giant-killers—as are today's amateur clubs coming face to face with the big battalions—but as gents who had condescended to perform before their inferiors. Class distinctions were as clearly defined on the running track, the cricket pitch and the football field as in the outside world.

Except perhaps in cricket, techniques were unsophisticated. The emphasis in football was not on tactics but on attack, and there was a good deal of what would now be considered over-

Mr. Jerry Builder, who desires to purchase building plots, is directed to Snowheath Estate.

The crowd, imagining him to be going to the great football match, follow.

Fearing that he has mistaken his way, the builder again inquires.

This time the "footer" crowd overhear his inquiry, and mildly explain to him that he has taken them miles out of their way, causing them to miss the football match.

Hoping to arrive by half-time, they quickly retrace their steps, having briefly explained their opinion of himself to Mr. Jerry Builder.

The poor were devoted to football; it was their sport, and they would go to a great deal of trouble to watch a match

Emphasis in association football was on attack, and there was much over-zealous tackling and hard play

zealous tackling and hard play, though scheming fouls involving play-acting had not yet been codified. The customary practice was to play five forwards, with the backs up in attack somewhere in mid-field. Play therefore fluctuated from one end of the field to the other, there was little plan or purpose behind the attacks and none of the delicate by-play or strategy that marks the best football today. Association football employed professionals, who ran till they dropped for a maximum of £4 a week. It was lively, unquestionably, but lacking in subtlety; speed and dash were what the man on the terrace wanted.

The dominant force in the game was the Football League, a breakaway movement formed in 1888. This was orientated to the Midlands and the North; the teams in the Football League played for workers in industry, whose Saturday afternoons were consecrated to football, and occasionally other sports: cock-fighting was still practised in the North, and the working classes were also fond of whippet-racing and pigeon-racing. By the end of the nineteenth century, the South was getting the flavour of football, and typical of the immense interest being

The 1901 cup final at the Crystal Palace between Tottenham Hotspurs and Sheffield United drew 110,820 spectators, the largest crowd ever to watch a football match

shown was the 110,820 attendance at the 1901 cup final at the Crystal Palace. The game was between Tottenham Hotspurs and Sheffield United and ended in a draw, two all, including one disputed goal. During half-time the spectators flocked on to the pitch and milled about, and the police were powerless to stop them; it was the largest crowd ever assembled to watch a football match.

The Football League was free from the affectation and gentility that had marked public school football, previously the bastion of the game. The commercial game was hard and rough, and although the amateurs had competed for the F.A. Cup in the past they soon dropped out of the running—all except the Corinthians—and started their own cup with its own rules, refusing to recognise the penalty kick which they considered the prerogative of the common professionals with their propensity for foul play.

Although there was plenty of money in professional football, if only on account of the large gates at the Saturday afternoon games, little of it rubbed off on the players. In 1901 it was ruled that no player should receive more than £10 for a signing-on fee, and when, in 1905, a player was transferred from one club to another at a cost to the buyer of £1,000, the Football Association stepped in with a ruling that £350 was to be the top transfer fee—a petty move that fell into disuse within a few months. There was a certain amount of bribery and corruption, and football clubs and officials were wealthy.

In international matches there was virtually no competition from abroad, and all comers were soundly trounced, whether it was Germany in 1901 (beaten 12–0 and 10–0), or Austria in 1908. There was no doubt at all who would win the Olympic football tournament in 1912.

In Rugby football, too, there had been a breakaway movement in the late nineteenth century to differentiate between amateurs and professionals. Rugby Union and Rugby League pursued their separate paths according to different rules. Rugby League was played mostly in the industrial north. Wales, weak in soccer, was strong in Rugby, and in 1905 was the only side to beat the New Zealand All-Blacks. In England there was sufficient interest in Rugby Union to merit the building of the stadium at Twickenham, which thereafter became its headquarters. Those who played Rugby Union were gents, those who played Rugby League were common; there were also class differences between Rugby and soccer, and middle-class grammar schools with aspirations made a point of saying in their prospectus that Rugby, not soccer, was played.

Amateurs and professionals in football, gentlemen and players in cricket. Cricket pervaded the whole fabric of Edwardian life, and although it was never followed with the intensity of football by the industrial working classes, they found pleasure in watching the giants of the age. One of the few areas in which Edwardian democracy operated was village cricket, where for the space of a few hours class distinctions were brushed aside and there was no dishonour in the squire being eclipsed by the blacksmith. In the great country houses cricket was a feature of the leisured life, with full-time groundsmen committed to maintaining pitches equal to that of the Oval and pavilions that vied with those on county grounds.

Village cricket was a great leveller, and squire vied with blacksmith without loss of dignity

The Grand Old Man of English cricket, W. G. Grace, had just left first-class cricket when the reign opened—he could afford to; in 1895 a testimonial of over £5,000 was raised for him by the *Daily Telegraph*. Although he played in a few minor matches and lived until 1915, the Edwardian public had to be content with his legend and his successors.

They were days of good wickets and fast scoring. In 1901 in six consecutive innings, C. B. Fry scored 106, 209, 149, 105, 140 and 105. In that same year sixty batsmen scored more than 1,000 runs each, and three topped the 3,000 mark. In 1902 Sussex scored 705 for nine declared against Surrey at Hastings; in 1903 Jessop scored 286 in 180 minutes for Gloucestershire, and in 1904 in the match between Derbyshire and Essex both sides topped 500 runs in the first innings. The match between Worcestershire and Oxford University produced 1,492 runs. In the Test Matches against Australia in 1905 the Hon F. S. Jackson captained England, won the toss five times out of five and headed both the batting and the bowling averages. In 1906 T. Hayward scored a record 3,518 runs, and in the same year

G. H. Hirst scored 2,385 runs and took 208 wickets—the only double 'double' ever completed. In 1909 Hobbs and Hayes scored 371 runs in 165 minutes for Surrey against Hampshire. The decade was, indeed, notable for the brightest of cricket. One of the feats of 1911 was the scoring by E. Alletson of Nottingham of 189 runs in 90 minutes, his last 89 being made in 15 minutes.

Nor was there any shortage of bowling triumphs. In both 1906 and 1908 T. Wass of Nottinghamshire took 16 wickets in a day; in 1901 Yorkshire dismissed Nottinghamshire for 13 runs, and in 1902 Australia was dismissed for 36 runs with Wilfred Rhodes taking 7 wickets for 17 runs. The English team on that occasion is generally regarded as the best-balanced side ever put into the field by this country. In 1905 Rhodes demonstrated his supremacy by taking six wickets for nine runs for Yorkshire against Essex.

The captain of the 1902 side against Australia was C. B. Fry, who epitomised the quality of Edwardian sportsmen. Born in 1872, Fry was the gentleman autocrat at his most unselfconscious. In 1892 at the inter-university sports taking place at Oxford he put down his cigar in the dressing-room, went out and set a world record for the long jump that held for 21 years, then went back to his cigar. He played football of the highest standard, taking part in a cup final, and was a boxer, a fine swimmer, a golfer, played competitive tennis, was adept at the javelin, and was a good shot, fisherman and horseman. He was also a talented writer, promoted naval training for boys, and was a keen motorist. All in all, a *Boy's Own Paper* hero. Typical of the aristocratic players was the Hon F. S. Jackson, who split his time between soldiering (serving in the Boer War), hunting, shooting and cricket. In the Gentleman v Players match at Lord's in 1894 he and his fellow opening bowler bowled unchanged throughout the match, Jackson taking 12 wickets for 77 runs. Born in 1870, the son of Lord Allerton, he was educated at Harrow and Trinity College, Cambridge, and personified the well-born cricket amateur.

Cricket was the sport everyone could participate in without

loss of dignity. Urchins played it in the squalid streets of the East End with dustbins as wickets; the lower middle classes set up their stumps on the beaches of the south coast; the rich spent their week-ends at the game, and attendance at the Eton-Harrow match was a must on the social calendar. Of course, there were those who complained that it was a slow game, out of key with the frenzied tempo of the new age. In 1901 *Punch* put forward a number of suggestions for shortening the game: let the batsmen go in fetters; extend the distance between the wickets to a quarter of a mile; have two bowlers at each end, both bowling simultaneously; increase the fielding side to twenty-two but allow only six to bat (chosen by ballot); have six stumps at each end; let the bat be abolished in favour of the broom-stick; instruct umpires to treat every application in the most favourable sense to the 'outs'; let the innings of a batsman be closed at twenty runs and a match come to an end when declared by a tenth of the spectators as 'tedious'—all of which were scorned by the MCC.

To the man in the street, rowing was the University Boat Race, a free spectacle with opportunities for celebration in the riverside pubs. The purists rather resented the interest of the masses in this contest, were disgusted by the betting that 'contaminated' the event, and deplored the ungentlemanlike behaviour of members of the crews in writing about rowing for the press. Athletics was also of limited appeal, and the 1908 Olympic Games passed without extravagant press coverage, despite British supremacy in most events. The fastest time for the 100 yards sprint was 9.8 seconds in July 1901, and for the mile 4 minutes 16.8 seconds in July 1902; these remained unbroken by the 1908 games. The record for the high jump was less than 6 ft 6 in, the long jump record was just under 25 ft. In the tug-of-war at the Olympic Games the United Kingdom had a walk-over for third place, as only the Americans decided to compete against the three United Kingdom teams (all made up of policemen).

Hockey, widely played in the universities and public schools, was now considered a suitable sport for young ladies, who were

Croquet was still widely played, and at one time it seemed as though it would eclipse lawn tennis in popularity

also entering the male purlieus of cricket and football. 'Have you not observed', asked a *Punch* humorist:

That all the girls you meet
Have either hockey elbows or
Ungainly cycling feet?
Their backs are bent, their faces red,
From cricket stoop or football head.

Hockey represented an early instance of what might be called the St Trinians syndrome ('I caught her a crunch on the knuckle. A clip on the knee and the cheek'), and mixed hockey, energetically called for by the women, was invariably declined by the men. England dominated the hockey scene, and were never beaten in an international (though the only country outside the British Isles that participated in hockey internationals was France).

Tennis vied with croquet for attention, and at one time it seemed that it would go under. The magazine *The World* reported that 'the lawns that were erstwhile cumbered with tennis

nets now bristle with croquet hoops, and the sedate mallet has
driven out the frisky racquet'. Competition tennis had yet to
make an impact, and it was mainly a sociable game or a source
of humour.

'I wonder why Mr Poppstein serves with three balls?'
'Old associations, I suppose.'

There were few links between lawn tennis and real tennis,
which was played in an indoor court. The latter form was
dominated throughout the period by one player, E. H. Miles.
Lawn-tennis was a late starter, deriving from a game called
sphairistike patented in 1874. In 1877 the All England Croquet
Club became the All England Croquet and Lawn Tennis Club,
and Wimbledon became the centre of the lawn tennis world.
Edwardian lawn tennis, compared with present-day standards,
was a slower game, with less emphasis on the serve and more
on placing the ball. Real, or royal tennis, called court tennis in
America, was a rich man's sport, for it cost £2,000 to build an
indoor court, whereas almost anyone could play lawn tennis.
It was ironically suggested that tennis matches could be played
with one's neighbours over the hedge; one would not necessarily
have to meet them. It was ferociously played by middle-aged
men under the illusion that they were young, and was a useful
adjunct to courtship, though the long skirts of the women players
handicapped them, and rushing the net was decidedly out.
Croquet was a much more amiable game, and part of the social
background rather than a competitive event. It gave women the
opportunity to cheat, as they could shuffle the ball forward under
their long dresses without fear of detection. Played on vicarage
lawns, it was the ideal way of spinning out the long Edwardian
summers. Both games were given prestige by Edward VII, who
took up lawn tennis shortly after it was invented and indulged in
croquet at Marienbad when he was on one of his cures.

Modern boxing, as distinct from pugilism, dates from 1866
when the laws against prize-fighting became more rigidly
enforced; though the fairground bruisers were still in operation
and the bouts organised in the East End were as vicious as

anything in the roll-call of bare-knuckle bouts. The Amateur Boxing Association, founded in 1884, made boxing respectable. Its major innovation was to restrict the number of rounds.

The upper flight of professional boxers aspired to appear under the aegis of the National Sporting Club. In 1901 a case was brought against the club for manslaughter when Billy Smith, fighting under the name of Murray Livingstone, died in the ring. The aim of the Crown was to put a stop to future competitions and, had the jury brought in a verdict of guilty, the history of boxing in Britain might have been cut dramatically short. Fairground boxing-booths provided a cadre for the professional ring; and for young working-class men who happened to be strong and quick on their feet, the ring seemed an escape from unemployment or menial jobs, the emoluments offered for one fight being usually more than a man would earn in a week of toil.

Heavyweight boxing in Britain was dominated by Bombardier Billy Wells, who held the title for nine years, and in the lesser weights Jimmy Wilde—still a name to be conjured with in public bars—had by 1914 fought 200 contests without being beaten. Britain's triumph in the boxing events in the 1908 Olympic Games was due to the non-participation of America. The aristocrat amateur was significantly absent from the boxing ring. Boxing was rough and tough, and little prestige was to be gained from being battered about the head and body, even over the three rounds that the Amateur Boxing Association specified. For every Jimmy Wilde and Bombardier Billy Wells, there were a score of punch-drunk has-beens shuffling round the streets.

Wrestling never made much of an impact on the industrial masses, but various regional forms were practised, each part of the country having its own speciality. There was the Cumberland and Westmorland, the Lancashire (known as 'catch as catch can'), the Cornish, the Devon, the Scottish, and the Irish. There were also a bewildering variety of foreign systems, including 'Glima', the national style of Iceland, which had a curiosity value during the 1908 Olympic Games. The English forms did not match with the Graeco-Roman style popular in Europe,

A Golf Story

(*A golfer recently, in attempting to loft over a house, landed his ball down the chimney. That is the story as reported. We have ventured to supply the remainder*)

" My good woman, don't make such a fuss. Can't you see I'm badly bunkered in your confounded fireplace ? "

Golf was a very popular sport, and golfing stories made their rounds, a source of inspiration to cartoonists

and the British felt that they were at an unfair disadvantage, as the Graeco-Roman style had little resemblance to classic wrestling and derived from the French wrestling schools of the 1860s. Competitive wrestling had little appeal as a spectator sport; it was too slow-moving and the rules were too obscure to excite spectators nurtured on the slap-bang-wallop of professional boxing or the frenzied running about of association football.

The prime minister, Balfour, made golf an in-sport, but even so it would have made headway as a sport eminently suitable for overweight middle-aged men, with someone to carry the clubs, and respectable for women and the lower middle classes. It was a sport that did not need any great mental or physical preparation, and businessmen found that a round of golf did not take too much out of them. Where there is demand backed by money there is supply, and new courses sprang up with startling rapidity in the outer suburbs of the cities and towns. The new golfers soon got to grips with drivers, spoons, brassies, mashies, irons, niblicks and putters, and were discreetly pleased when the solid gutta-percha ball, which had been in use since 1848, was replaced in 1902 by the more easily played, rubber-cored and wound so-called Haskell ball, a mass-produced American invention.

The handicapping system made it possible for apprentice golfers to match themselves against experienced players without a round becoming too one-sided. Golf, unlike cricket, was never a social leveller; if anything it acerbated the class divisions, encouraging businessmen to gather together in exclusive cliques. A good deal of informal business could be done over eighteen holes. Golf also initiated a modest revolution in domestic matters; for it provided a man with a viable excuse to go off for an afternoon without his wife sensing another woman in the offing.

The age was dominated by three players, J. H. Taylor, James Braid and Harry Vardon, but in anticipation of the future an American won a major tournament in 1913 against the best that Britain could offer. In many sports the Americans were becoming a threat to British supremacy. An interesting, as yet unbeaten record was set up in the same year; on a course at Herne Bay a golf ball was driven more than a quarter of a mile.

Cricket of a fairly high standard was played by such luminaries as cartoonist Bernard Partridge, playwright J. M. Barrie, actor C. Aubrey Smith, and novelist A. E. W. Mason, while golf had the prime minister as its most valuable PRO. More prestigious than either of these sports was horse-racing, a sport in which Edward VII had an almost psychotic interest, possibly justified by the immense sums of money he made at it. Between 1886 and 1910 his stallions earned £269,495 in stud fees, and his horses won £146,345. Wealth was always a criterion of what was worth while to the king. He maintained that the happiest day of his life was in 1896 when he led in his Derby winner, Persimmon. To cap his delight the horse had been quoted at 5-1 against. The Jockey Club took action against anyone who infringed the rules, bloodstock breeding improved, and the 'monkey crouch' style of riding changed horse-racing tactics.

On Derby Day the British from all ranks of life gathered together. Ascot was a fashionable event in the social calendar;

every year King Edward moved to Windsor for Ascot Week in the middle of June, and towards the end of July he made a regular visit to the Duke of Richmond for the races at Goodwood. The French nobility were always in evidence at Ascot; 'they appreciated the *haute école* and that observance of the things *stylé* that is dear to their hearts'.[1]

It was well known that the ladies who went to Ascot to show off their finery did not know much about horse-racing. One joke of the period made this clear:

> Uncle: 'Ah, Milly, I'm afraid you've lost your money over that one. He's gone the wrong way!'
> Milly: 'Oh, no, uncle, I'm all right. George told me to back it 'both ways'.'

After the death of Edward VII there was a surrealist touch in the so-called 'Black Ascot', when everyone appeared dressed from head to foot in black.

> The men wore black silk top hats with morning or frock coats, black trousers, black waistcoats, black ties, while in their black-gloved hands they carried tightly rolled black umbrellas. Their funereal ladies must have seemed like strange giant crows or morbid birds of paradise strutting at some Gothic entertainment.[2]

Perhaps the gesture would have appealed to the king; the last thing he was told before he died was that one of his horses had won a race at Kempton Park, and the Ascot extravaganza might have pleased him. Anyway, pretty women always looked well in black.

Showbiz

To many of the rich showbiz was life, and life was showbiz. They pursued their pleasures with a diligence that was lacking in any other aspect of their lives, and prominent amongst these pleasures was the theatre. The cinema had arrived on the scene, but it was in its early stages, and there was no kudos in being seen in picture palaces in the suburbs—the cinema had yet to make the West End.

Edwardian theatre encompassed a wide variety of genres. The frivolous did not flock to the theatre of Galsworthy or Bernard Shaw, kept going by the patronage of the intellectuals and the improved working classes, but they did to the new respectable music halls of the syndicates, the theatres showing inane farces and spectacular melodrama, and, especially, musical shows.

Music hall had passed its best; the drive and the verve that characterised it in mid-Victorian times had been replaced by the cult of the comedian. Twenty years before Edward came to the throne, an Act of Suitability, demanding safety curtains and the exclusion of food and drink from the auditorium, had forced most of the smaller halls to close down and the local stars into other professions. The emphasis shifted to large music halls with a wide appeal, for 'family' entertainment with a minimum of smut, and this led gradually to the control of halls passing to one group, who despatched their stars from one place to another, feeding the demand for hero and heroine worship.

The Coliseum in St Martin's Lane was the dream music hall come true. Opened in December 1904 and costing £80,000 more than anticipated, it had a triple revolving stage that could be rotated at 20 mph, a stage of 10,000 square feet weighing 160 tons, and a special tramline leading directly into the Royal Box, on which ran a tram made entirely of glass. The Coliseum contained an information bureau, a multitude of confectionery stalls, a telephone box (at a time when telephones were few and far between) and a letter box. With four shows a day, presented with a panache that few music hall owners had ever been able to afford, the theatre was lavish, expensive and gorgeously vulgar. It was not surprising that King Edward soon availed himself of the opportunity to use the glass tram so kindly placed at his disposal by the progenitor of the Coliseum, Oswald Stoll.

Stoll was born in Australia in 1866, and when his father died his mother brought Oswald to England, and married into the provincial music hall business. Her new husband owned the Parthenon music hall in Liverpool, and after his death she and her 14-year-old son managed it, then moved to Cardiff to open

a music hall there. It might be supposed that Stoll knew all there
was to know about the music hall by 1904. Though not yet forty,
he was old-fashioned in his ideas, and although clean, the shows
at his Coliseum were dull, and it was known as the Morgueseum.
A simulated Derby was put on (at one performance a jockey
was thrown off his horse and killed), chariot races were run,
there were massive choirs clothed in surplices, and although the
Coliseum's motto, blazoned across the programmes, was 'Pro
Bono Publico', the public were not interested in their own good
but only in being entertained. Spectacle and music did not necessarily guarantee amusement.

Stoll introduced the novelty of making all seats bookable,
including the sixpenny balcony (not gallery, for gallery had low
connotations), but this back-fired for the sixpenny public was
not used to this procedure. The box office became ankle-deep
in postal orders, without accompanying names or addresses,
the resulting chaos necessitating the employment of a chartered
accountant to sort out the mess, which he did by giving tickets
to everyone who declared that he had sent in his money.

The Coliseum, the mirror of the new improved Edwardian
music hall, did not get off to the start that Stoll had hoped for,
but he was sanguine, for he was chairman and managing director
of a chain of music halls that included Empires at Hackney,
Holloway, New Cross, Stratford and Shepherds Bush in London,
and Hippodromes, Coliseums, and Empires scattered throughout
the United Kingdom, in Leeds, Bradford, Birmingham, Liverpool,
Newcastle, Manchester and Nottingham, and other towns where
family fun was in demand. Occasionally the managers were not
so strict with their artists as Stoll, and when a comedian at the
Shepherds Bush Empire overstepped the mark and cracked a
blue joke, this lapse cost Stoll ten guineas. No doubt it proved
even more expensive to the unfortunate comedian, for the circuit
system was in operation, and a black mark registered against a
performer would affect his career not only in the Stoll empire
but in that of Edward Moss, whose major property was the
London Hippodrome. The circuit system of sending stars from
hall to hall meant that select performers could earn more than

£1,000 a week, and the glamour attracted the small fry, who clamoured for work in the life-enhancing environment of the music hall. Seven hundred chorus girls once attended an audition for a show, only twenty of whom were acceptable.

To counter the effect of the Moss and Stoll chains, previously unallied theatres and music halls joined together in self-protection. One of these syndicates comprised the Tivoli, the Oxford, the London Pavilion, the Canterbury and the South London. It was an indication that the independent music hall, catering for a local audience, was dying, though one or two of them, including the Britannia in Hoxton, kept going against all the odds. Shows were becoming stereotyped for the mass audience. Although Sarah Bernhardt and Ellen Terry appeared at the Coliseum, and good one-act plays were staged as part of the programme, the basic elements of the spectaculars were blandness and unction, pseudo-Cockney song and sweet melody, an eagerness not to offend. Stoll received a knighthood in 1919, as the man who cleaned up music hall and made it respectable.

Many of the qualities of respectable music hall entertainment promoted by Stoll were present in musical theatre, the dominant form of which was the musical comedy. This had been gaining popularity over burlesque and comic opera since 1892 when *In Town* brought the new genre to the public. *The Belle of New York* (1898), with Edna May as the leading lady, established the American musical in Britain.

In 1903 the new Gaiety was opened in the presence of the king and queen, neither of them averse to entertainment that did not demand too much of their mental powers. The musical comedy presented then was the now forgotten *The Orchid,* which made a star of Gabrielle Ray, so that she became a 'postcard queen'; a favourite Edwardian way of conferring immortality was to portray stage heroines on picture postcards. The Gaiety became a cult, with the Gaiety Girls the epitome of desirability. Show girls had always been fair game for stage door johnnies, whether Victorian swells or Edwardian knuts, but the charisma had never been exploited with so much energy. Whether or not the Gaiety stage door was, as historians put it,

London's West End was rich in theatres and music halls. In this superb Edwardian night photograph of Leicester Square the Alhambra can be seen through the trees

the gateway to romance, the girls became transformed into the Baroness Churston, the Countess Poulett and the Countess of Drogheda. The inane vacuous stories being unfolded on stage were transferred to real life.

The keynote of Edwardian musical comedy was escape. Musical comedy had started as being refreshingly modern, but now audiences wanted to be wafted into a never-never world. The promoters tended these delicate blossoms, and saw that it paid handsomely. Frank Curzon was a typical entrepreneur of the period. Having made money in tailoring, he built the Piccadilly Hotel and resurrected the Strand theatre, opening it in 1901 with *A Chinese Honeymoon* that had been tried out in the theatrical outback of Hanley in 1899. With songs such as 'Martha Spanks the Grand Piano' and 'Twiddly Bits' the show was a runaway success, notching up 1,076 performances. By 1903 Curzon controlled the following theatres: Avenue, Camden, Coronet, Prince of Wales, Comedy, Criterion, Wyndham's and the Strand. For prestige reasons he occasionally dabbled in straight theatre, putting on Gerald du Maurier at Wyndham's.

Producing a musical comedy was not exactly a licence to print money. Some shows were too banal even for an Edwardian audience and the more discriminating favoured the meatier light operas of Edward German—*Merrie England* (1902) and *Tom Jones* (1906). But whereas *Merrie England* ran for only 120 performances the later musical comedies enjoyed a more popular success; *Our Miss Gibbs* (1909) ran for 636 performances, *The Arcadians* (1909) for 809, and *The Quaker Girl* (1910) for 536.

The most dramatic triumph of fantasy over reality, of long drawn-out sweetness, was Lehar's *The Merry Widow*, put in production as a stop gap when the supply of English musical comedies was running out. It ran from June 1907 until July 1909, and King Edward VII saw it four times. An Eton schoolboy, Osbert Sitwell, saw it, and later pondered over its significance:

> It held a suitably designed mirror to the age, to the preference for restaurant to palace, for comfort to beauty, and to the idealization of Mammon. Mammon underlay the smudgy softness and superficial prettiness of the whole performance, as the skull supports the lineaments of even the youngest and freshest face.[1]

For the farewell performance the theatre was besieged all day long, the earliest arrival taking his place at 5.30 in the morning.

Franz Lehar, born in 1870, a young Austrian bandmaster, followed this up in 1911 with *The Count of Luxembourg*, which he composed in two months. It was the kind of plot the audiences loved. A comic grand duke wanted to marry a music hall girl, but before he could do so the girl needed a title, so a marriage was arranged between the girl and a spendthrift count, on condition that he did not see her and divorced her after three months. There was £20,000 on the deal. Naturally the count (hero) did see the music hall girl (heroine) and what was £20,000 to a man in love? What indeed? echoed the audience, entranced. But Lehar's second offering to the English stage did not have the success of *The Merry Widow*, and *Gipsy Love* of 1912 faded even faster.

The mood had changed. In 1907 when *The Merry Widow* opened war was far away, but five years later there were rumblings of a change. The old-fashioned burlesque was being remodelled into the modern revue, and in 1913 *Hullo, Ragtime* broke vulgarly on to the scene, thin in plot and music, but fast paced and abounding in vigour. It brought new thinking into the theatre and new dances into the ballroom—the bunny hug, the chicken scramble, and many of the devotees of the older school breathed a sigh of relief when, during the war, *The Maid of the Mountains* proved that romance was not dead. Also in the pre-war format was the record-breaking *Chu Chin Chow*, of which, because of a certain degree of nakedness in the production, Sir Herbert Tree quipped: 'More navel than millinery'.

Nudity, in fact, was becoming a draw in the theatre, and paralleled the emphasis in fashion on the sensuous and the alluring. Gaby Deslys had appeared in London in 1903 as a soubrette, singing naughty French songs and wearing naughty French clothes. As early as 1900 Annette Kellerman did a physically revealing swimming and diving act, and was a dominant influence in persuading women to adopt the close-fitting bathing costume, hiding little. Maud Allan was one of the first women to appear on the stage with bare arms and legs. But no matter what went on after the show, when it was tacitly recognised that the goal of the show girl was a liaison with a toff, the accent was on teasing and titillation, as far from Victorian strip tease (*poses plastiques* and *tableaux vivants*) as they were from present frontal nudity. The titillation was given a veneer of spurious artistry; Maud Allan received most applause for her dance of Salome, when she was a good deal more naked than when expressing Mendelssohn's 'Spring Song'.

Male impersonators were enjoying a vogue. Vesta Tilley in frock-coat, spats, silk hat, and lavender gloves was perhaps of more consequence as a singer than a woman in drag, but she bought her clothes from men's outfitters and for a time set men's fashions.

In *Our Miss Gibbs* the hats worn by the chorus girls cost sixty guineas each. Salaries for the principals were reaching astronomical heights, the choruses were getting larger, and were being subdivided into front row chorus, who would participate in the singing, dialogue and action, and the also-rans. The members of the front row chorus, experienced and wooed for rival shows,

Maud Allan in her celebrated Salome dance

were becoming as much in demand as the stars, and marriage
was always breaking into their ranks. Musical theatre was big
business. In 1913 one management spent £18,000 in producing
the now little-known show, *Come Over Here*; in the course of an
evening the chorus girls wore 650 frocks. The producer of
The Arcadians spent £12,000 on improvements to the Shaftesbury
Theatre in preparation for the musical comedy that only he had
any faith in. £13,000 could go into a loser such as *The Dashing
Little Duke*, while *The Duchess of Dantzig* lost £15,000. These were
both attempts to capitalise on the vogue for Ruritanian high
jinks. Even long-running shows such *A Country Girl* failed to
show profits in London, and although *The Girl from Kays* ran for
432 performances in 1902, the loss of £20,000 was only recouped
from the provinces and America. Nevertheless there were vast

profits to be made for everyone—200,000 copies of the sheet music of the waltz from *The Merry Widow* were sold within a few years, an encouragement to music publishers to back promising outsiders. In an age in which the stage was never short of backers, it is not surprising that promoters occasionally ventured their arm on projects that everyone on the outside could see were doomed.

The disarming quality of the best of the musical comedies was that they were musically unpretentious, and composers such as Franz Lehar provided large numbers of excellent tunes. There were those, of course, who saw musical significance in *The Merry Widow* and its contemporaries, who persuaded themselves that they were in contact with great art rather than being self-indulgent. G. K. Chesterton in his column in the *Illustrated London News* lashed out at the pretentiousness of these people: 'The fact is that we have reached so high and rarefied a condition of humbug that the most serious things we have left are the comic songs'. *The Merry Widow* was a historical phenomenon, and it is interesting to note that it was Adolf Hitler's favourite entertainment.

In straight theatre, only one production in three was a success despite the low cost in putting on a play. A play running at half capacity could show a modest profit. There was not the backing for drama that there was for the musical, but pioneers such as Harley Granville Barker forced playgoers to face the facts of life with his own plays; *The Voysey Inheritance* and *Waste* have survived the froth and frivolity that constituted much of the West End theatre. Barker's management of the Court Theatre between 1904 and 1907 has been described as 'without question the most noteworthy episode in English theatrical history since Shakespeare and Burbage ran the Globe on Bankside'.[2] Granville Barker encouraged the resurgence of provincial repertory theatre, and at the Court he put on Euripides, Maeterlinck, Yeats and Galsworthy, but it was Shaw who made this theatre financially viable. One of his lesser works, *John Bull's Other Island*, was a runaway hit, seen by Balfour four times; on two of these occasions Balfour took with him Asquith and Campbell-

A scene from a domestic melodrama of the period, Alfred Sutro's John Glayde's Honour, *performed in* 1907

Bannerman, the leaders of the opposition. King Edward, who had earlier dismissed Shaw as a 'damned crank', went to see this play, and laughed uproariously, breaking a chair in the process. Shaw described the playgoers who went to the Court as 'not an audience but a congregation'. *Man and Superman* made Shaw the key figure of the period to the intelligentsia, and *Major Barbara* and *The Doctor's Dilemma* played to full houses. The Court Theatre had neither the capacity nor the location to attract large audiences, and the Shaw plays were transfered to the Savoy and the Haymarket theatres. Fashionable playgoers did not relish having to work at enjoyment, however, and this fact, combined with crippling rents, forced the plays to close. The Shaw/Barker regime was not typical of Edwardian theatre; away from the Court theatre it had to face the opposition of farcical drivel and spectacular melodrama using real railway trains at Drury Lane, and, as often was the case in Edwardian London, the second-rate triumphed. Later plays by Shaw, *Getting Married* (1908) and *Misalliance* (1910), ran in the West End, but not for long. His *The Shewing-Up of Blanco Posnet* was refused a licence by the Lord Chamberlain for blasphemy, and only a pot-boiler, *Fanny's First Play* (1911), could be rated a success in terms of number of performances.

The new school of playwrights did not obey the cardinal rule of giving the public what it wanted, and only when Shaw wrote *Pygmalion* for Mrs Patrick Campbell did the highbrow and the middlebrow theatre meet. The paying audience on the whole did not wish to be reminded of industrial unrest, as in Galsworthy's *Strife*, much preferring the saccharine of Barrie or the calculated daring of Somerset Maugham. The test of a successful Edwardian play was to be burlesqued, and this dubious dignity was conferred on Barrie's *What Every Woman Knows* (1908). Several of his other plays, such as *Quality Street* (1902), were almost parodies in themselves.

A scene from a Drury Lane spectacular, The Whip, *performed in* 1909

Nevertheless there was frequently an integrity in the intelligent Edwardian theatre that one is at a loss to find elsewhere, and one can have nothing but praise for Granville Barker and others for not only putting on meaty and demanding English fare but for encouraging foreign drama. Granville Barker also put on superb productions of Shakespeare when, from a box office point of view, they spelled death.

To a certain degree, drama had a clear field in visual story-telling. Maugham's dramas were in no way better than the average television play of today, but they were patronised by the public who wanted to see what ordinary people would do in set circumstances; the interest was in dialogue and narrative. The middlebrow theatre was doing what the cinema could do far better. However, in Britain the cinema had got off on the wrong foot, and was treated as a gimmick, with cinematography an auxiliary to music hall turns. Film clips of the funeral of Queen Victoria and the coronation of Edward VII were treated as fit entertainment for the groundlings, and it is characteristic of the lack of imagination shown that when Edward VII saw himself on film he was concerned mainly because his medals were on the wrong way round (the film was in negative).

The cinematograph was born towards the end of the nineteenth century; in 1893, Edison had done a one-minute film of the execution of Mary, Queen of Scots; in 1894, kinetoscopes had been set up in force on Broadway; in 1895, the Lumière Brothers had begun operations; but perhaps the most significant event was a fifteen-minute film in twelve scenes on the subject of the Dreyfus affair made by the pioneer Méliès in 1899. The British lagged behind, and one of the few manifestations of interest was the Brighton school of film-making from 1900 to 1905, in which the innovation of close-up was used. Whereas Méliès made his adventurous *A Trip to the Moon* in 1902 and the Americans produced the first 'classic' film, *The Great Train Robbery*, in 1903, the main contribution of the British was the trivial snippet of film to enliven a music hall programme. All the elements were there to exploit, but no one bothered. As with the typewriter and the telephone, development was left to the Americans, though it was the Italians who foresaw the possibilities of the cinema for spectacle when they made *Quo Vadis* in 1912, a year before the development of Hollywood and three years before Griffiths' *Birth of a Nation*.

The British also ignored the cinema's comic possibilities and let Charlie Chaplin, who had been a wolf in the first performance of *Peter Pan* in London and who had demonstrated his capabilities in the Karno Comedy Co, get out of their grasp. Chaplin made thirty-five films for Mack Sennett in 1914, while the British, leaders in visual humour, twiddled their thumbs. In the sphere of cinematography, as in many others, the British were too idle to capitalise on an entertainment winner and only the demand of the masses for this new medium caused it to be taken up. The home-grown product was cheap and vulgar with the aura of a second-rate music hall turn, and although by 1914 all the large towns in Britain had picture palaces, their offerings gave no indication that the cinema was to be one of the most important art forms of the century.

The middle classes and the intellectuals scorned cinema, the former because it reeked of innovation, the latter because it was common; the left-wing intelligentsia were even more contemptuous, for the cinema made a point of giving the lower orders exactly what they wanted (sex and violence) without attempting to improve them.

Innovation had a habit of nonplussing the English paying public, and when Debussy's *Pélleas et Mélisande* was produced at Covent Garden in 1909 they were caught between incomprehension and the desire to appear knowledgeable, states of mind shared by the critics. Opera came dimly within the orbit of showbiz. Provided that English opera was not put on, there was always a public for Covent Garden productions of the standards, under-rehearsed and shabby as they might be; the only stipulation the opera public made was that there should be a name singer (preferably not British). The operas of Richard Strauss were always good for a shudder, on account of his plots, and a laugh, on account of his music. Ballet was an integral part of the music hall scene, and it was via the Coliseum in 1909 that Russian dancers made themselves known to the British public. They heralded the invasion of the Diaghilev ballet in 1911, and the mellifluent absurdities of Isadora Duncan and Maud Allan were submerged in a riot of exotic dancing, exciting music and colourful costumes.

Strange new trends had already been forced on the public mind by the Post-Impressionist exhibition of 1910, called into being by the fact that the Grafton Gallery had a gap between exhibitions. Cèzanne, Gauguin and Matisse provoked lectures from psychiatrists and a chorus of disapproval from the established artists. Thesauruses were looted for the right words to describe this barbaric invasion—jejune, barbarous, imbecility (*The Queen*), weird, uncouth, tortuous (*Daily Telegraph*). Painters of the English establishment saw the show as a bad joke that would devalue art; art was concerned with conspicuous display. The new rich had their portraits painted by Sargent, and city councils commissioned artists like Brangwyn to decorate their walls with appropriate scenes. The status symbol of the genteel was the set of Francis Wheatley's street cries of London, reprinted in a limited edition.

Philip Burne-Jones, who had made for himself something of a corner in languorous hermaphrodites and was thought by most people to be dead, wrote to *The Times* a letter incoherent with rage, in which he suspected that the exhibition of Post-Impressionist paintings 'is a huge practical joke, organised in Paris at the expense of our countrymen'. The *Morning Post* complained that art students would find these 'hysterical daubs' . . . 'a justification of their own worst endeavours'.

The chorus of disapproval that greeted this quite small exhibition was out of all proportion to its impact on the general public, which rarely visited any of the minor galleries, and whose artistic horizons were governed by the Royal Academy exhibitions. It was symptomatic of a feeling of helplessness. It is understandable that the French artists on show were regarded as the vanguard of chaos, paving the way to the naked barbarism of the Russian ballet of the following year. To the establishment it seemed that a crack was appearing in the whole framework of civilisation, and anxieties about the cultural basis of the western world were mixed with general apprehension at the way more mundane things were going. Similarities were drawn between the anarchy of art and the anarchy of industry, the *malheurs* of Richard Strauss and the perversity of Debussy were matched with the incomprehensible behaviour of the suffragette movements.

No wonder that the disciples of the old order were outraged that not only did these sinister manifestations occur, but that the only response seemed to be tepid jibes in *Punch* and a rustle of order papers in parliament. The warmth and *schmalz* of *The Merry Widow*, the flattery of Sargent's brush, the harmless knockabout and cheeky Cockney of the music hall, all these were fading, rendered insignificant by the new brutal spirit of the times, a counterpoint to dark doings in Europe.

Notes to this chapter are on page 295.

CHAPTER EIGHT

CRIME AND PUNISHMENT

The Policeman's Lot

IN SPITE of the unrest and unease that pervaded the years 1901–14, crime remained at a modest level. This table showing the numbers of criminals convicted at superior courts in England and Wales makes illuminating reading:

	population	convictions
1850	17,773,324	20,537
1860	19,902,713	12,068
1870	22,090,163	12,953
1880	25,714,288	11,214
1890	28,763,673	9,242
1900	32,249,187	8,157
1910	35,796,289	11,987

In 1906, a typical year, there had been a total of 59,079 indictable offences committed, compared with 50,469 in 1899. This, incredibly, was less than two crimes per policeman and despite the strong feelings of hostility by the poor, who had constantly suffered at the hands of the police throughout the Victorian period. The police were then looked upon as instruments of class war, and were harried and mocked whenever the chance arose. A clear indication of this can be found in a host of music hall songs, where the police are shown as corrupt, vicious, unintelligent and comic. 'If You Want to Know the Time, Ask a P'liceman' indicates that this was all he was good for.

There was no equivocation about right and wrong. There was a criminal class, just as there was a working class and a middle class. Criminals were easily recognised, and when caught fair and square they would own up and make a clean breast of it; they abided by the rules of the game. According to the criminologist Dr Lombroso in 1876 'the born criminal has projecting ears, thick hair and thin beard, projecting frontal eminences, enormous jaws, a square and protruding chin, large cheek bones, and frequent gesticulation'. Moral insensibility, a dull conscience and a freedom from remorse were attributed to the criminal, and as he was generally lacking in intelligence he never took proper precautions before or after committing a crime.

By the start of the Edwardian period, the Metropolitan Police had settled in at new headquarters in Scotland Yard, and were acquiring new techniques. Although the principle of finger-printing had been laid down in 1892, the police were still involved in anthropometry—the classification of criminals by physical characteristics, such as the shape of the head. A system of fingerprinting, introduced in 1902, caused alarm throughout the underworld, especially when fifty-four men were arrested on Derby Day for various offences, notably pickpocketing, and it was discovered, by comparing their fingerprints with those on record, that twenty-nine of them were old lags.

The possibilities of the use of this technique in crime detection were brought to the attention of a sensation-seeking public when a finger was found on a Clerkenwell warehouse-gate after a break-in. At Scotland Yard, the finger was identified as belonging to a pickpocket who operated in the Elephant and Castle area. Eventually he was picked up, and the absence of a finger provided excellent evidence. Fingerprints by themselves were not fully accepted by the courts, though a precedent was formed on 14 September 1902 when the perpetrator of a burglary in

Denmark Hill was brought to justice on the evidence of fingerprints alone and sentenced to seven years' imprisonment.

It was hoped that with new methods, such as fingerprinting, there would be a rise in the numbers of cases solved. In 1878 the CID had investigated 21,792 felonies, and arrests had been made in 10,849 of these cases. Yet of £157,283 stolen, only £19,785 were recovered. The public was not slow to accuse the police of incompetence, and something worse, and throughout the Edwardian period very few months went by without the police being charged with accepting bribes from prostitutes and brothel-keepers.

As for incompetence, the Metropolitan Police in the early 1900s was 2,000 under strength, the new techniques had yet to be tested, and the recording systems were in a mess—not until 1914 was the Criminal Record Office formed from the various individual departments dealing with records. The *Police Gazette* continued to use woodcuts for illustrations long after photography became a viable proposition for this purpose. Although the introduction of the telephone had revolutionised business life, the Metropolitan Police still preferred the telegraph, where messages had to be tapped out one letter after another, maintaining that this was safer than the telephone, where operators could listen in. This idea that telephones were not 'secret' persisted until about 1910, though as late as 1917 there were two police stations which were not on the telephone.

In 1903 Sir Melville Macnaghten took over as Chief of the Criminal Investigation Department. Born in 1853, he had been educated at Eton before taking over the management of the family estates in Bengal. He joined the CID in 1889.

He determined to make the Metropolitan Police a force above reproach. In 1904 a constable charged with perjury—accused of planting a knife and a hammer in the pockets of a suspected man—was sentenced to five years' imprisonment. The case was given wide publicity by the tabloid press, and the general public was well pleased that its intuitive suspicions about the police were justified. In 1906 a constable arrested Eva d'Angely as a common prostitute; she had, he maintained, been behaving in a riotous and indecent manner in Regent Street, and she duly appeared at Marlborough Street police court. To the reporters of the London weekly press, that depended for its success on juicy court cases, it seemed an open and shut case, but Eva d'Angely protested that she was a respectable married woman who had been waiting for her husband, and this plea was accepted by the magistrate. The police, the popular press reported, were celebrated for their persecution of innocent women, and it was high time something was done about it. The public image of the police would seem to have been irrevocably tarnished, but when the newspapers tried to get hold of Mrs d'Angely to keep the story boiling they found that she had disappeared to Paris. Discreetly it was decided not to pursue the matter for Eva d'Angely was, indeed, a common prostitute.

Another case stirred the fires. Two men were arrested on Boat Race night for being drunk and disorderly, and were incarcerated in Vine Street police station. Again it all seemed a cut and dried case, and only when the magistrates decided that the two men had suffered from 'brutal methods of treatment and procedure, denoting culpable negligence' did it become newsworthy.

It was not surprising that when the suffragettes appeared on the scene the police were in two minds how to tackle the problem. The statement by Mrs Pankhurst that 'the argument of the broken pane is the most valuable argument in modern politics' did not endear her to them. The police authorities could hardly pull punches when letters were being set on fire in pillar-boxes, and other targets for arson included empty houses, sports pavilions, boat houses, grandstands, railway stations, plus a school or two. Nor could the police ignore the fact that the British Museum and the Tower of London were attacked, pictures slashed, golf greens dug up, the glass of orchid houses at Kew Gardens smashed and telephone wires cut. The policeman's lot was decidedly not a happy one.

That the Metropolitan Police were not reduced to a chronic state of anxiety says much for the calibre of the average constable. There were cases that could not backfire. When a house in

Richmond Road, Kensington, was raided in 1904 in the belief that it was a brothel there was relief all round when twenty-five couples were found (including three coloured women) distributed amidst the five bedrooms, plus indecent photographs in the upstairs rooms. In the same year the police were involved with the Rev Mr Kendall, rector of Holsworthy, Devon, who was accused of having saucy photographs of Plymouth actresses and suspected of having unlawful relations with a Miss Andrews. The rector was awarded £1,000 damages for slander, and there were more red faces.

Constable Pullen was luckier. William Morris and Cecil Proutt one night in 1908 missed the last train from Liverpool Street station, and walked through Bishopsgate Street, meeting

"CAN YOU TELL ME?"

THE POLICE SAY THEY HAVE FOUND A CLUE AND DO EVERYTHING IN THEIR POWER TO MAKE SURE OF THEIR MAN. IS IT ANY FAULT OF THEIRS IF HE GETS AWAY?

(*Drawn by* G. L. STAMPA)

The police were always good for a laugh, as reflected in this humorous drawing of 1907

The girl looked down at the sinister patch of red on her skirt.
"It l·oks like—like blood," she stammered.

It was the age of the suave amateur sleuth, such as Freeman's John Thorndyke, here about to solve another baffling crime

Constable Pullen en route and deciding to bait him. They asked the constable 'What's the time?' and Pullen pointed to the clock over the road. This procedure was repeated several times, and eventually the two men broke into the song 'If you want to know the time ask a p'liceman' whereupon Pullen, his patience exhausted, took them into custody. Next morning the men were fined 10s. Such cases were the small change of police business.

Britain's police forces were guaranteed a bad press if they slipped up, and journalists were certain of getting their names in print if they exposed a scandal involving the police. And not only journalists. In 1903 Sir Arthur Conan Doyle came across the case of George Edalji, the son of a Parsee country vicar, sent to prison for horse-maiming. Thinking the sentence of seven years was somewhat harsh, Conan Doyle decided to emulate his own Sherlock Holmes and investigate. He found that Edalji had been convicted because he was coloured, and that he was a studious, shortsighted man who had worked in a solicitor's office and written, at the age of twenty-seven, an authoritative book on railway law. Conan Doyle's series of articles in the *Daily Telegraph* in 1907 once more cast doubt on the quality of the police.

It was the age of the fictitious amateur detective; apart from Sherlock Holmes, there were, among others, Chesterton's Father Brown, Freeman's John Thorndyke, and Baroness Orczy's Old Man in the Corner. The 'old man in the corner' figured in two Edwardian collections published in 1905 and 1909; he sat in an ABC teashop drinking milk and tying and untying knots in strings, solving crimes that had baffled the police, for the benefit of a girl reporter. 'There is no such thing as a mystery in connection with any crime, provided intelligence is brought to bear upon its investigation', he stated. And intelligence, it was implicit, was notably lacking in the baffled police, who were invariably portrayed in fiction as incompetent inferiors to the brilliant sleuths.

Baroness Orczy was at one with the suffragettes in her belief that everything a man could do, a woman could do—better, and this included, for the baroness, police work. In 1910 *Lady Molly of Scotland Yard* appeared, featuring Lady Molly Robertson-Kirk 'head of the Female Department'—in fact as late as 1926 the CID had only one woman detective, and women police were not introduced until 1919.

It sometimes seemed that criminals were taking their tone from A. J. Raffles and other gentleman crooks. Violent crime was rare. Besides keeping the crime rate down, Macnaghten stopped major crime escalating as it had done in the United States. Murder was sufficiently uncommon for there to be no homicide squad at Scotland Yard, and firearms were generally eschewed. There were two instances during the period where the smooth fabric of the crime pattern was shattered and the police engaged in armed conflict with law-breakers.

The first occurred in 1909, when Paul Hefeld and Jacob

*Violent crime was rare, but when it occurred it was relentlessly exploited by the press,
who found it good copy. A payroll robbery in Tottenham in 1909 inspired several
magazine serials*

Meyer, described as 'Russians of doubtful character', snatched a
payroll of £80 from outside a Tottenham factory. They were on
foot, and were pursued by two policemen in the car that had
brought the money from the bank. Hefeld fired three shots at the
car; one missed, one smashed the windscreen, and the last
pierced the radiator, stopping the engine. The policemen
continued the chase on foot, with the two men firing at them.

A small boy who came along to see the fun was shot dead, and as the action moved towards Tottenham Marshes a bullet killed one of the policemen. Nothing like this had ever happened before. The telegraph began tapping out its slow message to the various police stations, and—knowing that this was a case where they could not be rendered speechless by acid-tongued magistrates— the London constabulary flung themselves into the pursuit on horseback, on bicycles, in carriages and motor cars, and even a bus. They were hindered by a vast crowd of well-wishers, and two men with shotguns who were bird-shooting on the marshes watched the whole cavalcade go by, not knowing the reason for it. By the time the two fugitives had reached the Chingford Road they had killed two persons and wounded twenty others.

An electric tramcar on the Chingford Road was held up at the point of a pistol to allow the two men to get aboard. An elderly passenger who objected was shot, and from the back of the car Meyer fired at the pursuers who had requisitioned a horse-trap. The horse was hit and the occupants thrown out; a tram-car travelling in the opposite direction was stopped, and reversed with the police on board. A car drew ahead of the leading tram and Meyer and Hefeld were forced to get out. They took over a milkcart, which was wrecked, and then a greengrocer's cart, which they abandoned before taking to the fields, heading for Epping Forest. Sportsmen with shotguns had now joined in. Hefeld fell wounded, but before he could be captured he turned his gun on himself and blew his brains out. Meyer carried on alone. He made for an unfinished building, where a plasterer threw bricks at him and was shot. Meyer took refuge in a cottage and tried unsuccessfully to hide in the chimney. He fled upstairs, locking himself in a bedroom. There was some doubt as to whether he killed himself or was shot by two armed policemen who followed him into the cottage. The whole affair was quite outside the experience of the police. The public felt that at last real life was taking on the colours of adventure fiction. This view was confirmed less than two years later when other foreign criminals demonstrated that gun battles were not, by act of God, restricted to the eruptive continent of Europe.

In December 1910 a small gang of aliens resolved to rob a jeweller's shop in Houndsditch; they took the premises next door, intending to break through the intervening wall. While they were busy with the crowbar, the proprietor of a fancy goods shop heard suspicious sounds, and summoned the police. The four investigating policemen were inquisitive rather than bent upon arrest, but a foot was put in the door when one of the gang tried to slam it in the leading officer's face. The gang panicked, shooting the four policemen and their own leader. Another policeman was killed when he tried to tackle one of the gang who left the house.

In the confusion the criminals escaped, and took refuge in Grove Street, Whitechapel. They had with them the shot member of the gang. A doctor, who was summoned, accepted the story that the dying man had been accidentally shot in the back, and did not report the matter to the police. When he returned to the house to see how the man was getting on, he found him dead and the others gone; only then did he tell the police, who searched the place and found a loaded pistol. There was a round-up of revolutionaries, and a small arsenal and a collection of anarchist literature were found in a house in Gold Street, off the Whitechapel Road.

The police came to a dead end in their investigations, and it seemed as though the whole affair would turn out to be inconclusive. A year went by before information reached the police that two of the wanted men had taken refuge in 100 Sidney Street, a squalid thoroughfare running between the Mile End Road and the Commercial Road. The police were told that the men were armed with Mauser pistols and a large stock of ammunition. It was perhaps typical of the lack of preparedness for any such contingencies that the ninety policemen recruited for the assault of Sidney Street were armed with inferior revolvers and rifles from a minature rifle range.

It was difficult to clear the surrounding houses and to winkle out the occupants of the building; an elderly couple on the ground floor, no doubt thinking that their worst fears of the police were justified, screamed and had to be removed by force.

Notwithstanding such events as the Sidney Street siege, the public's image of the policeman was stable enough for it to appear in advertisement form

Gradually the police cordon reached two hundred, and at dawn the door was knocked and gravel thrown at the windows. This drew the fire of the inmates, and one policeman was hit.

It was soon realised that the police weapons were nothing but toys, and a detachment of Scots Guards was summoned from the Tower of London. Everybody was keen to have a go. Sportsmen with shotguns saw this as their hour of glory (after all, only two men were up there, and they were foreigners and therefore of little account) and were disappointed that they were not called upon; so were the police, who offered to carry the house by frontal assault. Historic significance was given to what was afterwards called the Siege of Sidney Street by the arrival of Winston Churchill, the home secretary, who suggested that artillery should be brought to the scene and Royal Engineers should drive tunnels beneath the house. In the event, though the artillery arrived, it was not used, but the owners of nearby property had a few uneasy moments.

The police fired at the house, the gang fired back, and the crowd of spectators became bored. Their unspoken thoughts were answered by a wisp of smoke at an upstairs window; the house was on fire. The flames forced the two men down to the ground floor, and after a time the firing from the house ceased. The police and fire-brigade entered the burning building, but for a time they could not find the bodies of the two men—raising the suspicion that the police had in some curious manner let the men get away through the back of the house. Eventually the two charred corpses were found. Two hundred policemen, nineteen Scots Guards marksmen, and two pieces of artillery had been set against two armed men locked in a house from which there was no escape. A mystery grew up around the name of Peter the Painter, though there was a good deal of doubt concerning who he was, where he was, and what he had to do with the Sidney Street charade.

Such deeds of 'derring do' proved a welcome relief from the humdrum business of everyday life for both police and public, and helped to avert attention from the activities of the suffragettes, who had done nothing so spectacular as to engage in a pitched gun battle with the constabulary. It might be too cynical to say that the only thing learned at the Siege of Sidney Street was how to carry unwilling civilians from their homes; this proved useful in dealing with militant suffragettes.

Forgery and Fraud

Where there are large sums of money about and the motivating spirit of the period is greed then there will be fraud. Money was the god of the Edwardian age, and was pursued with a passion that the Victorians would have considered ill-bred. There was nothing disgraceful in the making of fortunes, and the shopocracy, the tradesmen who had lifted themselves out of the middle classes by the making of millions, were endlessly courted by the aristocracy. They could do no wrong, and their social gaffes were politely ignored. It was a shock to all, aristocracy and shopocracy alike, when William Whiteley, the 'universal provider' of Bayswater, was killed by his illegitimate son.

A gullible public eager for easy money were a ready prey for anyone with get-rich-quick schemes, such as the South and South-West Coast Steam Trawling and Fishing Syndicate, which was run by Charles de Ville Wells, a picturesque scoundrel immortalised as the man who broke the bank at Monte Carlo, not once but half a dozen times in the space of a fortnight. By 1906 Wells had come down in the world, having made and lost millions, and done a spell in prison. His colleague in the syndicate was an unfrocked clergyman named Moyle.

Wells and Moyle followed the standard pattern by inserting advertisements in the leading daily newspapers, offering a monthly income of £20 on every £100 invested. Hundreds applied and, although for the first month or so they received their 'interest', payments soon ceased. The syndicate also claimed to own a patent life-saving apparatus, the 'Enforced Breathing Apparatus', and had so much confidence in it that they displayed it at a fisheries exhibition in London. Wells had lost his touch and was soon convicted, being sentenced to three years. Other financiers and entrepreneurs were more astute.

A. W. Carpenter worked along the same lines as Wells and Moyle only on a larger scale. There were still a considerable number of private banks in existence and, notwithstanding the collapse of several of them in the nineteenth century, many people preferred to put their money into these small banks, encouraged by the large rates of interest offered. Carpenter owned the Charing Cross Bank, which he had started in 1886 as a corollary to his money-lending business. He offered six per cent interest for six-month deposits, seven per cent for twelve months, and ten per cent for five years. Carpenter had a gigantic ego, and was confident that his investments, using the money deposited in his bank, would pay off handsomely; his main interests were in Canada and in South African gold. In 1907 the magazine *Truth* began to have doubts about the Charing Cross Bank, but little was done and the public's attention would not have been drawn to Carpenter's machinations if he had not employed an accountant to put the bank's internal affairs in order. The accountant found evidence of incompetence and dishonesty on the part of Carpenter's underlings, and also became aware that the bank was based on very shaky foundations. The accountant asked advice of his solicitors, and in due course the affairs of the Charing Cross Bank were examined with a view to prosecution; it closed down in October 1910 with a deficit of nearly £2 million.

A good deal of fraud was possible because of the lenient attitude of a number of the large banks towards forgery, partly due to the lapse of the Bankers' Association which once prosecuted in all cases. Any moves that reflected on the unreliability of the banking machine were avoided, and bank employees involved in embezzlement were rarely punished; one offender was given £100 and a passage to Canada to get him out of the way. When the banks did prosecute they often used inexperienced barristers who were friends of bank officials. This rebounded, for the offenders gave their cases to better advocates, and frequently got off.

When prosecutions were undertaken, gangs of forgers were often uncovered, whose principals remained in the background to avoid risk. The usual method employed by forgers was to use a messenger boy, who would take a forged cheque to a bank and cash it. Outside the bank he would be followed unobtrusively by one of the gang. The messenger had previously been told to go to a certain shop and buy something. If the transaction went through, the forger would know that the coup had been successful; if the messenger boy had been stopped in the bank, or did not emerge from the shop with the goods, the watcher would slip away.

Specialists in forged cheques usually put in a good deal of homework on their subjects, and took pains to obtain genuine signatures to copy. One master forger went into business partnership with Mrs Hughes, known as the queen of begging-letter writers. Those who believed in the 'criminal type' were thwarted by the forging fraternity, many of whom came from good families and utilised their inner knowledge of society and the vulnerability of the bank manager class when faced by their betters. Typical of the well-bred forgers was Captain Henry Fane, a former officer of the Rifle Brigade, and a member of the Army and Navy Club. The club had the quaint habit of supplying blank cheques to those members who asked for them, and with the aid of such cheques Fane and his colleagues got away with a good deal of money, using the messenger boy gambit. Of an even more ingenious cast was Robert Hutchinson, Etonian and Leicestershire country gentleman who, as chairman of the local conservative association, organised a Budget Protest League against Lloyd George's soak-the-rich budget. One of those approached for a guinea subscription to this league was the local conservative candidate, Thomas Paget.

Armed with this cheque, Hutchinson called at Paget's house in London, and purloined a supply of headed notepaper. On this paper Hutchinson requested Lloyd's Bank, Leicester, to send a cheque-book to the Burlington Hotel, Eastbourne, into which a collaborator had booked under the name of the conservative candidate. On leaving the hotel, 'Paget' instructed the hotel to post his correspondence to 28 Upper George Street in the West End, which turned out to be a holding address for correspondence. Hutchinson made out a cheque for £975, which was duly cashed, though several of the nine £100 notes paid out by the bank eventually led back to Hutchinson's own bank account in Manchester.

The method adopted by Gerald Kennaway was cruder but no less effective—it involved stealing letters from pillar-boxes. Cheques contained in letters had their endorsements removed with acids, and Kennaway, a gentleman, had no difficulty in cashing them. Retribution was never far behind and he served several sentences in prison, in 1900, 1902, 1910 and 1916. Much of this was due to increased energy and perseverance on the part of the prosecution, and Sir Richard Muir, the prosecutor of Crippen, made himself a specialist in forgery cases. As the years went by, courts increased their sentences in cases of fraud, especially the so-called 'bucket shop' frauds. The names of small investors were uncovered from the files of various companies, and these—often country clergymen, a class never averse to financial dabbling—were circularised, fascinated by the prospect of fortnightly dividends. A company would be started with a formidable title and offices in a prestige thoroughfare in the City, and after sending out cheques for a few shillings the organisers of the frauds would disappear into obscurity, emerging soon afterwards with another company and another set of circulars. Even when caught, their sentences were light, and they thought a few months' imprisonment worth the risk. With years substituted for months, the 'bucket shop' frauds lapsed.

Society was not worried by the spate of minor frauds perpetrated on banks, which could afford to lose the money anyway, or on unimportant middle-class dabblers. Apprehension was felt only when society itself was involved, or worse, when frauds were carried out by people who were known and had been entertained socially on account of their money-making abilities. A man who could make millions was, by definition, a man worth cultivating.

One of the most spectacular of the grand masters of fraudulence was Ernest Terah Hooley, who in 1896–7 made £7 million profit, got rid of the lot, was made bankrupt to the tune of £1.5 million, and started again from scratch. His biggest and most dramatic coup was in 1896 when he bought the Dunlop Tyre Company for £3 million and refloated it a few months later for £5 million. This put him in line for a baronetcy, but whispers of his bankruptcy deterred the promoters. As soon as Hooley had got over the bankruptcy, he threw his energies into Siberian gold, and floated a £1 million company, but this was repudiated by the Russian Government and came to nothing.

From his house, Papworth Hall in Cambridgeshire, Hooley organised his empire, persuaded the Privy Council to make him

High Sheriff of Cambridgeshire, and disdainfully lent money to those members of the aristocracy who would creep low enough. He spent £250,000 on improving Papworth Hall, endowed the conservative party with large sums of money, and carried on his operations until 1912 when he found himself at the Old Bailey, charged with swindling a young Rochdale engineer of £2,000. Hooley was a challenge to the legal profession, but by 1912 his charisma had dispersed and he had outlived his period. When Hooley operated again in 1920 he was pounced upon, and made an example of for speculating in the Lancashire cotton boom.

Whitaker Wright reached his peak at the same time as Hooley. He broke into the London financial scene in 1889, promoted the West Australian Exploration and Finance Corporation in 1894, and the London and Globe Finance Corporation in 1895. These two companies floated venture after venture, and financed the Baker Street and Waterloo Railway, later known as the Bakerloo line. The West Australian venture proved immensely profitable and paid out millions in dividends. Whitaker Wright was accepted into aristocratic circles and the seal of respectability was given to his projects when the Marquis of Dufferin and Ava became chairman of the board of the London and Globe.

Whitaker Wright's home, Lea Park near Godalming, was perhaps one of the most spectacular private residences in Edwardian England. Bought in 1896 for £250,000, Wright spent £1 million on improvements, one of which was a conservatory beneath a large artificial lake. His architectural and landscaping visions transcended mere vulgarity. A marble fountain weighing sixty tons had to be hauled to its site by traction engines as it was too heavy for the railway to carry. A private theatre costing £15,000 was built inside the house and there were stables for fifty horses.

Behind this façade things were not as they seemed. In 1899 the Marquis of Dufferin declared that the London and Globe Finance Corporation possessed more than £500,000 in cash—actual figure £29,300. The crash was not far off. In 1901 an order was made winding up Whitaker Wright's companies, and the shareholders in the London and Globe, which had a capital of

£2 million, got nothing. Many were affected by the debâcle, and one firm of stockbrokers lost £365,000. Whitaker Wright still had friends in high places and it was considered that a prosecution would prove fruitless, though when he fled to France in 1903 it was decided to extradite him.

It was difficult to ascertain how many millions were involved in the crash, and Wright's habit of switching millions from one company to another made the case complex and arduous. Many lawyers privately confessed that they would never again officiate in a case where financial wizards were involved. Wright received, for that period, a fierce sentence of seven years, but committed suicide by taking cyanide in the lavatory at the Old Bailey. The verdict of suicide while of unsound mind would have been disputed by the envious. Whitaker Wright had made and lost millions, had the pick of mistresses and given yachts away as other men proffer drinks. In an age that worshipped wealth and conspicuous consumption, Wright was a subject for emulation; his death was seen as the departure of a god.

Murder Most Foul

Murder trials were very popular in Edwardian England, which saw a number of interesting cases. It also saw the beginning of the intriguing practice of forensic medicine, the supreme exponent of which was Sir Bernard Spilsbury. There were some picturesque advocates, such as Sir Edward Marshall Hall, who were as newsworthy as music hall stars and whose appearances at the Old Bailey were watched by their admirers. Marshall Hall defended Robert Wood in what was known as the Camden Town murder, and among those attending the trial were the actress Gertie Millar; Lady Tree, wife of the celebrated actor-manager; the playwright Pinero; the actor Henry Irving and the novelist Hall Caine.

This 1907 murder trial, though not one of the classic cases, featured Sir Charles Mathews for the Crown, and public saw it as a battle of the giants. By and large, there was not much interest in the accused, an artist who had once been praised by William Morris, and little sympathy with the victim, a prostitute.

Emily Dimmock, known as Phyllis, was found naked on her bed, her throat cut from ear to ear so savagely that the head was only attached to the body by a few muscles. The question was whether the artistic Wood could have done this deed to the girl whom he described as 'a crushed rose—that had not lost all its fragrance, and had been thrown aside. She seemed a girl who might have seen better days, who might have made a good wife in other circumstances'.[1]

Emily Dimmock was living with a man named Shaw, whose name she had taken, and the case revolved around a postcard sent to her from 'Alice' inviting 'Mrs Shaw' to meet 'her' at the Rising Sun public house, depicted in a sketch of a rising sun. The postcard was reproduced in a Sunday newspaper where it was seen by Ruby Young, a model who had been seduced by a medical man; she had turned prostitute and was on affectionate terms with Wood. She recognised the handwriting and style as belonging to him, and sent him the newspaper clipping. In great distress, Wood admitted to her that he had met Emily Dimmock at the Rising Sun, the Friday before she was murdered, that a boy had been touting picture postcards and he had bought one, and sent it to her. He had seen her on the Monday, had been with his brother on the Tuesday, and on the Wednesday had been walking alone. Wednesday had been the night of the murder. He persuaded Ruby Young to give him an alibi, to tell the police if they came to her that she had spent every Monday and Wednesday with him. He protested that there was nothing between Emily and himself, that he had signed the letter 'Alice' at Emily's request because 'the guv'nor might cut up rough', and that he liked Emily's company because she was intelligent (and had, though he did not tell Miss Young, a kink about prostitutes).

Ruby Young was frightened, and put the matter in a hypo-thetical way to a woman friend, who saw through the fabrication and introduced her to a journalist. He obtained the full story and introduced Ruby to a police inspector. It was not long before Wood was arrested, and he was recognised by a bookseller as having been with Emily as late as 10.30 pm at the Eagle public house on the evening of the murder. It seemed as though it was all up with Wood. However, his employers pooh-poohed the idea that the gentle, foolish youth was a murderer, and were willing to back him with expensive counsel. Counsel considered the evidence was all circumstantial and applied for bail, whereupon the arresting inspector disclosed that Wood had been recognised as a man leaving the murder house at 5 am on the morning of the murder. The witness was a carman who said that the man he saw had a peculiarity in the way he walked. This was denied by everyone who knew Wood—except Ruby Young, seemingly intent on slipping the noose around the neck of her lover.

The evidence of the carman was ruthlessly broken down by the defence. He agreed with the defence that it was a drizzly, foggy morning (which it was not), and that but for the street lamps it would have been impossible to identify anyone who left the house. The defence had a lighting-chart from the electric lighting company stating that the current had been switched off at 4.37 am, fifteen minutes before the witness had seen the alleged murderer pass beneath its glare. Nevertheless the collapse of one of the key prosecution witnesses did not prevent Wood being committed for trial, and at this point Marshall Hall was brought in.

For a year or two, partly due to a feud with Lord Northcliffe of the *Daily Mail*, Marshall Hall's stock had been low, but had picked up slightly in 1906. He had unsuccessfully defended a gamekeeper charged with stealing 20,000 pheasant eggs; he had prosecuted a mad woman for killing a child in a nursing home; and had been involved in a curious matrimonial case where a husband had pursued, in a tug, the liner in which his wife was travelling, to make sure that she was not joined by her lover. When Marshall Hall was offered the Camden Town murder case he realised this could restore his reputation, and he made the most of the opportunity, swaying public feeling on to Wood's side. A huge mob, solidly behind Wood, waited outside the court, which was surrounded by dozens of police. In the streets were fifty mounted policemen ready for riot and crowd control.

During the closing stages of the trial the judge veered from his animosity towards Marshall Hall and Wood, and in his summing up he indicated to the jury that he did not consider the prosecution's case strong enough. His statement that the jury was not bound to act on his view was inconsequential, for they too had swung round in favour of Wood, who was acquitted.

The Camden Town murder had the two vital ingredients—violence and sex—and no one was particularly worried that somewhere a prostitute murderer was on the rampage. A few sensationalists did not hesitate to point out that it might be Jack the Ripper repeating his performance in another subfusc area of London. The lynching of Ruby Young, who in the public's view deserved the same treatment as Emily Dimmock, was narrowly averted. All prostitutes were fair game to a hysterical mob.

The appeal of such cases as the Camden Town murder key in with the psychoanalyst's view that murder is a reenactment of the 'primal scene' of infancy, representing parental sexual intercourse; the victim is the parent, and the clues are 'symbolic representations of mysterious nocturnal sounds, stains, incomprehensible adult jokes'.[2] Even forgetting such an interpretation, it is not surprising that the Farrow murder case, though perhaps historically more significant than the Camden Town murder, proved less popular to the general public.

In 1905 an elderly couple named Farrow were found murdered in a small chandler's shop in High Street, Deptford. They lived over the shop and, according to gossip, there were large sums of money in the house (in fact, there was never more than £6 or so). A boy employed in the shop arrived one morning and found the shutters still closed. He peered through the letter-box, saw a chair upturned and called for help. Mr Farrow was dead in the kitchen, his head smashed, and his wife was dying upstairs in bed, also with head injuries. Two masks made from black stockings were discovered, plus an empty cash-box. Two milkmen declared that they had seen two men leave the shop at 7.15 am, and a man and a woman saw Mr Farrow come to the front door, look up and down the street, then go back. They observed with perfunctory interest that the old man was terribly injured about the head and face. The police assumed that Mr Farrow had regained consciousness long enough to go to the door, open it, look up and down the street, and return to the kitchen to die.

One of the first men on the scene was the chief of the CID, Sir Melville Macnaghten, who was excited by the appearance of a fingerprint on the cash-box. It was a blurred print, but it was a clue. The fingerprint section, now three years old, had something to go on, though there was momentary dismay when a young detective sergeant admitted that he had moved the box beneath the bed, fearing the ambulance men taking the body of Mrs Farrow downstairs would trip over it. The fingerprint, however, did not belong to the sergeant, nor to the couple.

Deptford was one of the lowest quarters of early twentieth-century London, and there were plenty of candidates for murder. Two brothers named Stratton seemed to merit especial investigation and a net was cast for them; this feeling was confirmed when the girl friend of one of the brothers contributed some evidence. The elder brother was easy to find, but it was decided to get them both together. As they enjoyed football, a cup-tie at the Crystal Palace seemed a logical Saturday afternoon venue. The brothers did not turn up. Instructions were issued to the police that either brother should be arrested if seen, and soon both were under lock and key with their fingerprints taken.

It was the first murder case in which fingerprinting was in evidence, and there was considerable delight when it was found that there were eleven points of resemblance between the print on the cash-box and the right thumb-print of the elder brother. (Today this would not be enough.) The whole system of fingerprinting had to be explained to the jurymen, who had a bonus by having their fingerprints taken and a lecture by the police. The defence called an expert, but as he had first offered his services to the prosecution his evidence was declared suspect. Representing the accused was Mr Rooth, later a London magistrate; he dismissed the whole concept of fingerprints contemptuously, saying that it savoured more of the French courts and was decidedly not suitable to 'the English mind'. The judge was more cautious, but commented on the 'extraordinary resemblance' between the photographs of the print on the box and the print from Stratton's thumb. The jury had little doubt abut the matter, and the Strattons were duly convicted and hanged.

In a letter to the criminologist William Roughhead, Henry James requested him to 'go back to the dear old human and sociable murders and adulteries and forgeries in which we are so agreeably at home'.[3] The Farrow murder was neither human nor sociable, nor did it have any tincture of adultery. The Crippen case had all three. There was also a vast difference in techniques between 1905 and 1910. The Crippen case produced a new hero for the masses—a real-life Sherlock Holmes in the person of Sir Bernard Spilsbury.

It is generally believed that the Crippen case was cut and dried, and that he richly deserved to be hanged for a cold-blooded and dastardly crime. Most people are a bit foggy about the actual circumstances of the case, and only know that Crippen was brought to retribution by the use of the new-fangled wireless telegraph.

Hawley Harvey Crippen was born in Michigan in 1862, came to England when he was twenty-one to pick up some medical knowledge, and returned to America, where he obtained a diploma in homeopathy and then one in ophthalmics, modest credentials that enabled him to call himself 'doctor'. He operated in fringe medicine in alliance with patent medicine companies, and married twice, his first wife dying in 1890 or 1891. During a stay in New York he met Cora Turner, real name Kunigunde Mackamotski, a seventeen-year-old girl of uncertain morals who had been the mistress of a stove manufacturer. She fancied that she had a voice worth cultivating, and Crippen paid for operatic lessons.

In 1900 his company sent him to England as its British representative. Later in the year he was joined in his rooms off the Tottenham Court Road by his wife, a bejewelled, vulgar,

Crippen, the most notorious murderer of the age

cheerful woman. Mrs Crippen set her sights on the English music hall, then in all its glory, and although she got one or two minor engagements she did not consider her talents were appreciated. When her husband was recalled for six months to America, she lowered her sights and entertained at 'smoking concerts' where cheap coarseness was much appreciated. While her husband was away she met Bruce Miller, an American music-hall performer, and was in all probability his mistress. On his return, Crippen took her away from the disreputable rooms in Guilford Street, and installed her in Store Street, Bloomsbury, loading her with expensive clothes which he could ill afford, as he moved from one area of fringe medicine to another. One firm with which he was involved was the Yale Tooth Specialists, where he employed the typist Ethel le Neve, a delicate, ailing and respectable girl.

In 1905 the Crippens moved to 39 Hilldrop Crescent in Camden Town, a large gloomy house in a district that had gone to seed, the idea being that they should take in lodgers so as to eke out Crippen's small income. Their domestic life was squalid in the extreme and, except when they were entertaining—for Mrs Crippen, under her stage name Belle Elmore, still had theatrical connections—they lived in the kitchen. They kept no maid, a circumstance that appalled their friends, for Crippen was technically a member of the middle classes.

Crippen took Ethel le Neve as his mistress, making guilty love to her in a series of hotel rooms. By 1909 the situation was deteriorating. The lodgers were always men with an eye for a buxom wench; Mrs Crippen, fretful and quarrelsome, knew about the two-year liaison with Ethel le Neve, and threatened to leave her husband, taking with her their joint savings amounting to £600. On 15 December she gave notice of withdrawal to the bank. A month later Crippen ordered five grains of hyoscin hydrobromide—a quantity so large that it had to be obtained from the wholesalers—and this he collected on 19 January 1910.

On 31 January the Crippens gave a little dinner-party. This was the last time Mrs Crippen was seen alive. Crippen gave out that she had gone to America and died on the voyage. Ethel le Neve moved into 39 Hilldrop Crescent (later renamed Filleted Plaice by a callous public), took the name of Crippen, and employed a French maid. She also decked herself out in Mrs Crippen's finery, and was indiscreet enough to go with her lover to a ball wearing one of his wife's brooches—a circumstance that was noted by acquaintances of the Crippens, though it was several months before the suspicions were told to the police. When they interviewed Crippen he changed his story, saying his wife had left him for another man, leaving her belongings behind. The police searched the house and, apparently satisfied, went away. Before completely dropping the matter, an Inspector Dew paid a visit to Crippen's consulting-room to ask a few supplementary questions, only to be told that the doctor had gone abroad. And so had Miss le Neve.

The police returned to the house, the garden was dug up, and a loose brick in the cellar encouraged them to concentrate their efforts there. Buried in quicklime under the floor were small pieces of flesh wrapped in an old pyjama coat, marked with the retailer's name. The specialists got to work. One piece of flesh was from the abdomen and had an operation scar. The flesh was therefore human. Analysis showed that it contained 2/7 of a grain of hyoscin.

The search was on for Crippen, and E. R. Henry, commissioner of police, offered a reward of £250. The response was incredible but largely irrelevant. The only lead came from Captain Kendall, of the liner *Montrose* bound from Antwerp to Canada, who had seen with puritanical disquiet 'Master Robinson' squeezing the hand of 'Mr Robinson'. He had sent a message by wireless to the owners who had contacted Scotland Yard. Inspector Dew travelled on the *Laurentic*, a faster vessel. In the guise of a pilot, he boarded the *Montrose*, and it was as he thought—the insignificant, polite, dapper, bespectacled Mr Robinson was Dr Crippen, wanted, as the reward poster put it, for, 'murder and mutilation'.

Without any further evidence, the presence of hyoscin and the abdominal scar would probably have sent Crippen to the gallows. The police thought so, and after Crippen had been brought back Dew was inclined to be languid, so much so that the prosecutor, Muir, suggested that Dew was suffering from sleeping sickness. The police bestirred themselves to find the final nail for the Crippen coffin. This centred around the pyjama jacket. If it had been bought before the Crippens moved to Hilldrop Crescent, it was possible, barely possible, that the remains had been put in the cellar by a previous tenant, Crippen maintained that he had bought the jacket several years earlier, but a buyer from Jones Brothers, the retailers, asserted that the material was not acquired until 1908 and that three pairs were supplied to Crippen in 1909. The jury was out for half an hour, their verdict was guilty, and the appeal failed. Crippen, the epitome of the little man who used the women's method of murder, was hanged.

Miss le Neve, tried as an accessory after the fact, was acquitted. Throughout the trial Crippen had done his best to protect his mistress. Marshall Hall, who was not involved in the case though he took an intense interest in it, maintained that Crippen would have made good his escape if he had fled alone, and Lord Birkenhead declared that Crippen 'was, at least, a brave man, and a true lover'. Marshall Hall had nearly been drawn into defending him, but Crippen's refusal to deviate from a suicidal line of defence would have afforded him no scope for his own astounding theory that the death of Mrs Crippen was due to an accident, that the hyoscin had been procured not to kill the woman but to reduce her sexual demands on Crippen, or render her unconscious so that he could take Miss le Neve to his house and have sex with her.

The drug was a comparatively new one, though in the form of henbane it was well-known in folk medicine. In small doses it produced drowsiness and sleep, and had the properties of affecting the memory centres. A person taking it would not know that he or she had done so, or realise that he or she had been unconscious. It was possible that Crippen had been drugging his wife for some time, gradually increasing the dosages as her resistance built up. That he bought a large quantity in one go does not indicate that he had never bought the drug before, either in its natural form as henbane—an easily obtained plant of the nightshade variety—or treated. A methodical, careful man, it was out of character for Crippen to betray himself by buying such a large quantity of hyoscin if his intention was to murder his wife, rather than put her into a state of oblivion while he dallied with his mistress.

Whether the prosecution felt any uncertainty about the verdict is a moot point. After the execution Muir made the cryptic remark that 'full justice has not yet been done'. This can only refer to either a belief that Ethel le Neve was an accomplice and should have shared Crippen's fate, or that Marshall Hall's tentative line of defence was right. One commentator on the case said that either Miss le Neve had no character at all, or plenty. The question remains open as to whether she was the instigator of it all, and whether Crippen was not the monster of legend but a puppet manipulated by a deceptively innocent typist.

The public, who dearly loved a villain to look like a villain, were well served by Frederick Seddon, the Holloway superintendent of the London & Manchester Insurance Company.

In 1910 Seddon sublet part of his house to Miss Eliza Barrow and her entourage—an adopted son and some people named Hook. Miss Barrow was forty-nine, crusty, suspicious, difficult to live with, and a miser, distrusting banks and keeping hundreds of pounds in gold and notes in a box beneath her pillow. She had £1,600 in gilt-edged securities, and owned a shop and a public house. Her total assets amounted to about £4,000. Seddon wheedled his way into her confidence, and advised her to transfer her securities to him in return for just over £3 a week. On 1 September 1911, Miss Barrow became ill and the doctor sent her to bed. On the night of 13 September she died, with Seddon sitting outside the door, not bothering to send for a doctor, a fact he admitted when he was brought to trial. Without going to see the body, the doctor granted Seddon a death certificate stating that Miss Barrow had died from epidemic diarrhoea. Seddon went to the local undertaker and bargained for the cheapest funeral possible—£4 less his 12s 6d commission— then returned to the house and took the contents of her money box, leaving £10 from an estimated £800. On the evening of the funeral, Seddon and his wife went to a music hall.

The only known relatives of Miss Barrow did not hear of the death for several days, and when they went to Seddon's house they found that he and his wife had gone away on holiday. Suspicious, the relatives went to the police, and in November the body was exhumed and found to contain arsenic. It was proved that the Seddons had bought fly papers, from which it was assumed that Seddon had obtained the arsenic. Mrs Seddon had changed with local tradesmen many of the Bank of England notes belonging to Miss Barrow and been misguided enough to endorse them with a false name and address. The public and the jury did not need anything else; they were already determined

Crowds waiting outside the Old Bailey for the outcome of the Seddon trial

that Seddon was guilty because he looked it, having close-set eyes and an air of utter callousness. The fact that he and his wife had visited a music hall on the night of the funeral was as significant as evidence that was purely circumstantial; Seddon had also made a psychological bloomer in taking his commission on the £4 funeral. He was hanged in April 1912, protesting his innocence.

A good deal of apprehension was felt by the public over a number of unsolved murders. They were not particularly worried that the police were baffled by the prostitute murders— Emily Dimmock, of the Camden Town case; Dora Kiernicke, whose nude body was found in January 1904 in a room in Whitefield Street, Tottenham Court Road; or Esther Praager, of 3 Bernard Street, Russell Square, also killed in the nude, though she had been strangled whereas Miss Kiernicke had had her throat cut.

The murder of Mrs Luard, in a summer-house near her home

at Ightham Knoll, near Sevenoaks, was another matter. For she was a lady, the wife of Major-General C. E. Luard. She had been shot, and robbery had apparently been the motive, for four valuable rings had been torn from her fingers and her purse had been stolen. The case was interesting because Scotland Yard accused the local police of walking over all the clues and not calling them in until it was too late. They were also scathing about the opinion of a Dr T. A. Mansfield, who was brought in initially, and who, observing that there were two bullet wounds in the head, suggested that the dead woman had shot herself simultaneously with two revolvers, neither of which was found. A theory was put forward that the murder had been done by a tramp, but there were also rumours that Mrs Luard was involved in an eternal triangle situation (though she was about sixty and her husband seventy), and a number of anonymous letters and postcards were sent to the members of the jury at the coroner's inquest. Although General Luard was a quarter of an hour's walk from the summer-house when the shooting occurred, this did not save him from calumny, but even those who roundly dismissed the idea of the general shooting his wife must have had misgivings when they heard that he had killed himself by leaping under a train.

Public anxiety was also roused by an outbreak of seaside and railway murders. Yarmouth had witnessed two within twelve years, both involving women strangled with boot-laces. In January 1914, a strangled seven-year-old boy was pushed under the seat of a train bound for Broad Street from Chalk Farm; on this line the stations were only two minutes apart. In 1904 the body of a thirty-five-year-old female book-keeper was found gagged and mutilated in the mile-long tunnel between Victoria and Brighton.

The Edwardian public liked to read about these things. But in novels and detective fiction the murderer was always brought to book. In so many things, why did not life emulate the good taste of fiction?

Notes to this chapter are on page 295.

CHAPTER NINE

PRELUDE TO WAR

AFTER 1910 there was no question for most people that war was coming. The apparatus of war was all about. Maggie Benson, the sickly sister of the Benson family of authors, wrote a letter on the train to Cornwall: 'We have just crossed into Cornwall by the great harbour at Devonport, with battleships and torpedoes lying in it, looking like great ugly noxious beasts . . .'[1] Few could avoid seeing the portents. As early as 1908 the once-popular society preacher, Stopford Brooke, who had, at a time when such things were of consequence, created a furore by leaving the Church of England to become a Unitarian, realised the implications of a world war: 'But war, such as it is now, is not only a crime, it is the worst of follies. And it ought to be impossible. If it is not soon rendered so, the whole fabric of civilization will be expunged, and Europe will go back to savage conditions'.[2]

The death wish consumed Britain. Sir Edward Grey was aimlessly procrastinating, waiting for conditions to settle down; King George V was timid, incapable of the intimate diplomacy of his father; Asquith was an effete bystander from another age, waiting for the stab in the back. There were troubles with strikes, suffragettes and the Irish, as well as distrust and antagonism between and within the services. It appeared to some that a war would solve these difficulties; to others that war would be categorically welcome, as it was to the notorious Frank Harris, quondam friend of Oscar Wilde. England, Harris considered, was effete, puritanical and poisonous (if only because W. H. Smith's book stalls had refused to sell the *English Review* which contained one of his short stories). D. H. Lawrence was of much the same mind, for similar reasons. 'We ought to be grateful to Germany', he wrote shortly after the outbreak of war, 'that she still has the power to burst the bound hide of the cabbage'. Rupert Brooke was 'extraordinarily happy' at the prospect of conflict.

In August 1911, Lloyd George wrote to Churchill: 'I have been reading the FO papers. They are full of menace. The thunderclouds are gathering. I am not at all satisfied that we are prepared, or that we are preparing'. The Admiralty was 'so cocksure, *insouciant* and apathetic, so far as one can judge from all that one sees and hears'.[3] The replacement of Sir John Fisher as the key man in the remodelled navy had perhaps not been so politically convenient after all.

Supporters of Haldane's 'model army' were also over-sanguine. Despite a study of the Russo-Japanese war, few experts had realised the devastating effect of small-arms fire employed in defence or the implications of the machine-gun. The British Expeditionary Force was perhaps the best disciplined of all the contemporary armies; its riflemen were beyond compare, and could fire up to eighteen rounds a minute. There was a plentiful supply of small-arms ammunition. Employed in the role of a strike force, the BEF would have been unequalled. As a subsidiary to the big, lumbering French army it was astonishingly ill-equipped, with little heavy artillery and inadequate medium artillery; worse still, it was short of artillery ammunition. Although it was known that communication would play a major part in modern war, telephones were in very short supply. Despite the fact that Britain led the world in heavy motor transport, the mentality of the army was still geared to the horse and the mule. Close-support weapons, particularly mortars and hand grenades, were lacking; hand grenades had been used to great effect in the siege of Port Arthur by the Japanese in 1904, and were to prove invaluable in trench warfare.

The British Army was not prepared for the kind of war it was going to fight. Kitchener knew it, but few others did. In the year before the war the number of men in the army actually went down. The Royal Navy was less efficient than it might have been; though the dreadnoughts and battle-cruisers were handsome, they were rarely what was needed in the conditions imposed on them. The aeronautical side was ill-developed, while too much money and attention had been devoted to airships. Fortunately the French air force was stronger, as was their aircraft engine technology, devolving from their supremacy in motor-car manufacture.

The British politicians were not alone in being unable to foresee the kind of war it was going to be, nor did they have a monopoly in sloppy statesmanship. George V was weak, but so was the Tsar. When the Tsar was forced to order mobilisation, he specified that it was to be against Austria-Hungary alone. This effort to restrict the conflict was unsuccessful, for his ministers overruled him, making the mobilisation general and thereby implicating Germany.

Would it have been possible to avert the war? It is an academic point, for war would have broken out somewhere, if not in 1914 then in 1915 or 1916. All the elements had been drawn together to make conflict inevitable. If vacillating is immoral, there were plenty of culprits, but in retrospect none of the nations involved was totally culpable, with the exception of Serbia. Austria-Hungary not unnaturally wished to keep Serbia in their fold; the Russians wanted to protect their minorities, who by a quirk of borders lived in Serbia, and Germany was anxious that Austria-Hungary should not have a lump knocked off her as this would diminish her credibility as a leading power. Austria-Hungary was the one ally upon which Germany could depend; Italy was an ally in name only. The alliance between France and Russia meant that any involvement of Russia in conflict with Germany would necessarily bring in France. Had the Tsar had his way and mobilised only against Austria-Hungary, then the situation might have cooled, with the Germans able to gain prestige as the benevolent responsible nation anxious to lower the temperature.

The assassination at Sarajevo on 28 June 1914 of the Austrian Archduke Franz Ferdinand by Bosnian-Serb students Princip and Cabrinović, who thought to solve Austro-Hungarian repression by the murder of figureheads, was only really significant as a spark to a fuse. Five weeks were to elapse between the assassination and the outbreak of war.

To the average Briton, no country was so uninteresting as Serbia. A little perfunctory indignation had been roused on her behalf in 1909 when *Punch* published a cartoon in which Europa, intervening between Austria and Serbia, was saying to the former: 'I think I can persuade my young friend here to be reasonable, and I am sure you can afford to be generous', to which Austria retorted, 'I don't remember to have asked your opinion, madam. But—if he's prepared to lick my boots, I'll then consider whether I'll allow him to go on living.' The climate of opinion represented by *Punch* had one basic quality— the willingness to patronise, to forget that the indignities forced upon Serbia by Austria were paralleled throughout the British Empire. The British press could always tap a vein of easy sentiment by sympathising with a small nation menaced by a hostile neighbour. But in 1914 the fate of Serbia caused few hackles to rise.

Belgium was different. On the map of Europe, she looked tiny and vulnerable, and somehow cosy. Britain identified with her. On 1 August 1914 Germany and Russia were at war; on 3 August Germany and France were at war, and Germany marched into Belgium. At midnight on 4 August Britain and Germany were at war, Germany having declined to pull her troops back from Belgium. In retrospect there does not seem to have been any military advantage to Germany in invading Belgium. It was a psychological blunder of the first magnitude. It may be that the German mind considered that Britain would not go to war where there were no pickings for her. Unquestionably, Germany considered that British diplomacy was Machiavellian and cunning, and that altruism rarely entered into British calculations.

Furthermore, Germany had already been assured by George V that Britain had no intention of warring with her. And it was only natural to mistake British confusion and muddle for disinterest.

War was inevitable. But Britain's participation was not. Why, asked the Germans, should the British be concerned about the insignificant boundaries of Europe when they themselves had shuffled the map of the world about in such a robust manner? It must be admitted that the Germans had a point. Their record was good. Their colonial policy in Africa was reasonably enlightened, and the assimilation into the German confederation of such disparate states as Baden, Saxony and Wurtemberg had been accomplished in a civilised manner. Nor was there any atrocity or repression in Alsace-Lorraine, won from France after the Franco-Prussian War of 1870. They could have pointed out that their colonial administration was a good deal better than that of poor little Belgium, whose overseas empire, the Congo, was harshly run as a private preserve of King Leopold.

'To Hell with Servia' Horatio Bottomley had exploded in his paper *John Bull*. To Hell with Belgium? But the atmosphere was too charged for this. In the hours before war was declared, Winston Churchill wrote that it was like waiting for the results of an election.

The French had no qualms about a continental war, and were contemptuous of British hesitation and uncertainty. There were solid reasons for a war with Germany. In eastern France there were large deposits of iron but little coal, but in western Germany there was coal but little iron. France had recently leapt into a leading place in the technological race with her achievements in motor manufacture and aeronautics. If she succeeded in winning mineral resources from Germany and dulling the impact of German technology there was no reason why France should not overtake Britain, well-known to be on the decline. The economy demanded war, either now or in the near future. Unlike Britain, France had invested heavily in her army. In the preceding ten years she and Russia had spent £842 million on their military machines, considerably more than Germany and Austria (£682 million). The pace was killing. Current expenditure on armaments could not be maintained without bankruptcy.

France felt no indignation about Belgium. The treaty guaranteeing Belgium neutrality had long been obsolete, and, unknown to the sentimental British public, the French, British and Belgium general staffs had assumed that France and Belgium would form a single battlefield. Had the Germans not invaded Belgium, thus putting themselves outside the pale so far as the innocents went, the odds are that the French would have done so. There were even plans for a landing of British troops on the Belgian coast. There is room for speculation that France deliberately leaked these plans to the Germans, encouraging them to anticipate the situation and thereby guarantee British intervention.

The extraordinary euphoria aroused by the war reflected relief. The age of apprehension was over, and the issues were now clear-cut. In *The World Crisis* 1911–18, Winston Churchill quotes Dryden to demonstrate the mood; it is difficult to make Dryden appear saccharine and soppy, but somehow Churchill managed it:

Men met each other with erected look,
The steps were higher that they took,
Friends to congratulate their friends made haste,
And long-inveterate foes saluted as they passed.

At the outbreak of war, D. H. Lawrence descended from one of his rural fastnesses into Barrow-in-Furness. 'All went mad', he declared, with 'soldiers kissing on Barrow Station, and a woman shouting defiantly to her sweetheart'.[4] Big business had not wanted war. 'Money was a frightened and trembling thing. Money shivered at the prospect'.[5] The newspapers had realised that warmongering was totally different from actually going to war. On 4 August, the last day of peace, the *Daily News* had put in a plea for neutrality: 'if we remained neutral we should be . . . able to trade with all the belligerents . . . We should be able to capture the bulk of their trade in neutral markets'. Most sternly anti-war had been the *Manchester Guardian*: 'We care as little for Belgrade as Belgrade does for Manchester.'

Lloyd George had not wanted war. Even a German invasion of Belgium might be overlooked if they merely 'trespassed' on a corner of it to gain access to France, then evacuated it and paid compensation. To Lloyd George, however, war was less important than keeping the Liberal party together. Churchill wanted war, and so did the leader of the Conservative opposition, Bonar Law, on account of 'the honour and security of the United Kingdom'. In the best summing-up of the situation, Lloyd George wrote that 'the nations backed their machines over the precipice'.

Release was found for the masses by gathering 30,000 strong outside Buckingham Palace singing *God Save the King*, and smashing the windows of the German Embassy. Others were not so sanguine. Wrote Max Beerbohm: 'What a world! What a period to have been born into! It is very epical and all that; but the horror and sadness and absurdity of it all . . . But so far as one can foresee, the thing is not so much a purge as an additional poison'.[6] Only when the reality of war was brought home by the massive casualty lists did the euphoria succumb and Beerbohm's comment that it was not so much purge as poison make sense. 'The British nation surging forward in its ancient valour'— Winston Churchill again—moved more sluggishly as the cream of its young men were wiped out and bitterness took the place of gaiety.

Notes to this chapter are on page 295.

EPILOGUE

THE EDWARDIAN period can be seen as the first truly modern age, when the seeds of problems that bedevil us today were sown. Some have seen it as an overblown epilogue to the nineteenth century. There was certainly some overlap. Victorian manners and mores did not disappear with the death of the old queen, and, indeed, persisted throughout the war and into the 1920s. In many ways Victorian attitudes wore better; the Edwardian flower was forced too rapidly, an opulent and vulgar bloom that faded quickly, fostered on thin soil.

The Edwardians gathered in the fruit of Victorian energy and invention. Aids to industry and commerce, such as the telephone, the typewriter, and the electric motor, revolutionised life. There was also a spin off on the domestic front. A variety of labour-saving devices, such as the vacuum cleaner and the gas cooker, were assimilated into the home, and no longer were servants an essential part of middle-class life.

People had more time for entertainment, diversion and sport. Today's entertainment industry devolves from the Edwardian preoccupation with the pleasure principle. Women released from their homes occupied themselves with a variety of interests. There were not only bridge parties but women's leagues, and those well-brought-up women who fifty years earlier would have

The Edwardian preoccupation with the pleasure principle is well illustrated in this engraving

been condemned to a life of afternoon calls and needlework could opt for an outlet amongst the suffragettes—or they could even go out to work. The typewriter and the telephone offered increased opportunities for office-workers and made young women independent, heroines to the young writers of the time, such as H. G. Wells.

Edwardian women were more to be commended than their men folk. They brought a breath of life into the dull languid world of business, and in the newly-formed suburbs they

Edwardian women were everywhere, though their intrusion into men's preserves was not perhaps as idyllic as in this illustration

formulated a culture involving the gramophone, intellectual word games, cheap editions of the classics, and the new art. They bullied and cajoled their men into the great outdoor sport of the age, cycling, and the lanes of the home counties echoed to the ting-a-ling of their bicycle bells, occasionally punctuated by the shriek of a lady cyclist who had come face to face with the new-fangled motor car.

In a different category were the grand ladies, scorning the passage of time and living in the past, deploring the vulgarities of Edward VII and his court, looking askance at the shopocracy and the Jewish moneylenders accepted into society and basking in its calculated approval. There was a schism between the grand ladies of the old school and the fashionable society ladies, many of whom at some time seem to have been actresses and whose fate so often revolved around marriage to an American or to an aristocrat, or failing marriage, an alliance. Doll-like, brittle, with dresses and gowns costing hundreds of pounds apiece, and provoking underwear now named lingerie, these society ladies pervaded Ascot and Henley, motor car and balloon rallies, court and county ball, proving what money could buy.

No age was more conscious of money. Wealth was the criterion of merit. Financial wizards were welcomed into society, and only when they were sent to prison did their friends deplore their crooked behaviour. The preoccupation with money, no matter how it was obtained, extended to those classes formerly immune to the appeal of Mammon. Country clergymen eagerly fell victim to get-rich-quick schemes operated by the so-called 'bucket shops'.

A seven-roomed flat in the best suburbs could be rented for £50 a year, Scotch salmon was 2s per lb, and a Jermyn Street tailor would make a suit for six guineas. Champagne, sold on draught, was only 6d a glass in West End bars; postage was a penny; and income tax a shilling in the pound. £10,000 a year was a 'snug fortune'; one could keep a small house in town, a modest house in the country, and indulge in a little hunting. In London a fashionable bachelor could live exceedingly well on £500 a year.

The anomalies were evident. In 1903 it was reckoned that 21s 8d was the minimum living wage for a family of five. In 1914 nearly a quarter of the male wage earners earned less than 25s a week. Women in the sweated industries were lucky to earn more than 5s a week. Admittedly a six-roomed villa in subfusc Edmonton could be rented for 10s a week, but for the poor that was a fortune.

Bitterness between the haves and the have-nots underlay the whole period, and it is not surprising that this occasionally erupted in violence. Had the Liberal party not gained office and inaugurated the first feeble welfare state, the nation would probably have exploded, and only the outbreak of war prevented a full confrontation between capital and labour, a circumstance that was postponed until the 1926 General Strike. The assimilation of militant trade unionists into Parliament, where their

The contrast between haves and the have-nots was everywhere in evidence, no more so than in the City where street hawkers, bootblacks, billposters, and newspaper sellers rubbed shoulders with the richest in the land

claws were smartly trimmed, also did much to rob labour of its threat.

The ineptitude of management and government in coping with the upsurge of the poor has never been forgotten. The inability to come to terms arose from a refusal to recognise that things had changed. The poor were still poor, but they wanted to know why. They were served with greater information. They knew that the purchasing power of the pound was getting less and less, and also that dividends were increasing. The conclusion they drew was correct: the rich were only concerned with getting richer, preferably with no exertion, preferring to ignore the economic and industrial progress of France and Germany and investing in money-making schemes in the Empire, such as South African gold, rather than revitalising British industry by putting in new machinery, thus increasing productivity, and raising wages to a viable level. The moribund state of British industry was a result of laziness at the top, and greed.

Engaged in an orgy of spending, it is not surprising that the well-off preferred to suppress their anxieties and apprehensions. Had they devoted more attention to a cold study of the problems facing Britain rather than to yachting, motoring and sport, these problems might have been solved. It was not idle apprehension, however; the problems were real. Prestige-laden as was the Royal Navy, it could not be denied that there were things about it that were not as they should be, that the expensive dreadnought programme had been effectively countered by the Germans, and that control by the Admiralty was haphazard and disputed. The problems of capital and labour were only too real—no one could ignore the waves of strikes that every so often paralysed a section of industry.

The activities of the suffragettes also caused alarm. To the better off these were more dismaying than the machinations of the kaiser or the unruly workers. There had always been troubles with Europe and the lower orders had always to be watched and kept in check. That womenfolk, even those of breeding and education, should indulge in violence and destructive acts—this was frightening and difficult to combat, particularly as no one knew where the suffragettes would strike next. The Edwardians reacted instinctively to the threats to a life that was becoming increasingly complex and difficult to manage. The Victorians had made the internal combustion engine and the electric motor viable; nineteenth-century America had perfected a host of industrial marvels from the sewing machine to the telephone, and technical advances in the communication media, principally the newspaper, provided too much data for the consumer to assimilate.

The newspaper proprietors made certain that readers' half-hidden anxieties were prodded and probed. Every irritant was magnified by Northcliffe and his contemporaries; and international events that would have been dismissed with a nod by Lord Palmerston were gloated over and presented in frightening terms. The British newspaper magnates had learned of the power of the press from America, where the Hearst newspapers had been instrumental in starting a war with Spain over Cuba.

There was escape—into the countryside and to the seaside. It was a boom period for hotel and boarding-house keepers. Ramsgate was very popular among Londoners

British newspapers did not quite manage a war, but not for want of trying.

Instant communication produces instant knowledge, and when the lower and lower-middle classes had their prejudices played upon first of all by the *Daily Mirror*, and then, in 1911, by the *Daily Herald* (started by the London Society of Compositors as a strike sheet) there was sufficient ill-feeling and half-understood information on all sides to guarantee apprehension or even panic. The newly informed classes were acquainted with the trials and tribulations of the government, not realising that the vehemence between Conservatives and Liberals was a component of a highly sophisticated game. Timid readers of the *Daily Herald* on 25 January 1911 reacted like scalded cats to the motto on the front page:

> Like the rolling on of ocean
>   In the eventide of fear—
> 'Tis the People marching on.

It was easy to escape from pressures and anxieties. The rich had their motor-cars, the middle classes had their beloved bicycles and the young men their motor cycles. The increasing network of tramways made the countryside available to Londoners, motor buses became extremely popular, while the railways ran seaside excursions. Pleasure weekends were spent at the coast; there was a boarding-house boom, and Margate, Southend and Brighton echoed with the revelry of clerks out on a spree. For those with rural tastes the Edwardian age was an ideal one to live in, for, with the departure of farm workers to the towns, country cottages could be bought for a song by weekenders.

Life was more complicated, and so was commerce and business. Despite the eight-per-cent unemployment figure, there was a constant demand for white-collar workers, and with the coming of the welfare state the government needed a host of clerks to man the newly-formed labour exchanges and to unravel the mysteries of national insurance. Few would have guessed that there was industrial stagnation as London spread and new prestige

The dream of the future. Or was it a nightmare?

office blocks arose, and there was no shortage of money for vast metropolitan enterprises such as the continuation of the Thames Embankment towards Chelsea and the driving of Kingsway through the slums of Drury Lane. Hectic and noisy, the new London seemed to indicate that there was a master mind at work, creating a great new capital for the Empire.

The redevelopment of London was deceptive. Planners preferred not to think of slums and slum clearance, and as Lutyens and others designed country houses for those who could afford them—it was the last time a sizeable country house could be economically built—the poor lived in squalor, a squalor made more profound by the fact that many charitable organisations of Victorian times had disappeared, and there were few to sponsor working-men's dwellings.

Muddle and go-as-you-please resulted in an untidy and meandering London. Ribbon-building extended along the roads made civilised by the coming of the tram. The motor car and the motor bus did not come neatly and methodically, but were crammed into the dusty London streets alongside horse-drawn buses, lumbering waggons, coal carts, and the assortment of personalised horse-drawn vehicles. The Underground railway was a stop-go project, only made viable by the introduction of the electric engine. Businesses and shops were drawn as if by a magnet to the Piccadilly and Oxford Street areas, creating traffic problems that are with us still. London was a mess, and no one cared. There were palliatives but no remedies; the attempt to capitalise on magic Oxford Street failed—New Oxford Street never caught on.

Much the same was true in the provinces—a dashing new building here, a new road there, and, above all, a suburbia brought into being by better road communications—a wasteful and bitty suburbia undisturbed by town planning acts and left much to itself for more than forty years. We are the inheritors of Edwardian *laissez faire*, in housing, in roads, in dispute between capital and labour, management and workers, and of Edwardian unwillingness to replenish the life blood of British industry.

The 1914–18 war solved many problems. Although it created more unemployment no one, except the Germans, could be blamed any more. It brought new life to industry, and the munitions and arms factories moved into top gear with a fluency that would have gratified the giants of the Industrial Revolution. The war helped to solve the suffrage problem; the four years did more for feminine self-sufficiency than half a century of vociferous agitation. The troubles of the Irish drifted into a lower key, and the domestic wrangles between Liberals and Conservatives became dull and vacuous. The politicians no longer had to wait and see. The event they had dimly foreseen had happened, and it was not so bad as they had thought.

NOTES AND REFERENCES

Death of a Great Queen (PAGE 13)

1 Gladstone, Mary. *Diaries and Letters* (1930), 454
2 Strachey, Lytton. *Queen Victoria* (1921), 269
3 St Helier, Lady. *Memories of Fifty Years* (1910), 352
4 Beerbohm, Max. *Letters to Reggie Turner* (1964), 124
5 Ward, Mrs E. M. *Memories of Ninety Years* (1922), 84
6 Bowley, A. L. *The Change and Distribution of the National Income* (1920), 21
7 Lane, Margaret. *Edgar Wallace* (1936), 173
8 Escott, T. H. S. *London Society in the New Reign* (1904), 90
9 Sitwell, Osbert. *Left Hand, Right Hand!* (1945), 241

King and Queen (PAGE 27)

1 Lane, Margaret. *Edgar Wallace* (1936), 195
2 Fitzroy, Sir Almeric. *Memoirs* (1926), 99-100
3 Athlone, Princess Alice, Countess of. *For My Grandchildren* (1966)
4 Paget, Lady Walburga. *Embassies of Other Days* (1923), 152-5
5 Young, Kenneth. *Arthur James Balfour* (1963), 236
6 Redesdale, Lord. *Memories* (1915), 185
7 One of His Majesty's Servants. *Private Life of the King* (1901), 89
8 Redesdale, Lord. *Memories* (1915), 187
9 Gore, John. *King George V* (1941), 117
10 Hearnshaw, F. J. C. *Edwardian England* (1933), 62
11 Conan Doyle, A. *Memories and Adventures* (1924), 331
12 Playne, C. E. *Society at War* (1931), 115

The Men at the Top (PAGE 42)

1 Escott, T. H. S. *London Society in the New Reign* (1904), 75
2 Raymond, E. T. *Uncensored Celebrities* (1918), 118
3 *The Free Trader* (31 July 1903)
4 Owen, Frank. *Tempestuous Journey* (1954), 142
5 Raymond, E. T. *Uncensored Celebrities* (1918), 87
6 Owen, Frank. *Tempestuous Journey* (1954), 143
7 Buchan, John. *Memory Hold the Door* (1940), 161
8 Raymond, E. T. *Uncensored Celebrities* (1918), 82
9 Magnus, Philip. *King Edward VII* (1964) 412
10 Maurice, Sir Frederick. *Haldane* (1937), 165

London—The Great Sprawl (PAGE 57)

1 Burke, T. *Nights in Town* (C 1915), 75

Society in Jeopardy (PAGE 71)

1 Esher, Lord. *Journal and Letters* (1934), 383
2 Conan Doyle, A. *Memories and Adventures* (1924), 266
3 Wells, H. G. *Experiment in Autobiography* (1934), 635
4 Sitwell, Osbert. *Left Hand, Right Hand!* (1945), 182
5 Bennett, Arnold. *Journals 1898-1910* (1932), 274
6 Cardigan, Countess of. *My Recollections* (1911), 174
7 Nevill, Lady Dorothy. *Reminiscences* (1906), 121
8 Escott, T. H. S. *London Society in the New Reign* (1904), 102
9 Cunnington, C. Willett. *English Women's Clothing in the Present Century* (1952)
10 Escott, T. H. S. *London Society in the New Reign* (1904), 125

Suburban Life (PAGE 84)

1 Nowell-Smith, Simon, ed. *Edwardian England* (1964), 365
2 Hobhouse, L. T. *Democracy and Reaction* (1904), 70
3 *Magazine of Art* (1903), 276
4 *Magazine of Art* (1903), 325
5 *Magazine of Art* (1903), 379
6 Gaunt, William. *The Aesthetic Adventure* (1945), 182
7 Bentley, E. C. 'The Inoffensive Captain', *Strand Magazine* (1914)
8 Blackwood, Algernon. *Secret Worship* (1908)
9 Benson, E. F. *The Room in the Tower* (1912)
10 Swan, Tom. *Edward Carpenter* (1905), 24
11 Benson, A. C. *Diary* (1926), 252
12 Greenwall, Harry J. *Northcliffe* (1957), 94

The Condition of the People (PAGE 103)

1 Masterman, C. F. G. *The Condition of the People* (1909), 15
2 Bosanquet, Helen. *Poor Law Report* (1909), 145
3 Bosanquet, Helen. *Poor Law Report* (1909), 148
4 Bosanquet, Helen. *Poor Law Report* (1909), 149
5 Bosanquet, Helen. *Poor Law Report* (1909), 172
6 Bosanquet, Helen. *Poor Law Report* (1909), 180
7 Rowntree, Seebohm. *Poverty* (1903), 103
8 London, Jack. *The People of the Abyss* (1902)
9 Owen, Frank. *Tempestuous Journey* (1954), 171

The Rural Exodus (PAGE 118)

1 Haggard, H. Rider. *Rural Britain* (1902), II, 542
2 Haggard, H. Rider. *Rural Britain* (1902), II, 542
3 Carpenter, Edward. *My Days and Dreams* (1916), 282
4 Lyttelton, Rev Hon E. *Memories and Hopes* (1925), 194
5 Green, Peter. *Kenneth Grahame* (1959), 294
6 Benson, A. C. *Diary* (1926), 166

The Coming of the Motor Car (PAGE 128)

1 Northcliffe, Lord, et al. *Motors and Motor Driving* (1906), 61
2 Northcliffe, Lord, et al. *Motors and Motor Driving* (1906), 307
3 Peel, Mrs C. S. *100 Wonderful Years* (1920), 119
4 Blumenfeld, R. D. *Diary*

Eugenics and Birth Control (PAGE 143)

1 Ussher, R. *Neo-Malthusianism* (1897), 93
2 Schuster, Edgar. *Eugenics* (1913), 75
3 Ellis, Havelock. *Man and Woman* (1914), 529

Edwardian Love and Romance (PAGE 155)

1 Aldington, Richard. *Portrait of a Genius But* (1950), 137
2 Wells, H. G. *Experiment in Autobiography* (1934), 438
3 Wells, H. G. *Experiment in Autobiography* (1934), 478

The Feminists (PAGE 166)

1 Wells, H. G. *Experiment in Autobiography* (1934), 483–4
2 Pankhurst, E. S. *The Suffragette Movement* (1935) 209
3 Pankhurst, E. S. *The Suffragette Movement* (1935), 332
4 Wells, H. G. *Experiment in Autobiography* (1934), 485

The War Lords (PAGE 186)

1 Fisher, Lord. *Memories* (1919), 274
2 Fisher, Lord. *Records* (1925), 174
3 Nowell-Smith, Simon, ed. *Edwardian England* (1964), 520
4 Wolseley, Lord and Lady. *Letters* (1922), 380
5 Raymond, E. T. *Portraits of the New Century* (1928), 289
6 Esher, Lord. *Journal and Letters* (1934), I, 401
7 Fitzroy, Sir Almeric. *Memoirs* (1926), I, 212
8 Maurice, Sir Frederick. *Haldane* (1937), 134
9 Magnus, Philip. *King Edward VII* (1964), 331
10 Raymond, E. T. *Portraits of the New Century* (1928), 164

The American Threat (PAGE 203)

1 Adams, W. S. A. *Edwardian Heritage* (1949), 74
2 Woodward, W. E. *A New American History* (1938), 571
3 Bennett, Arnold. *Journals 1898–1910* (1932), 73
4 Roosevelt, Theodore. *Edited Correspondence* (1922), I, 200
5 Morton, A. L. *A People's History of England* (1948), 476
6 Nevill, Lady Dorothy. *Leaves from the Note Books* (1910), 31
7 Young, Kenneth. *Arthur James Balfour* (1963), 277

The Sporting Life (PAGE 217)

1 Ribblesdale, Lord. *Impressions and Memories* (1927), xxii
2 Laver, James, ed. *Edwardian Promenade* (1958), 33

Showbiz (PAGE 230)

1 Sitwell, Osbert. *The Scarlet Tree* (1946), 290
2 Pearson, Hesketh. *Bernard Shaw* (1948), 240

Murder Most Foul (PAGE 262)

1 Marjoribanks, Edward. *Sir Edward Marshall Hall* (1929), 250.
2 Symons, Julian. *Bloody Murder* (1972), 14
3 Roughhead, William. *Tales of the Criminous* (1956), 254

Prelude to War (PAGE 275)

1 Benson, A. C. *Life and Letters of Maggie Benson* (1917), 381
2 Jacks, L. P. *Life and Letters of Stopford Brooke* (1917), II, 653
3 Owen, Frank. *Tempestuous Journey* (1954), 212
4 Aldington, Richard. *Portrait of a Genius But* (1950), 267
5 Beerbohm, Max. *Letters to Reggie Turner* (1964), 176

BIBLIOGRAPHY

Adams, W. S. *Edwardian Heritage* (1949)

Alden, P. *The Unemployed* (1905)

Anon. *Private Life of the King* (1901)

Bailey, L. *Edwardian Scrapbook 1900–1914* (1957)

Baker, H. T. *The Territorial Force* (1909)

Beaton, Cecil. *The Glass of Fashion* (1954)

Bennett, Arnold. *Journals 1896–1910* (1932)

Beveridge, W. H. *Unemployment* (1909)

Bosanquet, Helen. *The Standard of Life* (1906)

Bosanquet, Helen. *The Poor Law Report* (1909)

Bowley, A. L. *The Change and Distribution of the National Income* (1920)

Briggs, Asa. *Seebohm Rowntree* (1961)

Bryce, Lord. *Hindrances to Good Citizenship* (1909)

Burke, T. *Nights in Town* (1915)

Campbell, Lady Colin. *Etiquette* (1911)

Carter, E. F. *Edwardian Cars* (1955)

Cecil, Robert. *Life in Edwardian England* (1969)

Clegg, H. A. *A History of British Trade Unions* (1964)

Cole, G. D. H. *World of Labour* (1913)

Cornwallis West, G. *Edwardian Hey-Days* (1930)

Cowles, Virginia. *Edward VII and his Circle* (1956)

Cowles, Virginia. *1913: The Defiant Swan Song* (1967)

Cunnington, C. Willett. *English Women's Clothing in the Present Century* (1952)

Cust, Sir Lionel. *King Edward VII and his Court* (1930)

Davies, Maud F. *Life in an English Village* (1909)

Dickinson, G. Lowes. *The International Anarchy* ,1904–14 (1926)
Dilnot, G. *Scotland Yard* (1926)
Doyle, A. Conan. *Memories and Adventures* (1924)
Edes, Mary, ed. *Age of Extravagance* (1955)
Ensor, R. C. K. *England 1870–1914* (1936)
Escott, T. H. S. *Society in the New Reign* (1904)
Esher, Lord. *Journal and Letters* (1934)
Farrer, J. A. *England under Edward VII* (1922)
Fisher, Lord. *Memories* (1919)
Fitzroy, Sir Almeric. *Memoirs* (1926)
Frere, J. A. *The British Monarchy at Home* (1963)
Fulford, R. *Votes for Women* (1957)
George, W. L. *Women and Tomorrow* (1913)
Gilman, C. P. *Woman and Economics* (1905)
Gladstone, Mary. *Diaries and Letters* (1930)
Gooch, G. P. ed. *British Documents on the Origin of the War* (1928)
Gretton, R. H. *Modern History of the English People 1880–1922* (1912–29)
Grey, Viscount. *Twenty-Five Years* (1928)
Haggard, H. Rider. *Rural England* (1902)
Halévy, E. *The Rule of Democracy* (1952)
Heath, F. G. *British Rural Life and Labour* (1911)
Hearnshaw, F. J. C. *Edwardian England 1901–10* (1933)
Hobhouse, L. T. *Democracy and Reaction* (1904)
Hobson, J. A. *Psychology of Jingoism* (1901)
Hobson, J. A. *The Social Problem* (1901)
Hobson, J. A. *The Industrial System* (1909)
Humphreys, A. W. *History of Labour Representation* (1912)
Hynes, S. *The Edwardian Turn of Mind* (1968)
Jones, L. E. *An Edwardian Youth* (1956)
Kennedy, R. *Book of the Motor Car* (1913)
Lane, Margaret. *Edgar Wallace* (1936)
Laver, James. *Edwardian Promenade* (1958)
Lee, Sidney. *King Edward VII* (1925–7)
Liddell, A. G. C. *Notes from the Life of an Ordinary Mortal* (1911)
London, Jack. *People of the Abyss* (1903)
Maccoby, S. *English Radicalism 1886–1914* (1953)
MacDonald, Ramsay. *Socialism and Society* (1905)
Magnus, Philip. *Kitchener* (1958)
Magnus, Philip. *Edward VII* (1964)
Mann, H. H. *Life in an Agricultural Village* (1905)
Masterman, C. F. G. *In Peril of Change* (1908)
Masterman, C. F. G. *Condition of England* (1909)
Maurice, Sir Frederick. *Haldane* (1937)
Minney, R. J. *The Edwardian Age* (1964)

Money, L. G. C. *Riches and Poverty* (1905)

Morton, A. L. *A People's History of England* (1938)

Muirhead, J. H. *Service of the State* (1908)

Nevill, Lady Dorothy. *Reminiscenses* (1906)

Newnham-Davis, Lt-Col. *Dinners and Diners* (1910)

Nicolson, Harold. *King George V* (1952)

Northcliffe, Lord, ed. *Motors and Motor-Driving* (1906)

Nowell-Smith, Simon, ed. *Edwardian England* 1901–1914 (1964)

Owen, Frank. *Tempestuous Journey* (1954)

Pankhurst, E. S. *The Suffragette Movement* (1935)

Peel, Mrs C. S. *How to Keep House* (1902)

Peel, Mrs C. S. *Life's Enchanted Cup* (1933)

Petrie, Sir Charles. *Drift to World War* 1900–14 (1968)

Playne, C. E. *Society at War* (1931)

Ponsonby, Sir Frederick. *Recollections of Three Reigns* (1951)

Pope, W. MacQueen. *The Melodies Linger On* (1950)

Priestley, J. B. *The Edwardians* (1972)

Prothero, R. E. *English Farming Past and Present* (1912)

Purdom, C. B. *The Garden City* (1913)

Raymond, E. T. *Uncensored Celebrities* (1918)

Raymond, E. T. *Portraits of the New Century* (1928)

Reeves, Mrs Pember. *Round About a Pound a Week* (1913)

Rowntree, B. S. *Poverty* (1901)

Russell, G. W. E. *Prime Ministers and Some Others* (1918)

Spender, J. A. and Asquith, Cyril. *Herbert Henry Asquith* (1932)

St Helier, Lady. *Memories of Fifty Years* (1910)

Strachey, Ray. *The Cause* (1928)

Street, G. S. *People and Questions* (1910)

Tweedsmuir, Susan. *The Edwardian Lady* (1966)

Wallas, G. *Human Nature in Politics* (1908)

Warwick, Frances, Countess of. *Afterthoughts* (1931)

Webb, S. and B. *English Poor Law Policy* (1910)

Wells, H. G. *Anticipations* (1901)

Wells, H. G. *A Modern Utopia* (1905)

Wells, H. G. *First and Last Things* (1908)

Wells, H. G. *Experiment in Autobiography* (1934)

Young, A. B. F. *The Complete Motorist* (1904)

Young, K. *Arthur James Balfour* (1963)

The following newspapers, magazines and reference books of the period also provide interesting material:

Cassell's Magazine; Daily Herald; Daily Mail; Daily Mirror; Daily Telegraph; Girls' Own Annual; Illustrated London News; The King; National Review; News of the

World; Nineteenth Century; Pall Mall Magazine; Pearson's Magazine; Punch; Quarterly Review; Queen; Reynold's Newspaper; Sphere; Strand; Tatler; The Times; Woman at Home; Woman's World.

Annual Register; Daily Mail Year Book; Whitaker's Almanack

INDEX